HUGH MILLER'S MEMOIR
FROM STONEMASON TO GEOLOGIST

Edited by
MICHAEL SHORTLAND

EDINBURGH UNIVERSITY PRESS

© Michael Shortland, 1995

Edinburgh University Press Ltd
22 George Square, Edinburgh

Typeset in Linotronic Pilgrim
by Speedspools, Edinburgh, and
printed and bound in Great Britain

A CIP record for this book is available from
the British Library

ISBN 0 7486 0521 5

The Publisher wishes to acknowledge subsidy
from the Scottish Arts Council towards the
publication of this volume.

CONTENTS

PREFACE

Hugh Miller (1802–56) is barely remembered today, but for much of his life he was a visible and impressive figure on the Victorian scene. After fifteen years as an obscure Scottish stonemason, in middle age Miller won for himself a considerable reputation as a geologist, man of letters, and ecclesiastical controversialist. He launched and edited one of the most successful newspapers of the day. In this role and as the author of several best-selling books, he helped to shape the opinions and attitudes of a whole generation. Dickens, Carlyle, Chalmers, Darwin, Ruskin, Huxley . . . no one in the early Victorian period who thought about the development of science and its impact on belief escaped the influence of Miller's writings. Shortly after his death, Miller's many admirers erected a great monument to him in Cromarty: a tall, gaunt pillar standing on a base of old red sandstone, with a statue of Miller gazing out across the bay. The event was reported throughout the English-speaking world, from London to Sydney, from New York to San Francisco. So too was the celebration of his centenary nearly half a century later in 1902.

Miller still looks out across the waters off the eastern coast of Scotland, but few notice or, still less, look up to him. History has not been kind to Hugh Miller. From our vantage-point, he seems a remote figure, alien to those features of our culture we value and deem natural. Certainly he would cut an odd and graceless form in our secular, cosmopolitan, Darwinian age. Even so, Miller's life and work are of extraordinary interest, as this book is intended to show. It consists principally of an autobiographical memoir written when Miller was still a stonemason labouring in the graveyards of Cromarty. This memoir, greatly modified and embellished, later appeared as *My Schools and Schoolmasters* (1854), a classic work of Victorian self-improvement, self-expression, and self-realisation. A quarter-century earlier, at the age of twenty-six, Miller had drawn up a list of 'Things which I intend doing, but many of which, experience says, shall never be done'. Under the heading, 'Prose Composition', he wrote:

> 1. I intend writing a work, humorous and descriptive, to be entitled, 'Four Years in the Life of a Journeyman Mason.'

It is this work which now appears in print for the first time, accompanied by an introductory essay on its significance and place in Miller's work. A series of appendices reproduce and appraise some other of Miller's other early writings, which in part fulfilled the second of his literary designs:

> 2. I intend writing a history of my varying thoughts of men and manners, right and wrong, philosophy and religion, from my twelfth to my twenty-sixth year.

The manuscript itself, originally handwritten in a letterbook, was transcribed first by Harry Hanham, and, later, independently by me. I had spent several years undertaking research on Hugh Miller's life and work unaware of the labours of Professor Hanham, working in Scotland and the United States. With the help and encouragement of Dr Jon Hodge (a friend and colleague to whom we are much indebted), we have been able to co-operate on the introduction to this book.

The original manuscript is in the Library of New College, Edinburgh. The text is reproduced with permission of the Librarian of the University of Edinburgh. Carlyle's copy of Miller's *Testimony of the Rocks* which we have used is held in The Norman and Charlotte Strouse Collection of Thomas Carlyle, University of California at Santa Cruz. We thank Jerry D. James for his help in obtaining access to this volume.

Professor Hanham would like to thank Ruth Soule Arnon and Henry Binford for their help. I express my indebtedness to the scrupulous editorial assistance of Woody Horning and Zara Griffin, and to Vivien Eime, Ann Goodsell and Shari Lee for their help.

Michael Shortland, December 1994

INTRODUCTION

WHO WAS HUGH MILLER?

Lord Byron claimed that he awoke one morning to find himself famous. For Hugh Miller, it was death, on Christmas Eve, 1856, that transformed a reputation into far-flung fame. The Scottish press and establishment were shaken, and the news carried far. Obituaries, reviews of his life and work, personal testimonials and public obsequies followed. Miller's burial took place under an appropriately gloomy sky spread across the face of nature (as a reporter lamented) 'like a pall'.[1] The Lord Provost of Edinburgh, several members of Parliament, luminaries of the Free Church, and Miller's family were joined by several thousand ordinary citizens of Edinburgh for the funeral procession to the Grange Cemetery. Half the city, it seemed, had turned out to witness the last journey of Hugh Miller.[2]

For several days before the funeral, the circumstances of Hugh Miller's death had been clouded in mystery and wild speculation. The *Witness*, the newspaper Miller edited, reported that he had died in a tragic accident. Awoken by a ghastly nightmare, he heard noises and suspected a burglary. Grabbing a loaded pistol he kept in his bedroom, he lost his step, fell, and accidentally shot himself in the chest.[3]

Three days later, a different version emerged. According to a family friend, Miller's death was attributable to mental confusion brought about by overwork.[4] His characteristic capacity for unrelenting labour was – appropriately, if tragically – the

indirect cause of his death. Had Miller then taken his own
life? Was he a self-murderer? In an era when suicide was subject
to severe stigma, the suggestion seemed to brand Miller a villain
or a coward. Within living memory, after all, suicides had
been buried at a crossroads by night with stakes driven through
their hearts.[5] Though effectively decriminalised, suicide and
intimations of suicide prompted gossip and journalistic speculation.[6] People became intensely curious about the circumstances
of Miller's death and the life that preceded it. Many who
knew Miller, or had read his work or merely glimpsed him on
one of his habitual walks about the city, would have felt
grief. But the thousands lining Princes Street to see Miller's
ornately decked hearse and the procession of coaches, must
have been impelled more by curiosity and that prurient commo-
tion described by a historian as 'un petit frisson . . . une emotion
delicieuse'.[7]

Not that Miller was by any means unknown in his lifetime.
Many thousands admired him and mourned his passing out of
fondness for his writings. A strong and commanding author
pervades Miller's work. Whether he was scribbling for pence
on the subject of North Sea herring stocks or pouring venomous
ink on abusive landlords and rival newspaper editors, Miller's
voice is never less than clear and distinct. Readers surely felt –
one senses it to this day – that, with his latest volume in their
laps, they had Hugh Miller looking over their shoulders. In
choosing him, readers were choosing a friend.

The questions posed by Miller's suicide were to some degree
settled in some people's minds by reports that Miller had been
impelled by ill health as well as overwork. It now transpired
that he had been plagued by the conviction that his brain
'was deeply and hopelessly diseased – that his mind was on
the verge of ruin'.[8] Two days before his death, he had called
on his physician for help and been advised to rest well, eat
lightly and go to bed early. Professor James Miller (no relation),
an eminent surgeon at the University of Edinburgh, corrobor-
ated the physician's advice after examining the patient. 'I left
him', Professor Miller later recalled, 'little doubting that a
short time of rest and regimen would restore him to his full

vigour.'[9] Though Miller did not adhere to the prescription, it would not in any event have been effective. For while the immediate cause of death was a pistol shot 'inflicted by his own hand', the *post mortem* concluded from 'the diseased appearances found in the brain, taken in connection with the history of the case,' that 'the act was suicidal under the impulse of insanity'.[10]

'[I]n no case of suicide which ever took place,' wrote Miller's biographer Peter Bayne about the official account of his death, 'can the evidence of insanity have been more express or conclusive.'[11] By declaring Miller mad at the time of his death, a complicated story was simplified and the victim was rendered eligible for the proper Christian obsequies. A verdict of *non compos mentis* allowed for Miller's escape from obloquy to sympathy.[12]

Sympathy, like scandal, was good for business. Under the careful (and lucrative) superintendence of his widow, Miller's books sold as never before. Who could fail to be curious about a man whom the *Times* had described as uniquely governed not only by 'indifferent health' and 'nervous excitement', but also by 'eccentric manners' and 'unusual strangeness'?[13] Under this watchful superintendence of his widow Lydia, a steady flow of Miller's writings began to run off the presses in Britain and America. Within twenty years of his death, five editions of Miller's 'collected works' had appeared, along with commentaries, criticism and collections of his unpublished essays. Miller was now recognised as a great writer – 'the most remarkable man of the age', in one critic's opinion.[14] Even the literary lions of the day now found bonds in common with him. Charles Dickens called Miller 'a delightful writer, an accomplished follower of science, and an upright and good man'. John Ruskin wrote to his widow of 'your husband's genius'. Even Thomas Carlyle, more prone to stabbing than elevating with his pen, wrote of 'the world's great loss' and of Miller's posthumously published *Testimony of the Rocks* (1857) as 'full of grave and manly talent, cleverness, eloquence, faithful conviction, knowledge . . . It will teach me and others much'.[15] By the end of the century, *The Old Red Sandstone* (1841), *First Impressions* of *England* (1847), *Foot-prints of the Creator* (1849) and *My Schools and Schoolmasters* (1854) had each sold over 50,000 copies in Britain and been carried to all corners of the Empire and beyond. 'They were to be found', the geologist Sir Archibald Geikie wrote, 'in the remotest log huts of the Far West'.[16]

'A plain working man'

The circumstances of Miller's death, coupled with the opportunism of his widow, explain much about the growth of his reputation in the second half of the nineteenth century. While the sentimentalist in him would have been touched by the emotion displayed at his funeral, Miller would also have found it more than a little distasteful. Men whom he had never met – shopkeepers, bankers, printers and other common folk – mourned him as they might have a relative or dear companion. To a man who created his own world and lived in it with unusual self-sufficiency, this posthumous intimacy would have been profoundly discomfiting.

There is more than a touch of irony here, for Miller had few friends in life; he appeared, indeed, to lose friends as he gained admirers. Towards the end of his days, even Lydia seemed to shy away from him. The greater his renown, the greater his loneliness. It was as though writing were a prison-house and his circle of readers its walls.

Ironic too, in light of Miller's capacity to win friends through his work, is how little he set out to do so. Early in his literary career, he had sought patronage and courted favour; the memoir published here was his boldest such effort. But as Miller found his powers, he renounced all deferential gestures. By the time he published *Letter from One of the Scotch People to the Right Hon. Lord Brougham* in 1839, Miller had determined to say what he had to say, unalloyed and undiluted. 'I sat down', Miller wrote later, recalling the circumstances that produced this important pamphlet, 'to state my views to the people'.[17] The mixture of grandiloquence and self-assurance in this magisterial affirmation is a hallmark of Miller's mature style. But in 1839 he still had not completely shed the air of humility that runs through the *Letter*. Miller later had little trouble ridding himself of the false modesty that characterises the opening of the *Letter*:

> MY LORD, – I am a plain working man, in rather humble circumstances, a native of the north of Scotland, and a member of the Established Church. I am acquainted with no other language than the one in which I address your Lordship; and the very limited knowledge which I possess has been won slowly and painfully from observation and reflection, with now and then the assistance of a stray volume, in the intervals of a laborious life.[18]

This paragraph would become as famous as any in its day, but Miller was being less than honest in choosing such self-effacing rhetoric. He was by this time well acquainted with 'other languages' and had experimented a great deal with different styles and idioms. Nor had his self-education been limited to 'a stray volume'; he had by 1839 read widely and deeply in the classics and contemporary prose and verse. Miller had, it is true, been a stonemason. But since 1835 he had worked as an accountant at the Commercial Bank in Cromarty, an undemanding job that earned him the comfortable salary of sixty pounds per annum.[19] The learning he confessed to in his *Letter* is more likely attributable to moments of boredom at the bank than to intervals snatched from hard labour in the quarry.

The *Letter* was a deeply reactionary and polemical piece of writing, heralding the conjunction in Miller of the conservative and the controversialist. Miller generally disliked change and opposed those who commended it. Indeed, even when he supported change he often found reason to take issue with his apparent fellow partisans. Those who moved too fast, or too slowly, or not at all – in fact, anyone who did not adhere to the letter Miller's own recipe for social, religious and cultural rectitude – earned his disdain. The Free Church of Scotland, which Miller had worked tirelessly to bring into being, received his sanction and profited greatly from it, but heaven help any who strayed from the Church or from whatever faction within it was currently championed in the pages of the *Witness*. Like any partisan, Miller's harshest criticisms were reserved for those

ideologically closest to home (although those more remote
were not spared: Mormons, Hindus, Buddhists and Muslims
were all pilloried in his editorials).[20] Architects whose plans
for new churches Miller disliked, ministers whose sermons tried
his patience, and choirs whose renditions of popular hymns
bruised his musical sensitivities were all called to account.
His victims retorted that he had little knowledge of architecture, no skill at public speaking, and a tin ear. No matter:
from his *prises de position* he would not budge. The masthead
of the *Witness* bore the words of John Knox: 'I am in the place
where I am demanded of conscience to speak the truth, and
therefore the truth I speak, impugn it whoso list'. This declaration became for Miller an inviolable creed.

Le style est l'homme même

Miller conceived of himself not as a reporter or essayist, but
rather as a critic and campaigner. Even in an age when criticism
was more acerbic and campaigns harder fought than they are
today, Miller's fierceness stood out. He may well have taken
his cue from the *Edinburgh Review*, renowned for its exceedingly sharp style, whose contributors were encouraged by editor
Francis Jeffrey to 'make war upon the whole tribe of authors,
and mangle them for the amusement of the public'.[21] Miller
referred favourably to the *Review*'s 'gladiatorship', and surely
saw something of the gladiator in himself. He also liked Bos-
well's depiction of Dr Johnson as a Christian fighting the lions
of prejudice and secularism in a Roman amphitheatre.[22] If
biography has the power to transform a human being's life
into allegory – which it surely does – this may well be the
allegory Miller would have chosen for himself.

Miller's literary pugnacity grew out of the critical culture of
his day, his sense of mission and simple morality. That it also
had deep roots in his conception of self lends added significance
to his autobiographical writings. Miller's prose was bombastic
and martial because he saw himself as a man battling against
the odds. Having fashioned himself thus, everything he (or his
pen) touched turned on him, as though he were in combat.
To put it another way, Miller created for himself a world

constituted metaphorically as a battleground. The image of himself as struggling on this battleground became how he perceived and experienced reality. Once established, the concept of world-as-contest acquired pre-emptive power. Miller conceived of his writing as ammunition, servicing arguments that were either to be won and defended or attacked and demolished. The grip of this notion was such that, soon enough, any writing or argument not presented in combat dress was not seen by him as worthy – nor, indeed, as writing or argument at all.

'Here was a life-drama', observed the *Annual Register* in its obituary of Miller 'full of noble lessons and manly and successful struggles'.[23] A drama, yes. Miller certainly believed it to be full of noble lessons: his intention in his memoir is to convey those he had learnt in early adulthood. As for his struggles, they were not always successful; Miller's death was testimony to that. It was plainly in struggle that the drama and lessons of Miller's life were forged, yet the sword Miller wielded was two-edged. Fending off the enemy, real or perceived, forced him into a kind of internal exile of his own designing. Writing was a means of attaining power over others and of resisting their power over him. Any who dared to come close, whether bearing a white flag or not, appeared potentially hostile. He would not have welcomed, or perhaps even recognised, the affection he won from his readers.

If Miller is remembered at all today, it is probably as the author of two books, *The Old Red Sandstone* and *My Schools and Schoolmasters*.[24] Miller's enormous written output gave him during his lifetime any number of not altogether conformable reputations. To many he epitomised the possibilities of working-class emancipation and a 'cheering message of self-respect to the masses', but others never forgave his attacks on the Chartists and considered him a political traitor to his roots.[25] His writings on the relationship of science and religion won admirers and detractors in roughly equal proportion. In the eyes of his partisans, such works as *The Two Records: Mosaic and Geological* (1854) and *The Testimony of the Rocks* (1857) broke new ground in demonstrating the harmony between reason and revelation, but his critics dismissed him as merely ploughing old fields, disinterring 'the ghost of a defunct Biblical geology'.[26] The boldness of Miller's geological researches and the brilliance of his contributions to popular science drew the admiration of such figures as Sir Archibald Geikie, Sir Roderick Impey Murchison, and Professor Richard Owen. Others, like Professor Baden Powell, an Oxford astronomer, judged his scientific work 'greatly overrated'.[27]

On one point admirers and critics alike were agreed at his death: that, for all his idiosyncracies and anxieties, Miller had been a major force in shaping early Victorian culture in Britain and beyond. From the vantage-point of today, this may be difficult to credit. Indeed, interest in Miller's work is often said to have died with the publication of Darwin's evolutionary theory in 1859. After the appearance of Darwin's *Origin of Species*, according to the recent *Encyclopedia of Evolution*, 'no one would ever read Hugh Miller's books again'.[28] In fact, this was far from the case. Such 'anti-evolutionary' works as *The Old Red Sandstone*, *Foot-prints of the Creator* and *The Testimony of the Rocks* were repeatedly reprinted on both sides of the Atlantic in the second half of the nineteenth century: by the 1880s, each had gone through over 20 editions and sold over 30,000 copies. The influence of these books was profound: 'no American geologist of the generation now in the full swing of its activity', wrote the journal *Science* on Miller's centenary in 1902, 'can have failed to come, in his early days, under the inspiration of this unique man'.[29] Even Miller's history of Cromarty, his travel books *First Impressions of England* and *Cruise of the Betsey*, and his *Sketch-book of Popular Geology*, a posthumous ragbag compiled by his wife, continued to sell well into the 1900s. The wonder is not that anyone continued to study and enjoy Hugh Miller but that so many did.

Miller's posthumous hold on a large readership may be attributable in part to the paradoxes of his life and work that attracted crowds to his funeral. Here is a man unmade by the toil he had claimed 'made the man'. Here is a cowardly act of self-negation committed by the author of tracts commending courage and honesty as the most honourable of virtues. Here is a man whose recipe for success in life lay in tatters. Such paradoxes, though not explicitly manifest in Miller's memoir, are a compelling frame through which to view his earliest full-scale performance. By exploring these and other perplexities in Miller's early life and career, we can begin to answer question 'Who was Hugh Miller?'.

A LAD O' PAIRTS

The Business of Poetry

Scotland in the eighteenth and nineteenth centuries, almost alone among the nations of the world, prided itself on an educational system open to all, peasant and peer alike. The farmer's boy who tended the plough in the summer and trudged off to college in the winter with a bag of oatmeal on his back had a special place in the national pantheon. He was the symbol of 'Scottish democracy', flesh-and-blood proof that there was no cleavage or animosity between the classes and that in Scotland advancement and career were open to the able long before the French Revolution.[30] Indeed, the Scottish 'lad o' pairts' became a celebrated phenomenon all over the world: wherever there were engineers, Presbyterian ministers, ships' captains, army officers, colonial administrators, or merchants, there was a community of self-made, literate Scotsmen, admired for their hard-headed devotion to the matter at hand and their talent for disputation.[31]

Though the term 'lad o' pairts' only came into use in the 1890s, those it described had long been lauded – and mythologised – as the glory of Scotland's uniquely accessible educational system.[32] Since the days of John Knox, open paths for ability had existed throughout Scotland, and particularly in rural areas, allowing 'men of genius' to become ministers, doctors or schoolmasters. Of course, thoroughgoing equality of opportunity was itself a myth. Having boasted of Scotland's success in overcoming the 'gross ignorance and stupidity' of its people, Adam Smith conceded that 'rank and fortune' would also guarantee far better instruction.[33] Most 'lads o' pairts', after leaving in their early teenage years one of the public schools established by statute in every parish, went promptly to work, usually

as apprentices to skilled craftsmen or professional men. They
proved their quality on the job and moved on to responsible
posts elsewhere.[34] Scottish gardeners and engineers became as
renowned for their shrewdness and skill as Scottish ministers
and doctors. Even bakers and shoemakers might become celebrated if they combined scientific pursuits with the everyday
business of earning a living, as Samuel Smiles' biographies of
Robert Dick and Thomas Edward attest.[35]

The passport to success was book learning. Education was a
valuable commodity that every man of sagacity wished to
possess. Poor but talented Scots were, indeed, as greedy for
learning as popular wisdom held them to be shrewd about
money. Learning was their peculiar treasure, an invaluable
resource in their struggle to rise in the world. A popular culture
of libraries, debating societies, and self-help classes thrived in
the towns and villages.[36] Miller vividly depicts this milieu in
his memoir and in *My Schools and Schoolmasters*. Indeed, the
remarkable expansion of the Scottish economy in the late
eighteenth and early nineteenth centuries was at the time
attributed to its educated populace, low rates of pauperism,
and social contentment. A pamphlet by Alexander Christison,
one of many on the topic, forthrightly announced its argument
with its title, *The General Diffusion of Knowledge One Great
Cause of the Prosperity of North Britain* (1802).

Book learning alone was not greatly valued: every Scot knew
of supposedly learned schoolmasters who were utter failures
in life, and many Scots had unqualified teachers because qualified men could command better jobs. Even a college education
conferred no benefits, it was assumed, without the knack of
knowing how to make use of it. Scots, as a result, reserved
special admiration for the self-educated man: the man who
had sought learning because he knew what to do with it, and
who made his knowledge the foundation for a distinguished
career.

Respect was even accorded to those who put their learning
to use writing verse. Remarkably enough, verse-writing was
a marketable skill. Competent verse-writers attracted public
attention and the patronage of the Edinburgh literati long

before Robert Burns appeared on the poetic scene. Newspapers and magazines in the capital – indeed, virtually every newspaper in the country – ran a poetry column, and editors were inundated with verses; every social class was struck by the Muse. Most would-be poets were impelled by personal enjoyment, and never entertained high ambitions. But for others poetry represented an honourable means of improving their social and economic standing. To them, Burns's success demonstrated verse-writing to be a means of upward social mobility.[37]

For most rural versifiers, however, the importance of Burns was that his work seemed dignified. Burns had made no concessions to the great in order to rise in the world. He was proud to be a countryman and proud to have earned his living by the sweat of his brow. The weaver toiling at his loom anticipated turning to verse-writing at the end of the day not just as a solace and a lonely hobby, but as a shift from honest toil to the more refined but equally honest toil of the world of letters. The workingman-poet usually drifted into a non-manual occupation – as a minor government official, schoolmaster, or shopkeeper – but he continued in most cases to regard himself as simply a working man who had done well for himself. If not exactly a champion of proletarian values, he did at least articulate what he regarded as working-class virtues.

The Poet from Cromarty

Scotland was until the beginning of the nineteenth century essentially a land of small towns. Even after population growth and industrialisation had transformed Glasgow, Edinburgh and Dundee into cities, the social environment of most of the population was still centred on the farm and on communities of fewer than 2,000 inhabitants.[38] Thus the seemingly paradoxical absence in Scotland, even by mid-century (by which time it had become the second most urbanised country in the world, after England), of a culture that took into account – or even acknowledged – town and city life.[39] Literature instead idealised the folkways of small-town and lowland life. The need to earn a livelihood led many a workingman-poet to the big towns, but few regarded them as home. Allan Cunningham, the stonemason-poet from Dumfriesshire, lived for thirty years in London devoting all his leisure time to writing about the Scotland of his childhood.[40] And the craziest of all workingmen-poets, William McGonagall, a handloom weaver, professed to see in the nineteenth-century cities of Scotland only leafy squares and greenery.[41]

The Scottish Lowlands maintained longest the conditions in which working-class poets thrived. North of Aberdeen there were no towns of any size, and the parish school system was in better order than elsewhere in Scotland. The people, though poor and isolated from the rest of Scotland, enjoyed strong traditions and, as a seafaring folk, many connections with the outside world – notably the West Indies and India. Located as they were almost at the end of the world, they found it necessary to make their own amusements. Inverness, Elgin and Wick each had its own little circle of literary folk and, in time, newspapers, and educated ladies of good family kept an eye open for young men of talent. A workingman-poet could hardly fail to be noticed in such an environment.

Such was the background of Hugh Miller, who grew up in one of the backwaters of the north. He was born at Cromarty on 10 October 1802, into a family of seamen and craftsmen. The small, neat town of about 2,000 inhabitants had prospered as a herring-curing station in the early years of the nineteenth century, but had begun to decline by the time Miller published his *Letters on the Herring Fishing* in 1829, never to recover.[42] Far from the main trade routes, Cromarty fared badly by comparison with Wick to the north. Thomas Chalmers on a visit in 1839 commented that he had had 'no idea of this being so primitive and sequestered a place'.[43] Miller himself spoke of Cromarty towards the end of his life as a 'deserted place' with 'ruinous houses' and a 'general aspect most desolate'.[44]

Although he was to spend most of his adult life in Edinburgh and spoke sometimes disparagingly of his birthplace, Miller was generally prone to rhapsodise on the semi-mythical world from whence he came, and to which he often returned and seems never to have left in spirit. As David Alston has recently shown, Cromarty not only fascinated Miller but was essential

to his sense of place in the world.[45] He was wont to recall, for
example, the gale-lashed and windswept bay in Cromarty,
prompting his biographer Peter Bayne to describe the district
as 'one of the most bleak and uncongenial' in Scotland. This is
in fact inaccurate, for the eastern tip of the Black Isle has a
mild, sheltered climate and is almost completely free from the
'chill fogs' also mentioned by Bayne; nor do severe gales blow
in from the North Sea at every season to 'pierce every nook
and cranny of the shivering town'.[46]

Why did Miller, born and raised in a prosperous, cosmopolitan
town (whose building boom in the early 1800s may well have
persuaded him to become a stonemason) choose to portray
Cromarty as isolated and desolate?[47] This choice was an important ingredient in his own self-fashioning – particularly evident
once he settled in Edinburgh – as a rough, even untamed,
man. Cromarty offered Miller a sense of place and also a sense
of origin. Or, rather, several. Though born and raised in Cromarty, Hugh Miller was well aware that his mother was one of
a long line of Highlanders (her great grandfather was the renowned seer Donald Roy), while his father was of local, seafaring stock. Harriet Miller was a voluble and excitable woman
who evidently aroused strong passions in all who knew her
and her relish for myths, tall stories, and the northern occult
– some went so far as to denounce her as a mental weakling,
'fit only to stir a cauldron in company with the witches of
"Macbeth"'.[48] Hugh Miller's father, by contrast, was sturdy,
powerful and taciturn: the product of a more intellectually
advanced and socially prosperous culture. As we shall see,
one of the severest challenges Hugh Miller faced was to make
sense of the symbolic and social history of Scotland, of its
Highlands and Lowlands, a project he viewed through the
diffracting lenses of memory, loss and guilt. His response to
that challenge was sometimes brilliant but never wholly successful: the value systems of his mother and father dwelt in
him in perpetual, but immensely resourceful, tension throughout his life.

Despite – or, according to Miller, because of – its harshness,
Cromarty proved an uncommonly fertile soil for native literary

paragons and self-educated 'mechanics'.[49] Hugh Miller had himself displayed precocious literary talent and ambition as a teenager, producing a series of little magazines devoted to news and views about the town.[50] In 1829 he launched what he hoped would be a literary career as a workingman-poet with the anonymous publication in Inverness of *Poems Written in the Leisure Hours of a Journeyman Mason*. The book, which runs to 268 pages, is a strange medley of juvenilia, commonplace patriotic effusions, and romantic verse. Like many another workingman-poet, Miller dwells on his life of labour:

> CERTES, 'tis true, that I was born to toil,
> To wend through life's remotest paths my way:
> I hew the pond'rous stone with ceaseless moil,
> And wake to labour each returning day.[51]

But his themes are not ordinarily those of everyday life, for to Miller poetry was essentially a means of escape from humdrum routines.

> The desire of happiness, so natural to man, has led me to seek for that pleasure elsewhere, which I cannot find in the circle of my labours; and I have found it in the study of poetry . . . While engaged among my brother workmen, in the labours of a tiresome and uncongenial employment, I have been wandering over the heaths of Ossian, a spectator of the battles of Fingal. While residing among strangers, in a bleak country, and exposed to the hardships and privations of the Journeyman Mason, I have seen all that is beautiful, and felt all that is pleasing. There is a pleasure in indulging in the dreams of imagination; there is a pleasure in making transcripts of these dreams, and in giving them a dress of words and a music of numbers; there is a pleasure in looking over these transcripts when the originals are forgotten.[52]

Miller's poems − or, rather, his decision to publish them − represented another form of escapism. He hoped that his poetry would improve his material circumstances and raise him out of the ranks of journeyman stonemasons. Other ventures had conspicuously failed; the notice he placed in the *Inverness Courier* in July 1828 seeking freelance work as a stonecutter had drawn no response.[53] He began to consider the course he ought to pursue:

> For years before I had indulged in the hope that I should one day become known as a writer; but in even my least phlegmatic moods, I considered that day as at a great distance; for I was aware that I had not yet attained the ability of making other than imperfect transcripts of what I either thought or felt; and I could not think of becoming a candidate for the approbation of the Public until I had first secured my own. I now, however, resolved on publishing a volume of poems. My poems, thought I, will give me no high place in the literary world; but if they do not show that I have a more cultivated mind and finer taste than commonly belong to men of my profession, my hope of yet occupying a respectable niche among writers of genius is certainly unfounded. If on the other hand they attract attention enough to show that my mind and taste are cultivated, my pretensions to superior skill as a mechanic will surely be credited; and the Public will bestow upon me what I consider its best patronage, – employment.[54]

The expression of hope that his poems will generate work as a stonecutter is remarkable, and it is impossible to be sure whether it is ingenuous or not – one cannot help (at least with hindsight) reading this passage as a piece of self-mythologising. In any event, Hugh Miller's ambitions as a poet did not survive. Reviewers of his collection in the *Edinburgh Literary Journal*, *Aberdeen Journal*, and *Inverness Courier* were kind enough, but he was also dealt some harsh blows. 'They have delivered every possible variety of opinion', he wrote to John Strahan in 1830 of his critics, 'I am a man of genius; – I am a blockhead; – my name is to be at once illustrious and obscure.'[55] Miller had half expected a cool reception from the critics; indeed, he had anticipated critical failure.[56] What seems to have shocked him is that the public was indifferent to the rag-bag collection: the

Poems failed miserably to sell. Desperate to see his pecuniary investment in the book returned, Miller sent copies of the work to the well-connected, to literary editors, and to friends and acquaintances.[57] When this marketing drive failed, Miller concluded that the *Poems* were destined for oblivion, and that he had no future as a poet. If he were to improve his social position by writing, it must be by writing prose. Robert Carruthers, the editor of the *Inverness Courier* who had published his poems, urged the distraught Miller to begin writing about his own experiences. Miller responded with a series of semi-autobiographical articles for the *Courier*, some of which were reprinted as *Letters on the Herring Fishing*. It was a small step to autobiography proper; soon Miller was set on a life of autobiographical writing.

AUTOBIOGRAPHICAL CAREERS
Miller and Principal Baird

Miller had been experimenting with prose before the *Poems* appeared. The task he had set himself was to reconcile the easy colloquial style of his own juvenile stories with the classical style of the eighteenth century, which he considered the only acceptable style for a writer of serious prose. By 1829 he had already written a number of experimental stories and articles, some of which were later published in the *Inverness Courier*.[58] But it was several years before his prose style settled down. Told in October 1834 that old Baron Hume the jurist had commended the excellence of his 'classical style', Miller responded at once (unusual for him). The response, to Miss Dunbar, raises, like Miller's expressed hope that his *Poems* would bring him employment, questions about his own sincerity:

> I owe my merit chiefly to accident; – to my having kept company with the older English writers, – the Addisons, Popes, and Robertsons of the last century at a time when I had no opportunity of becoming acquainted with the authors of the present time.[59]

Was Hugh Miller really too poor and isolated to have had

access to current authors, or is this a piece of self-dramatising? Obviously the latter since Miller in his memoir describes provincial Scottish culture as rich, vibrant and accessible. Presumably one of his objects in presenting himself to Miss Dunbar in this manner was to attract patronage, another to legitimise his rejection of modernity. Miller's chosen subject was the life of his native Cromarty. He had a wealth of anecdote and story to draw on, and every few weeks a new incident in the bay or out at sea, or in one of the neighbouring parishes, could be added to his stock. Moreover, life in Cromarty was highly routinised, as it usually is in small towns; thus any new or unusual event stood out clearly against its background.

Miller was soon diverted from his Cromarty stories by outside intervention. The Reverend George Husband Baird, who happened to be in Inverness in the summer of 1829, asked to see the stonemason-poet. Baird, then sixty-eight years old, had been Principal of the University of Edinburgh since 1793. He was by any reckoning an undistinguished occupant of the office, having risen to it not by contributing to learning but by having married the Lord Provost's daughter. Nevertheless, Baird had been on good terms with both Robert Burns and Sir Walter Scott, and had edited some verses of the eighteenth-century shepherd-poet Michael Bruce.[60] He was, moreover, known by repute all over Scotland as a firm supporter of the extension of Highland education.[61]

Some months later, Miller described his meeting with Baird to a woman who had taken an interest in his career:

> On the Saturday after the last of my letters on the Herring Fishery had appeared in the Courier, I received a note from my friend the Editor stating that Principal Baird who was then at Inverness was desirous of having some conversation with me. He added further that . . . such an opportunity ought not to be neglected. I accordingly went to Inverness and was introduced to the Principal. At first I felt how justly I could appreciate the feeling of the Jewish Spies 'We were as grasshoppers before them,' but the singular kindness of the reverend gentleman soon

restored me to a proper confidence. He related to me anecdotes of some of the eminent literati of both the past
and the present age. He had been the friend and correspondent of Burns, and the editor of the poems of Michael
Bruce. The offers he made me were startling. He proposed
that I should accompany him to Edinburgh; he asked me
whether I did not stand in need of money, adding that his
purse and credit were heartily at my service; he said he
would introduce me, if I desired it, to Professor Wilson, as
a suitable writer for Blackwoods Magazine; he informed
me, too, that he belonged to a Committee of the General
Assembly formed for the purpose of making some
alterations in the sacred poetry of the Church and some
additions to it; and then asked me whether I would not
become a contributor. I was much flattered by his expressing it as his opinion that my writings betrayed few of
the faults incident to an imperfect education; and by his
requesting me to state to him by letter the manner in
which I had attained my skill in the art of composition.
This request as it fell in with a previously formed intention of writing a memoir of 'Four years of the life of a
Journeyman-Mason' has furnished me with employment
for the greater part of . . . last winter.[62]

The main point of Baird's offer of sponsorship in Edinburgh
was to enable Miller to become a more skilful writer. In suggesting that Miller compose a letter explaining how he came to
write so well in spite of the deficiencies of his education, Baird
clearly had in mind a brief, analytical account that might be
useful in his efforts to promote rural education. Miller chose
instead to see in the request an excuse for writing his autobiography, a project he had already been contemplating. The
autobiography took the form of two letters to Principal Baird,
but its whole character suggests that Miller had mapped out
much of the plan well in advance. In a later account of
the meeting, Miller misleadingly describes Baird as requesting
something approximating a full-fledged autobiography.[63]
    To judge by the surviving correspondence, Miller failed to

give Baird a clear answer to his offer of help. Indeed, Baird
regarded the first instalment of the autobiography, however
lengthy, as non-responsive, and gently said so in his letter of
thanks:

> But you say nothing in your letter as to my suggestion
> when at Inverness of giving your busy hours to your pro-
> fession here during the winter, and your leisure hours to
> reading books, and plying your pen, and extending your
> acquaintance with the living as well as with the dead
> world of literature.[64]

To this query Miller returned a lengthy and ingenious answer:
he had found a way of combining literature and stonecutting
in the north of Scotland. He could not be sure of his reception
in Edinburgh, and might find it impossible there to preserve
the economic independence that gave him a sense of security
as a writer:

> I have at present several pieces of work on hand mostly
> tombstones which will keep me busy for the greater part
> of the winter; and I have besides some prospect of pro-
> curing employment next spring in the churchyards of
> Inverness; where I trust I shall hardly meet with any very
> formidable rivalry in the art of inscription cutting. . . .
>   From my engagements here and at Inverness I cannot
> avail myself of your kind invitation to spend the winter
> at Edinburgh, but I appreciate its value, and feel grateful
> for your kindness. My acquaintance with the dead world
> of literature is very imperfect, and it is still more so with
> the living; instead, however, of regretting this I think it
> best to congratulate myself on the much pleasure which
> from this circumstance there yet remains for me to enjoy.
> If I live eight or ten years longer, and if my taste for
> reading continues I shall, I trust, pass through a great
> many paradises of genius. Half the creations of Scott are
> still before me, and more than half those of every other
> modern poet. But though I can appreciate the value of an
> opportunity of perusing the works of such authors, there

are opportunities of a different kind to be enjoyed in Edinburgh, which from a rather whimsical bent of mind I
would value more highly. My curiosity is never more
active than when it has the person of a great man for its
object, nor have I felt more delight in anything whatever
than in associating in my mind when that curiosity was
gratified my newly acquired idea of the personal
appearance of such a man, with the ideas I had previously entertained of his character and genius. When I
resided in the vicinity of Edinburgh I have sauntered for
whole hours opposite the house of Sir Walter Scott in the
hope of catching a glimpse of his person, and several
times when some tall robust man has passed me in the
streets, I have enquired of my companions whether that
was not Prof. Wilson. But perhaps I am more ambitious
now than I was five years ago. Perhaps I would not be
satisfied with merely seeing such men, and I am yet
aware that I have not yet done any thing which entitles
me to the notice of the eminent though in one instance I
have been so fortunate as to attract it. I must achieve at
least a little of what I have hoped to achieve before I go
to Edinburgh. But even this intention must not be followed up with too great eagerness. . . . I must be careful
least by acquiring too exclusive a bent towards literary
pursuit I contract a distaste for those employments which
though not very pleasing in themselves are in my case at
least intimately connected with happiness. I do not think
I could be happy without being independent, and I cannot be independent except as a mechanic.[65]

Thinking now about the manner in which Baird approached
Miller, there is nothing strange about Miller's ready response.
Miller, who had steadfastly refused help from his uncles, seems
once again to have feared a kind of intellectual take-over, a
complete possession and domestication. Baird, to his credit,
did not lose interest in Miller after this stiff-necked rebuff.
Whenever Miller was in central Scotland, Baird welcomed
him to his home; and for the rest of his life, Miller was an

occasional visitor and correspondent. Indeed, one of Miller's most interesting letters describes a visit to Baird when the old man was prostrate with illness and grief at the extravagance (Miller suggests criminal extravagance) of his son.

What did Baird think of Miller's manuscript? He never saw it complete, since the second instalment was lost on the way to Edinburgh. His reaction to the first part, however, was not more than polite. Acknowledging receipt of the manuscript, which was accompanied by a copy of Miller's letters on the herring fishery, he wrote:

> Believe me that both of these have at once confirmed and increased my estimate of the claims which I had previously conceived you to possess on public estimation.
>
> I shall wait with anxiety for Chapter second of your life, detailing your intellectual and poetical history from the time of your 'finishing your school education,' and your 'boyish waywardness.' Chapter first resembles the deep dark cavern into which you and your young friend took the desperate, downward, twelve feet leap; – Chapter second will resemble, I doubt not, that cavern as it afterwards appeared 'crusted on with a white stone resembling marble.' I have a telescopic view of this result similar to what you had when looking to the sea and opposite coast from the cavern's inmost extremity.[66]

Nor did Baird's tone change on reflection. A later letter simply says, 'I am gratified at learning that you are obligingly proceeding with your interesting auto-biography.'[67] Two years later Baird wrote to ask whether Miller had any objection to the first part of his manuscript 'being referred to in one of the literary journals, and parts of it printed therein?'[68]

Baird's query about publication sent Miller back to his manuscript again. He was of two minds about its quality, and began to show it to his friends with a view to publication. The only other reaction to Miller's autobiography that has been preserved is outspoken. Miss Dunbar of Boath was belatedly shown the two parts of the manuscript in 1833 and responded candidly. She found it exciting reading, but intensely disliked

the evidence it gave of obstinacy and willfulness. 'I was often
angry with you', she observes. She also found the references to
prostitutes towards the end of the narrative distasteful.

> Every page, every paragraph has to me an interest, a
> novelty, a freshness, in both the things told and the
> manner of telling them, that I never found in any work
> of the kind before. I devoured it, and yet prolonged the
> perusal of it for several days; and am now sorry that it is
> done. . . . How did Principal Baird receive the manuscript,
> and what is he to do with it? I was often angry with you
> in the course of the narrative. Why were you so very
> wayward, when you could have been so much otherwise?
> Why did you so cruelly disappoint your excellent uncles
> when you could so easily have more than realised their
> most sanguine anticipations? How much pain have you
> not given to hearts that were fond and proud of you. . . .
> Your dreams, your digressions, your anecdotes, your de-
> scriptions, have all a rare interest, and your style I deem
> beautifully correct, – but there is one objectionable pas-
> sage [about prostitutes]. The fact it conveys is strikingly
> illustrative, but you have sufficiently established your
> argument without it; and it is not in accordance with the
> pure character of the rest.[69]

Did Principal Baird see in the narrative the deficits of character
that Miss Dunbar saw? If so, one can understand why he did
not press the wayward and headstrong mechanic to move south.
Miller would clearly come to Edinburgh in his own good time,
but not before. The old man was prepared to be polite and
wait. As for Miller, he took Miss Dunbar's comments as encouraging, and began to plan revisions. 'I am glad you like my
memoir', he wrote:

> It is a simple story of little promise; what indeed could be
> expected from the subject of it; but I have formed a plan
> regarding it which may convert it into a very readable
> sort of thing. I am not vain enough to think that it can
> have much interest as a memoir of the life and education

of an obscure mechanic, but I have seen a good deal of character as exhibited both in classes and individuals, and from a rather peculiar point of observation, and the study of character is perhaps of all others the most popular. What I purpose therefore is to recast the whole narrative, and break it into chapters, to add a great deal and subtract a little, to occupy in it as I have done in life the part rather of one who has observed than of one who has acted, and then, if I have succeeded to the satisfaction of my friends and of myself, to commit it to the Press.[70]

The proposed revisions took many more years. The *Scenes and Legends* demanded attention in 1833 and gave Miller great trouble until its publication in 1835. Miller simply never found the time to return to the memoirs until they became the basis for *My Schools and Schoolmasters* in 1854, nearly a quarter-century later.

But we may well wonder why it was that Miller had already been mapping out an autobiography. For he was also at work on the first stages of the *Scenes and Legends*. Are we to use what we know about Miller's relations with his parents to help us? If so, it seems reasonable to conclude that the two projects, the autobiography (that is, the memoir published here) and the *Scenes and Legends* reflect his different loyalties to his father and mother. The memoir, which, like *My Schools and Schoolmasters*, makes almost no mention of mother, sisters or womenfolk, stands for the active side of Miller's life, the life dedicated to the emulation of his father. The *Scenes and Legends*, by contrast – a work of the Highlands, rather than the Lowlands – belong to the fairy-tale world of his mother. Indeed, Lydia Miller attributes the latter book directly to her influence: 'From his mother Hugh undoubtedly drew almost all the materials for his *Scenes and Legends*'.[71] Neither work is exclusively father or mother oriented. But if we regard the two books as forming part of a single process of composition, we can understand both the masculine tone of the first autobiography and its concentration on a relatively narrow range of topics. Hugh Miller is a story-teller in both books, but in the first autobiography he plays down the miraculous, which figures so strongly in the *Scenes and Legends*.

While at work on his letters for Principal Baird, Miller received a letter from Isaac Forsyth of Elgin, who had helped him to publish his poems. His reply to Forsyth constitutes a sort of supplement to the letters to Baird, explaining his position generally and trying – on the whole vainly – to integrate his work on the *Scenes and Legends* with what he had recently finished writing in the memoir. It is reproduced in Appendix I, pp. 231–4.

Self-made Men

The working-class autobiography came into being in parallel with the formation of working-class conscience. At the beginning of the nineteenth century agricultural labourers, factory workers, artisans, sailors and the vast population of the marginally employed did not recognise themselves as belonging to the same economic and social class. Millhands did not feel any solidarity with farmers, nor stonemasons to wheelwrights. But by the 1820s, an immense change had occurred. Inspired by such writers as Thomas Paine, radicals founded corresponding societies and trade unions, as well as a vibrant and outspoken press – all of which, in E. P. Thompson's classic formulation, 'made' the working class.[72] In this context of unprecedented self-awareness, the working-class autobiography became a means both of self-expression and of contributing to political and social identity.[73]

The earliest working-class autobiographies appear uncertain of their audience and their own idiom. On occasion they touch on a harsh truth or two, but rudimentary political analysis and lengthy descriptions of village life were typically held together with the kind of serviceable but unsightly filler that builders call 'clunch'. In a vituperative survey of ten recently published autobiographies, the *Quarterly Review* in 1827 deplored the autobiographical urge that seemed to encourage 'every driveller to do his Memorabilia', resulting in a 'mania for this garbage of Confessions, and Recollections, and Reminiscences'.[74] Not until the 1840s did the possibilities of working-class autobiography begin to be explored in depth and with literary distinction.

Autobiographies of working-class poets seem to have developed somewhat earlier than political autobiographies. This may be attributable to the support of Robert Southey, the poet laureate, who went to considerable lengths to encourage working-class poets to publish both their verses and their life stories.[75] While such poetry was often treated with condescension, the lives of poets, even 'persons in humble life and of defective education', were judged capable of producing interesting memoirs.[76] The Lancashire weaver-poet Samuel Bamford's *Passages in the Life of a Radical* (1844) met with such commercial success that he recounted his childhood in another volume four years later.[77] In 1848 Alexander Somerville's well-known *Autobiography of a Working Man* appeared in weekly instalments in the *Manchester Examiner* before publication in book form under the authorship of 'One Who Has Whistled at the Plough'.

The Society for the Diffusion of Useful Knowledge, which drew much of its inspiration from the Scottish tradition of the 'lad o' pairts', took as its working credo that there were working men all over the country anxious to improve themselves. One of its publications, George Lillie Craik's *The Pursuit of Knowledge under Difficulties* (1830), attempted to tell the story of successful self-made men through the ages.[78] Despite its dullness the most successful volume in 'The Library of Entertaining Knowledge', it prefigured Samuel Smiles's much better-known *Self-Help* of a generation later.[79] *Chambers's Edinburgh Journal* also took an interest in the careers of self-made men, because the Chambers brothers considered it their mission to supply working men with useful as well as entertaining knowledge.[80]

Miller, who was constantly on the look-out for yardsticks by which to measure his own achievements, was surely aware that he was working in one of the boldest and most innovative literary modes. The one first-rate model that Hugh Miller might have learned from, he probably had not seen. This was the short autobiography of William Gifford, first editor of the *Quarterly Review*, which appeared as a preface to his edition of

Juvenal in 1802 and was later printed in a popular collection of memoirs and letters.[81] Gifford, like Miller, was the son of a seaman who died when he was young, and he too had been brought up in a remote country town. Having developed literary tastes, Gifford's boyhood ambition was to become a schoolmaster, but he was instead bound by his guardian as assistant to a sailor and then as apprentice to a shoemaker. When his literary abilities became apparent in his early twenties, he was rescued from his apprenticeship by a perceptive surgeon and in due course sent to Oxford. Much of the appeal of Gifford's autobiography is that it is the story of a man already successful and accustomed to writing with a certain polish. Concise and elegant, there is nothing about it of the working man trying to make good, nor for that matter of the self-made man risen to eminence who is 'studious to conceal the poverty of his early childhood'.[82]

In his memoir, Gifford was anxious to explain how his translation of Juvenal had come to be written and why it had taken him so long to complete. He did not need to establish his credentials: he already had powerful friends from his Anti-Jacobin days and was a literary lion in his own right. Miller, by contrast, was still working as a stonemason in the graveyard at Cromarty. His was the voice of the working men whom the Society for the Diffusion of Useful Knowledge was trying to reach.

Miller seems to have set greater store on the anecdotes and reminiscences of his old school friends than on those of published writers. When his schoolmate Alexander Finlay wrote to him from Jamaica in 1836, reporting that he had made good as the proprietor of the Twickenham Park Estate at Spanish Town, Miller was able to reply with a comprehensive account of their old classmates. Five had died, three had become shopkeepers, one an unsuccessful painter, one a clergyman, and one a broken-down and disreputable failure. Of all their classmates, only Miller himself, John Swanson the minister, and Alexander Finlay the West Indian proprietor had in any sense made good.[83] Both were, in different ways, important to Miller.

John Swanson was Miller's lifelong friend and, towards the

end of Miller's life, one of the few people he regularly visited. *The Cruise of the Betsey* is the record of a sojourn with Swanson, who, as minister of the Small Isles, used a small sailing craft to visit his isolated parishioners. Alexander Finlay, having dropped out of Miller's life for many years, suddenly re-emerged with the letter from Jamaica in 1836: he had come across an article by Miller in *Chambers's Edinburgh Journal*. Miller's response shows him at his most informal, rejoicing in the chance to relive his childhood and astoundingly well-informed about his schoolmates (see Appendix II, pp. 235–9).

Hugh Miller's correspondence is full of enquiries about the careers of working-class writers. He was particularly interested in the career of Allan Cunningham, a stonemason like himself, who had settled in London where he supervised the workshops of Sir Francis Chantrey, the distinguished sculptor, and wrote prolifically on the side. Miller also enquired avidly about his contemporaries in the north of Scotland. A minor writer for the *Inverness Courier* named James Calder he discovered to be the parish schoolmaster at Canisbay in Caithness, but Calder was reluctant to write about himself. Miss Dunbar of Boath's protégé, John Strahan, the weaver-poet of Forres, was more forthcoming. The two men were linked by the interest of Miss Dunbar and by the fact that both had published a volume of poems in 1829. Miller rather liked the poems in Strahan's *Walter and Emma: a Tale of Bothwell Bridge, and Other Poems*. But Strahan's career mattered more to Miller than his poetry, and with the help of Miss Dunbar he succeeded in extracting from Strahan an autobiography that paralleled his own. This narrative which offers us a glimpse of a different type of working-class career from Miller's, appears as Appendix III, pp. 240–5.

The memoir that Miller wrote for Baird clearly determined the shape of his career as a writer: autobiography became his principal literary form. The memoir, as we have seen, was reworked as *My Schools and Schoolmasters*. *The Old Red Sandstone* is the story of Miller's discovery of the fossils of the old red sandstone. *First Impressions of England* and *The Cruise of the Betsey* record the events of two of Miller's summer holidays.

Only in *The Foot-prints of the Creator* and some of his last works did Miller move away from autobiography, and even then not very far.

As a literary figure, then, Miller must be considered primarily as a man who found in his own experiences sufficient material for a considerable number of books. Indeed, critics who have seen him primarily as a man of science or as a churchman have missed a key to Miller's life. Miller was a man devoted to the maintenance of his personal integrity, and he could maintain it only by constantly refreshing himself from the springs of his own personal experience.

The price that he paid for using autobiography as his medium was considerable. Though always direct and honest in his writing, Miller increasingly cast his work in didactic form. The habit took hold with his articles on geology for *Chambers's Edinburgh Journal* (see Appendix IV), which were overtly aimed at encouraging working men to take up scientific pursuits. By the time of *My Schools and Schoolmasters*, Miller was writing as an established man of letters anxious to lend a helping hand. When he was not thinking about himself as an institution, his writing was still as unforced and natural as in his first autobiography. But *My Schools and Schoolmasters* suffers from Miller's greater acquaintance with self-improvement books like *The Pursuit of Knowledge under Difficulties*. It is still a remarkable book, but one wishes for more spontaneity, more of the directness of youth. One is conscious of reading a Georgian story dressed up in Victorian clothes. There is even some bowdlerisation of the first autobiography: prostitutes, for instance, no longer 'disfigure' Miller's pages.[84]

More serious for Miller was the distortion of his own history. He was driven to present himself as a Scottish 'lad o' pairts' who by dint of his own exertions had risen from obscurity in society to move on his own terms among the rich and the great. *The Old Red Sandstone* opens with an exhortation to the working man to follow him and become a geologist. *My Schools and Schoolmasters* is dressed up as a textbook of self-help. And the publisher of a cheap edition of Miller's works had no doubt about how he should advertise them:

To the higher and more cultivated classes of society he
appeals by the purity and elegance of his style, as well as
by his remarkable powers of description, and his profound knowledge of the marvels of nature. To the hum-
bler classes and the working man, the story of his life –
himself originally a working man in the strictest sense of
the word, pushing his way upward to the distinguished
position which he attained . . . cannot fail to prove of
special value.[85]

Miller's autobiographical writings demonstrate very clearly
that he chose the 'lad o' pairts' motif, less because it corres-
ponded to the facts of his career than because it supplied him
with a useful disguise. Like the great plaid he wore out-of-
doors (as much, one suspects, from desire to flout the conventions of dress as from habit), the trappings of the 'lad o'
pairts' gave him, so he thought, the greatest possible individual
freedom.

Much is explained if we approach Miller at the time of his
memoir not as an artisan determined to do well in the world
but as a shy, sensitive man of quite unusual diffidence. To be
an artisan was to be capable of enjoying an obscure and independent life outside the normal conventions of polite society.
Hence Miller's declaration in refusing Principal Baird's offer
to bring him to Edinburgh, that 'I do not think I could be
happy without being independent, and I cannot be independent
except as a mechanic'.[86] To be a mechanic may not have been
gratifying in itself, but it did assure Miller effective independence.

There were also pressing psychological reasons why Miller
chose to remain a mechanic. Miller suffered from an acute
case of what he called 'Diffidence'. When in 1834 Miss Dunbar
of Boath reproached him for not visiting her at Forres, Miller
pleaded not pressure of work (as he had done on previous
occasions) but that same diffidence:

I shall . . . give you a full view of what you are yet only
acquainted with in part. In a case like the present it is
policy to be candid; – Is it not partial views and half

glimpses that convert bushes and stones into ghosts and witches?

There are a few excellent people in Cromarty whose company I deem very agreeable and whose friendship I value very highly, but whose thresholds without a special invitation I never cross. Why? Just because diffidence tells me that I am a poor mechanic, regarded with a kind perhaps, but still a compassionate feeling, and that if I but take the slightest commonest liberty of social intercourse it is at the peril of being deemed forward and obtrusive. Well, I receive an invitation and accept of it. I come in contact with persons whom I like very much; the better feelings are awakened within me; the intellectual machine is set a working; and I communicate my ideas as they rise. 'You chattering blockhead,' says diffidence, the moment I return home, 'what right pray had *you* to engross so much of the conversation tonight? You are a pretty fellow to be sure to set up for a Sir Oracle! – Well you had better take care next time. Next time comes, and I am exceedingly taciturn. 'Pray Mr Block,' says diffidence, the instant she catches me alone, 'what fiend tempted you to go and eat the Lady's bread and butter to night, when you had determined prepense not to tender her so much as a single idea in return? A handsome piece of furniture truly to be stuck up at the side of a tea table! – Perhaps, however, you were too good for your company and wished to make them feel that you thought so.'[87]

Contemporaries, encountering a tall, physically powerful, and determined man, found it hard to believe in Miller's diffidence. Determination, recklessness, even ferocity, perhaps – but not diffidence. In his years as a banker in Cromarty he took to carrying pistols to protect his firm's money and the habit persisted after he finally moved to Edinburgh. His friends never knew, when they met him in an out-of-the-way place, whether to expect a cheerful welcome or a pair of pistols at the ready.

When Miller did finally thrust diffidence aside and give up being a mechanic, he was fortified by the example of his cousin George Munro. It was Munro's career that had first encouraged him to turn stonemason, and it was again Munro who emboldened him to give up stonemasonry. When Miller went south to become a banker, he found Munro already established nearby as an engineer of high repute. George Munro also seemed to have discovered the secret of personal independence, never worrying about what people thought about him. While Hugh Miller brooded and fretted lest people think he was merely an ignorant mechanic, George Munro went gaily about his business.

Miller never attained such gaiety. The independence he sought through autobiography – from the pressures of his childhood, the conflicting values of his parents, the values of his workmates – was, alas, only a paper independence. Miller remained bound all his life to his childhood, his parents, even his workmates.

LIGHT AND SHADE

'The Story of My Education'

Hugh Miller's father, the master of a small sloop engaged in the coasting trade, was lost at sea when young Hugh was only five, and the lad was largely brought up by his mother and her relations. He had for a time a fairly easy life of it, drifting through a succession of local schools, uncertain what to do with his life, and penning dark, brooding schoolboy verses.[88] His writing seems occasionally to have given him aspirations towards authorship. While still at school he read voraciously. Starting with the standard works of Scottish patriotic folklore, Blind Harry's *Wallace* and a life of Robert Bruce, he ranged widely, reading everything he could find in the nooks and crannies of Cromarty: theology and travel, classical romances and fairy tales, the poetry of Shakespeare and Milton, and the essays of Goldsmith, Addison, and Johnson. By the end of his apprenticeship, Miller had read most of the books an educated man would have been expected to know towards the end of the eighteenth century. Miller would later claim that he had learned nothing at school, and had had 'a sadly mis-spent boyhood'.[89] As is clear from *My Schools and Schoolmasters*, Miller was not a conventional product of the school of self-help; the autobiography is a moral tale, urging upon others the importance of making proper use of school and book learning, with the suggestion that his own school had been life, and his schoolmasters his fellow-workers.[90] Miller makes it perfectly clear that his educational deficiences were self-imposed, not the product of a humble or hostile environment. Even so, Miller probably learned more at school than he acknowledged. He read widely and was encouraged to do so, and fashioned for himself an identity as a teller of (often tall) stories. At Cromarty Grammar School, the teacher recognised Hugh's native talent and placed him in the Latin class. Not apparently convinced that the history of Rome was worth learning a foreign language to appreciate, Miller rebelled. Then and later he marvelled at the absurdity of sending out into the world 'Latinists who caught fish and made shoes'.[91] He also fought other absurd rigidities and the gratuitous severity he found in school:

> The class to which I now belonged . . . had its round of spelling; and in these last I acquitted myself but ill; partly from the circumstance that I spelt only indifferently, but still more from the further circumstance, that, retaining strongly fixed in my memory the broad Scotch pronunciation required at the dames' school, I had to carry on in my mind the double process of at once spelling the acquired work, and of translating the old sounds of the letter of which it was composed into the modern ones. Nor had I been taught to break the words into syllables; and so, when required one evening to spell the word '*awful*,' with much deliberation – for I had to translate, as I went on, the letters *a-w* and *u* – I spelt it word for word, without break or pause as a-w-f-u-l. 'No,' said the master, 'a-w, *aw*, f-u-l, *awful*; spell again.' This seemed preposterous spelling . . . and so I spelt it as at first. The master recompensed my supposed contumacy

with a sharp cut athwart the ears with his tawse; and again demanding the spelling of the word, I yet again spelt it as at first. But on receiving a second cut, I refused to spell it any more; and determined on overcoming my obstinacy, he laid hold of me and attempted throwing me down . . . We swayed from side to side of the school-room, now backwards, now forwards, and for a full minute it seemed to be rather a moot point on which side the victory was to incline. At length, however, I was tripped over a form; and as the master had to deal with me, not as master usually deals with pupil, but as one combatant deals with another, whom he has to beat into submission, I was mauled in a way that filled me with aches and bruises for a full month thereafter . . . [A]ll I could do at this time was to take down my cap from off the pin, when the affair had ended, and march straight out of school. And thus terminated my school education.[92]

Having rejected the schools of Cromarty, Miller then rejected the opportunity to attend college in Aberdeen, though he was as well prepared as many other country lads. His model, in so far as he had one, was apparently the self-educated Robert Burns. Miller's aim in *My Schools and Schoolmasters*, in fact, was to suggest an alternative to formal education, not *faute de mieux*, but as an act of deliberate choice. The generations of pupils who were awarded *My Schools and Schoolmasters* as a school prize must have been puzzled by the contrast between the prize sticker and Miller's own preface. A typical prize sticker reads:

KILMADOCK SCHOOL BOARD

YEAR 1910–1911

PRIZE

AWARDED TO

PETER SMART – 7 YEARS PERFECT

FOR MAKING 98 OUT OF 100 ATTENDANCES DURING THE YEAR

Miller, however, far from having a perfect attendance record, was a self-confessed truant. Furthermore, he reveals himself in his note 'To the Reader' as hostile to educationists, whom he finds incapable of offering encouragement, and as a champion of self-education over formal education of any sort. Miller himself would probably have seen no contradiction. Formal education in reading and writing he took for granted. What he intended was to suggest that there are other routes to success than extended formal education. The audience he hoped to convince was not schoolboys but working men, apprentices and journeymen:

> It has occurred to me, that by simply laying before the working men of the country the 'Story of my Education', I may succeed in first exciting their curiosity, and next, occasionally at least, in gratifying it also. They will find that by far the best schools I ever attended are schools open to them all . . .[93]

This intention gives *My Schools and Schoolmasters* an unusually vital and open character. One has only to compare it with its English counterpart Tom Hughes's *Tom Brown's School-days* (1857), to recognise Miller's commitment to experience and change and Hughes's acquiesence in the ethos of a prescriptive class society. Hughes's ideal, as Christopher Harvie has recently pointed out, is the English gentleman, energetic, docile, and dim. Miller, by contrast, conveys the excitement of education, the almost sensual pleasure of self-improvement, and the world-opening possibilities of the book. Hughes sees childhood as a time for being moulded by team sports and the regimen of the school; to Miller it is a period for venturing towards unknown, possibly foolhardy, regions.[94]

Tales and Stories

There is another oddity about Miller's appeal to the working man to educate himself: Hugh Miller was never an ordinary working man, as must be clear to any reader of his autobiographical writings. Even in simple economic terms, he belonged to the upper stratum of Cromarty. Unlike most of his working-class contemporaries, who started work at eight or ten, he did not have to seek employment until he was seventeen. There is nothing in the memoir or *My Schools and Schoolmasters* to echo the experience described in contemporary autobiographies of foregoing meals or walking dozens of miles to buy a book or pen and paper. His father was not a working man but a shipmaster. Miller himself confesses that he and his friends John Swanson and Alexander Finlay looked down on the congregation of the Gaelic chapel because it consisted largely of poor labourers and weavers.[95] Even after he had become a dreamy stonemason, Miller was sufficiently recognised as part of the Cromarty 'establishment' to be elected to the old unreformed town council as a self-avowed representative of the 'conservatives'.[96]

Indeed, Hugh Miller's background was such that he could afford the leisure to pursue a liberal education. His extended childhood before he began to work and the long winters when he could not work as a mason gave him the opportunity to range from subject to subject. His self-selected curriculum was dictated by the availability of suitable books, but its scope is enormous. In Miller's memoir we watch him moving from the study of fortifications to chemistry, painting, mosaics, and astronomy, and even to palmistry and other secret arts.

When the moment for decision finally arrived, however, Miller was ill fitted despite the breadth of his interests to pursue any specific career. He should probably have gone to college at Aberdeen, as his uncles suggested, but he refused their offer of help, having noticed at the age of seventeen that stonemasons enjoyed independence, long winter holidays, and a certain acquaintance with letters.

Miller's apprenticeship proved to be an discomfiting experience. His master, no great hand at stonecutting, was forced by lack of employment at home to seek work as a journeyman outside Cromarty. Young Miller could have abandoned him, but chose to sample the discomforts and enjoyments of life as part of a team of itinerant stonemasons, doing jobbing work up and down the country. Miller's experiences of life as an apprentice were also refracted and heightened by his own reading. Although the conditions of his apprenticeship seem no harsher than the norm, he fell under the spell of Crabbe's poem 'The Borough' (1810) with its revolting portrait of Peter Grimes, the master who murdered his apprentices by cruelty. Letters home speak of his miseries and despair, as though he were (as he later put it) one of Grimes's 'poor, helpless mutes'.[97] In fact, his master was his Uncle David, an elderly, plodding man, but perfectly fair and kind.[98] Miller learned his trade the hard way; within three years he was a competent mason. He then worked for a time as a journeyman on his own account, travelling as far as the Gairloch in the west and the outskirts of Edinburgh in the south. The conditions in which men were expected to live in the countryside were terrible. 'A wretched out-house, – the genuine bothy,– furnished with a few rude stools, a few deal bedsteads, a few bowls of tin or earthenware, a water-pail, and a pot, – serves miserably to accommodate some eight or ten labourers.'[99] Despite his later praise for 'noble, upright, self-relying toil', Miller held no illusions about the grimmer side of working-class life. The rampant drunkenness, bullying and womanising of the community he had joined struck him as brutal and atavistic.[100] At the time he found refuge in writing, building 'houses during the day, and castles during the night'.[101]

That Miller sought refuge in stories – that he was driven to them by loneliness – is not particularly unusual. He seems early on to have used literature to win admiration, by reciting aloud to groups at school and at home. His showing-off even extended, once, to fighting off the school bully, whom he stabbed in the leg.[102] If story-telling and scrapping earned him respect, it did not generate more than a couple of close friendships. Even as a schoolboy, he could be touchy and aloof. And so reading became in his later childhood more and more a form of communion with a private world rather than a means of access to public approbation. This transition enforced the formation of Miller's sense of self less in relation to others than through a kind of interior dialogue. In his reading, Miller found stories and characters he could recount to others and to himself; in the telling he began to forge his own identity. This formative process probably accounts not only for the extraordinary intimate connection he seems to have felt towards long-dead authors and their works, and the consuming need he felt to possess them almost as if they belonged to him, but also for his recurrent invocations throughout his life of defining images from literature.[103]

Miller as a writer did not simply draw on the experiences of other writers; that would have been conventional enough. What is striking is the extent to which he modelled himself on fictional heroes. His life at certain junctures seems almost to have been a kind of plagiarism, imitating literary reality. Miller tried on various literary styles: the polish of Pope and Gray, the vividness of Macaulay, the music of Milton.[104] It was finally Sir Walter Scott who won him over, body and soul. This is hardly a surprising choice: to have been alive and literate in the nineteenth century was to have breathed in the Waverley novels.[105] Many Scotsmen revered Scott: Allan Cunningham, when a mason's apprentice in Nithsdale, walked eighty miles to Edinburgh for the sole purpose of seeing his hero pass along the street, and Robert Chambers considered him an object of worship.[106] Miller, too, worshipped Scott.[107] One of the greatest joys of his adult life was to see a copy of his newspaper, the *Witness*, deposited in the stone foundation of the monument raised to Scott in 1840.[108] As Dorson has noted, Scott's name runs through Miller's *Schools and Schoolmasters*, 'like a Greek deity'.[109] It is striking that Miller almost always mentions Scott's name in an autobiographical context; that is, Miller makes Scott and Scott's narratives part of his own story. What Miller found in those narratives was a world of heroes and demons, of clear moral distinctions. Three particular features of Scott's fictional world seem to have had a striking effect on him.

First, Scott's work offered an approachable, if not wholly attainable, ideal of manhood and manliness, or what Samuel Smiles called 'a path and saviour of manhood'.[110] Scott himself was perceived as the archetypal 'manly' author, like his

fictional creations powerful, independent, courageous, patriotic, chivalrous and heroic.[111] A second feature of Scott's work
that resonated in Miller is the position of the male hero surrounded by dark and hostile forces, difficult to define or to
combat. Witches, demons, women disguised as men, and male
skalds people the Waverley novels and Scott's verse taunt-
ing, beckoning, luring men into their castles to isolate them
from their civilisation.[112] Scott's heroes, their courage notwithstanding, are thus understandably ill-at-ease. 'Apprehen-
sion', 'vexation', 'anxiety', and 'fear' permeate the novels,
from *The Heart of Mid-Lothian* through *Ivanhoe* to *Old Mortality*, giving the Waverley world a thickly menacing atmosphere.[113]

Calvinism as a system of belief failed Miller only once, but
in a way that was perhaps to prove fatal: it failed to provide
him an explanation of the supernatural. The great Highland
evangelical preachers of the eighteenth century had had no
difficulty accepting the supernatural. The celebrated 'Master
Lachlan' – the Reverend Lachlan Mackenzie of Lochcarron,
whose crazed sister figures in Miller's story of the Gairloch –
was famous for his power of divination, or second sight. Miller,
however, was torn. On the one hand, there were the Calvinist
seers of old, from one of whom, Donald Roy, Miller was descended. On the other hand, literate men no longer believed in
witches, and prophecy had very nearly died out. How was he
to reconcile the two?

Miller was at his best when writing about the supernatural.
He wrote in the simple, direct style of the born story-teller,
suggesting by a certain quizzical quality that part of the attraction of the tale arose from the fact that he and his audience
were consciously suspending the everyday rules of disbelief.
His writings are full of ghosts and spirits and prophecies. Even
the sober memoir describes a dream foreshadowing a friend's
death, a magical cure, and a discussion of the relations between
supernatural insight and madness in the aged Mrs Mackenzie.

Miller's stories of Cromarty suggest that his mother was by
no means alone in her preoccupation with the occult. The
neighbouring parish of Resolis was shaken by a series of witch-

craft cases in 1830, and there were several practising witches
in the locality.[114] Against bogus witches and mere superstition
Miller set his face. But he took it for granted that supernatural
forces were at work, and he liked to tell stories in which the
supernatural rose to the defence of Calvinism. One of the best
of these stories describes the journey of his ancestor Donald
Roy, one of the foremost eighteenth-century Highland evangel-
icals, to the parish of Urray with three laymen to assist at
communion.

> They reached the confines of the parish towards evening,
> and when passing the house of a gentleman, one of the
> heritors, they were greeted by the housekeeper, a woman
> of Nigg, who insisted on their turning aside and spend-
> ing the evening with her. Her mistress, she said, was a
> staunch Roman Catholic, but one of the best creatures
> that ever lived, and, if the thing was possible, a Chris-
> tian; – her master was a kind, good-natured man, of no
> religion at all. . . . Donald's companions would have de-
> clined the invitation, as beneath the dignity of men of
> independence, and elders of the church, but he himself,
> though quite as much a Whig as any of them, joined with
> the woman in urging them to accept of it. 'Sure I am,' he
> said, 'we have been sent here for some special end, and
> let us not suffer a silly pride to turn us back without our
> errand.'
> There was one of the rooms of the house converted by the
> lady into a kind of chapel. A small altar was placed in the
> centre; the walls were hollowed into twelve niches,
> occupied by little brass images of the Apostles. The lady was
> on the eve of retiring to this place, to her evening devotions,
> when the housekeeper came to inform her of her guests, and
> to request that they should be permitted to worship
> together, after the manner of their church, in one of the
> outhouses. Leave was granted, and the lady retired to her
> room. Instead, however, of kneeling before the altar, as
> usual, she seated herself at a window. And first there rose
> from the outhouse a low mellow strain of music, swelling

and sinking alternately, like the murmurs of the night wind
echoing through the apartments of an old castle. When it
had ceased she could hear the fainter and more monotonous
sounds of reading. Anon there was a short pause, and then a
scarcely audible whisper, which heightened, however, as
the speaker proceeded. Donald Roy was engaged in prayer.
There were two wax tapers burning on the altar, and as the
prayer waxed louder the flames began to stream from the
wicks, as if exposed to a strong current of air, and the saints
to tremble in their niches. The lady turned hastily from the
window, and as she turned, one of the images, toppling
over, fell upon the floor; another and another succeeded,
until the whole twelve were overthrown. When the prayer
had ceased, the elders were summoned to attend the lady.
'Let us take our Bibles with us,' said Donald, 'Dagon has
gotten a wearifu' fa', and the ark o' the Bible is to be set up
in his place.' And so it was; – they found the lady prepared
to become a willing convert to its doctrines; and on the
following morning the twelve images were flung into the
Conan. Rather more than twenty years ago a fisherman
when dragging for salmon in a pool of this river, drew
ashore a little brass figure, so richly gilt that, for some time,
it was supposed to be of gold; and the incident was deemed
by the country people an indubitable proof of the truth of
the story.[115]

Miller enjoyed the vividness and action that pervaded stories
of the supernatural. In an 1837 letter to Robert Chambers
suggesting that *Chambers's Edinburgh Journal* publish some
of his stories, he wrote:

> Superstition . . . is not at all the same sort of thing in
> these northern districts of the kingdom that it is in those
> of the south. It is no mere carcase [sic] with just enough
> of muscle and sinew about it for an eccentric wit to ex-
> periment upon now and then by a sort of galvanism of the
> imagination, but an animated body, re[d]olent with the
> true life. I am old enough to have seen people who con-
> versed with the fairies . . ., and as for ghosts, why, I

am not very sure but what I have seen of ghosts myself. Superstition here is still living superstition, and, as a direct consequence, there is more of living interest in our stories of the supernatural and more of human nature.[116]

Though Robert Chambers published the articles Miller submitted, he felt bound to reprove Miller for his preoccupation with superstition:

if you could avoid superstition and improbability, and shift the scene from your dearly beloved Cromarty my brother and I should be better pleased with your productions. We desire above all things a moral interest in our articles.[117]

Interest in the supernatural had weakened in Edinburgh, as it had not in Cromarty, and Miller was in danger of finding himself an anachronism.

But Miller never did give up his preoccupation with the supernatural. He worked away quietly at the *Scenes and Legends* long after he had moved to Edinburgh, and included a whole series of new ghostly stories in the expanded version published after he had become famous. The supernatural remained a phenomenon of everyday life for Miller because he continued in maturity to draw his ideas not from Edinburgh but from the Cromarty of his childhood. At bottom, only Cromarty had any real meaning for him. It was a community, not a chance agglomeration of individuals like Edinburgh. It prized Christian values even when it resisted them, and displayed none of the indifference and worldliness of the capital. Above all, in Cromarty men came face-to-face with eternal questions, questions of life and death, the past and the future, unconstrained by transitory intellectual fashions. Like other fishing communities on the east coast of Scotland, Cromarty was preoccupied with death, whether caused by rising tides, shifting winds, or divine or devilish intervention.

Once he had decided to become a prose writer, Miller's position was an odd one. His working hours were spent as a stonemason in the graveyards of Cromarty, his leisure hours in

writing newspaper articles and versions of the local traditions
and legends that he had been collecting, almost unconsciously,
since early childhood. A gangling figure, somewhat uncouth
and remote in behaviour, he was anxious to escape the drudgery
of stonemasonry. For a time he contemplated emigration to
America with Lydia Fraser, a middle-class girl with whom he
had fallen in love. Instead a local merchant came to his rescue
in 1834, arranging for Miller to become an accountant in the
new Cromarty branch of the Commercial Bank. Miller was dispatched to Edinburgh and Linlithgow to learn his business. Two
years later he married Lydia and settled down to the not-too-
laborious work of running a quiet country bank. Meanwhile,
in 1835, he had published by subscription his first substantial book, *Scenes and Legends of the North of Scotland; or,
the Traditional History of Cromarty*. Over the next four years
he published many occasional pieces in the Edinburgh magazines, but his work made no great impression until publication
of the ecclesiastical pamphlet *Letter to Lord Brougham* in 1839.

In the *Letter*, Hugh Miller revealed for the first time that he
had the makings of a first-rate polemical journalist. It sets out
resolutely and precisely the reasons why Miller and others
found intolerable the existing system of ecclesiastical patronage, which could force an unwanted minister on a hostile
congregation. Uncertain what to do with the manuscript,
Miller sent it to Robert Paul, the manager of the Commercial
Bank in Edinburgh. Paul passed it on at once to the Reverend
R. S. Candlish, who was to become one of the leaders of the
Free Church after 1843. The manuscript passed from hand to
hand in Edinburgh, causing a great stir within what was known
as the Anti-Intrusionist Party in the Church. Miller was sent
for and offered the editorship of a new anti-intrusionist newspaper, which he accepted. For the rest of his life Hugh Miller
was to be a working journalist.

Speculations and Successes

The decision to publish the *Witness* in 1840 was something of
a gamble. Miller had no experience as an editor, and the
established newspapers in Edinburgh, led by the *Scotsman*,

were relatively strong. Nor was there any certainty that a sectarian paper would find enough supporters to survive. But Miller proved himself a first-rate editor. The *Witness* became at once one of the leading papers of Scotland, and by far the most influential of those on the Free Church side at the Disruption in 1843. Appearing twice weekly, the *Witness* had a style all its own. The leading articles were occasionally so hard-hitting that Miller was accused of excessive violence of language; their subjects were quite unpredictable.[118] Though the *Witness* made Hugh Miller famous, it had very little effect on his character. He longed for the holidays so that he could return to the north of Scotland. He still wore his Cromarty plaid. He was still fascinated by ghost stories, and troubled lest there be evil spirits around him. His leading articles were interfered with by no one; he alone wrote the editorial columns.

The Free Church of Scotland, of which Miller was one of the best-known members, was the outcome of a movement for regeneration of the national life of Scotland. It began as a revival of the old evangelical party within the established Church of Scotland, but the enthusiasm it awakened was too great to be confined within the conventional limits of the establishment. In the face of a ruling by the House of Lords that the Church must accept ministers who held valid legal titles from a patron (whatever the views of the parishioners), the leaders of the evangelical party founded their own national Church. Within twelve months of the Disruption of 1843 the new Church was functioning smoothly and had begun to amass what turned out to be an astonishingly rich endowment. In some districts, notably in the Highlands, the overwhelming majority of the population joined the Free Church. A strong sense of destiny, and evangelical zeal of remarkable intensity, pervaded the movement.

From the first, Miller's relation with the leaders of the Free Church were uneasy. As Peter Bayne, his biographer, points out, they differed strikingly in style:

In religion Hugh Miller was an Evangelical, but in literature he belonged essentially to the Moderate school.

His literary ideal was that of grace and elegance, and quiet glow of imaginative fire; from declamatory vehemence and the strut and stare and swagger of the modern 'earnest' school, he shrunk with sensitive repugnance.[119]

Though Miller appears to have invented the name of the Free Church of Scotland, he clung to the vision of a partnership between church and state, and abhorred 'voluntaryism' – the ideal of a free self-governing church entirely independent of the state – which was increasingly the declared aim of the Free Church.[120] In politics he was not in the least a party man; he was, as he put it in 1847, 'more a Protestant than a Politician', disconcerting those Free Churchmen who saw an opportunity to strengthen their Church by forging an alliance with the Whigs and Liberals.[121] Even in social matters Miller was often at odds with the majority of the Free Church, expressing far more concern about the conditions of the Highlanders and the urban poor than about the feelings of the Free Church leaders. Small wonder that repeated attempts were made, notably in 1847, to put a more pliable man in his place.

The bent of Miller's mind was in every way speculative. Temperament inclined him towards speculation, and his reading confirmed his predilection. The bias of Scottish education towards philosophy rather than the classics, the Calvinist insistence of the Scottish Church on a comprehensive and highly structured system of belief, and the example of the great eighteenth-century philosophers all encouraged Miller, like many other Scots, to try to fit his own experience into a broader pattern. Miller was eager to construct a general theory about almost anything: the development of nations, the spirit world, the Church of England, poetry, a fossil.

Miller described himself as a Whig, by which he meant that he endorsed recognition by the state of the divinely ordained Presbyterian Church of the Covenanters as the central feature of the Scottish polity. After the Revolution of 1688, church and state, each in its own sphere, had entered into a blessed alliance for the spiritual and material good of the people of Scotland. The Revolution settlement embodied a grand principle: that Christianity requires men to behave as responsible beings and rejects all forms of irresponsible authority, whether kings or bishops. In an early pamphlet entitled *The Whiggism of the Old School* (1839), Miller wrote that

> The inevitable hostility of Christianity in its purer forms to irresponsible authority, however strengthened by ancient prejudice or unjust laws, arises . . . from two grand principles, – the recognition of a paramount code, to which every other code must yield, and an intellectual discipline, through which men are raised to a freedom and dignity of thought incompatible with a state of political servitude.[122]

Miller at first proposed calling the paper the *Old Whig*, so strongly did he feel about Whig principles. One of the aims of the paper, its prospectus proclaimed, was to advocate the 'spiritual independence of the Church' and to oppose the 'gross and selfish tyranny' that the Church had successfully fought off in the sixteenth and seventeenth centuries.[123] The government of the church and the nation was to be vested in men with sufficient character to bear the weight of responsibility, and not to depend on the counting of heads. What was needed, as in the seventeenth century, was a church whose ministers and elders were strong enough to lead the whole country.

In unregenerate man, guided by his own will, Miller had no faith whatsoever. His ideal society was one that embodied spiritual values and discouraged worldliness. His heroes were the Covenanters, godly peasants and god-fearing burgesses whose simple society prized spiritual excellence. Miller abhorred the degradation of modern urban life, and particularly the squalor of the Edinburgh slums. He saw corruption in every social class, however, and never ceased to condemn it. The *Witness* denounced landlords for championing false values: for valuing pride of ownership over religion in championing patronage in the Church, for setting sheep above men when they turned men out of their homes, forgetting that even tenants may be men and Christians, and by setting a bad example to the lower classes. Farmers he condemned for adopting the bothy or barrack system for housing their labourers. They were guilty, he said, of housing their labourers worse than their cattle.[124]

As early as the first edition of the *Scenes and Legends* (1835), however, Miller made it clear that 'no similarity of political principle' would ever lead him to support the Whig aristocracy as such.[125] They must prove themselves by just actions before he recognised them as true Whigs. The local Whig party leaders in Cromarty regarded him as a troublemaker because he charged them with putting personal ambition before principle. Not that Miller was in any sense a Radical. Quite the reverse. In one of his characteristically grim light-hearted moods he wrote in 1833 that 'we are much infested in Cromarty by a kind of vermin called Radicals, and have not yet got an act of Parliament for knocking them on the head'.[126] Derogatory remarks about Radicals are scattered throughout his letters, most notably in remarks on a meeting in Linlithgow, addressed by its Radical M.P.:

> The speech . . . might, perhaps, pass without remark in an inferior debating society; but there was a sad lack of taste about the parts in which the speaker attempted to be fine, and a deplorable deficiency of grasp when he strove to be sensible. His audience, too, seemed miserably low, and, with all the good-will in the world, had hardly sense enough to applaud. Wherever I looked I saw only low, narrow foreheads, and half-open mouths. What can such people know of the most difficult of all sciences – politics?[127]

The cornerstone of Hugh Miller's polity was the Church of Scotland, whether the undivided Church or the breakaway Free Church that claimed to be the true upholder of the Presbyterian tradition. For Miller, it was not just one Protestant church among many: it was the only church that succeeded in penetrating the mysteries of the universe and setting out God's plan for the world. Moreover, its sphere was unlimited. It was responsible for keeping watch over government and public order, as well as for preaching the Gospel. It was responsible, through the parochial schools and the poor law, for feeding the minds and bodies of the people as well as their souls.

The claims of the Church were all the more pressing for Miller in that he had discovered his religion for himself. Though well grounded in the Calvinism of his mother and his uncles, he had drifted away from religion quite young, and as a young man was something of an infidel. He writes in *My Schools and Schoolmasters* that 'wavering between the two extremes – now a believer, and anon a sceptic – . . . I lived on for years in a sort of uneasy see-saw condition'.[128] One can detect the traces of scepticism in his memoir, with its search for purely secular explanations of the human condition. Miller underwent a gradual spiritual conversion about 1830, and thereafter settled down into evangelical orthodoxy. The agents of this conversion were his school friend John Swanson, who was to become a well-known evangelical minister, and the parish minister of Cromarty, Alexander Stewart, esteemed by many as the leading evangelical preacher in Scotland after Thomas Chalmers.

Miller's evangelicalism was deeply rooted in the evangelical tradition of the seventeenth century, rather than the Methodist-oriented evangelicalism of the late eighteenth century (which Miller deplored).[129] Its central tenets were the grandeur of the divine order, the magnificent sweep of the orthodox Calvinistic system, the depravity of man, and the great joy of the Redemption. Miller's religion seems to have reconciled the various strands of his own experience: the teachings of his mother and his uncles, his urge to emulate his father, his own personal experiences, his discoveries as a geologist, and his quest for an all-embracing system. In the finest, most poetic passages in the *Testimony of the Rocks*, his last work, he was in effect preaching a sermon designed to reconcile his seventeenth-century Presbyterianism with modern scientific thought.[130]

The burden of running a newspaper virtually single handed occasionally tempted Miller to think of seeking an alternative career. He hoped at one point to become Professor of Natural History at the University of Edinburgh; the chair would have allowed him to pursue his geological studies and to become a professional scientist. But his lack of a scientific education –

indeed, any education – was too strong an obstacle to overcome. Other posts that were offered him, such as that of Distributor of Stamps for Perthshire, would have condemned him to a life of quiet obscurity. The *Witness*, for all its problems, gave him a public platform and made him a national institution.

MILLER AND THE BARBARIANS

Because most of Miller's sociological writing remained unpublished in his memoir, he has never received his due as a sociologist. That he was a keen student of sociology, however, no reader of the memoir can doubt. Indeed, an overemphasis on sociology threatens the unity of the narrative. Family and friends, even chronology, are pushed to one side to provide elbow-room for a serious discussion with Principal Baird, to whom the manuscript was sent in the form of two long letters.

Already Miller has a well-thought-out approach to social problems. His aim, he writes, is to use incidents in his own experience as a peg on which to hang general arguments:

> By the poor student of chemistry the iron spoon and tobacco pipe must be often employed in carrying on his experiments, instead of the retort and the crucible. It is thus with the student of human nature. He must often judge of such of the more striking and wonderful phenomena of his subject as can only be properly displayed in the midst of unusual circumstances, by minutely observing such of their partial half-defined lineaments as comparatively common occurrences render visible. . . . I cannot avoid being of opinion that human character, whether it be that of nature, – or . . . that of manners, and particularly the latter, is better delineated by enumerating its peculiar aberrations from the standards of reason and morality than by marking out its points of conformity to these standards. The least striking of all characters is the living manual and personified argument. (pp. 149–50)

This was also the method Miller used in geology: he would examine a fossil, however imperfect, and try to imagine its form and habitat. Then, relating it to other fossil creatures, he would move on to a general theory of the movements of the earth and tides, many millennia ago. In sociology, however, Miller does not confine himself to this method of argument. When it proves cramping, he chooses to treat his subject as a 'living manual and personified argument'. Thus he writes about the Highlands of Scotland in terms both of particular events and of general problems, which we would today classify under the general heading of underdevelopment.

Miller and the Highlands

Miller had a strong personal interest in the Highlands. Many of his ancestors were Highlanders, his uncles and cousins were Highlanders, the neighbours at Resolis who were plagued by witchcraft were Highlanders, and much of his apprenticeship had been served in the Highlands. Miller even occasionally regretted that he knew no Gaelic (his friend Swanson learned the language and preached in it). In *The Cruise of the Betsey* he writes nostalgically:

> It was my misfortune to miss being born to this ancient language, by barely a mile of ferry. I first saw the light on the southern shore of the Firth of Cromarty, where the strait is narrowest, among an old established Lowland community, marked by all the characteristics, physical and mental, of the Lowlanders of the southern districts; whereas, had I been born on the northern shore, I would have been brought up among a Celtic tribe, and Gaelic would have been my earliest language.[131]

To Miller the Highlands represented a double challenge, and one to which he reverted often during his life.[132] Superficially, there was the commonplace confrontation of Highland and Lowland values, which attracted the attention of so many eighteenth-century Scots. The Highlands, from this vantage-point, seemed to stand for a negative: rejection of the Enlightenment and rejection of material prosperity. The Highlands were also, as Miller knew well, proverbially credulous and superstitious.[133] But there was a deeper level of challenge for Miller whose childhood may well have encouraged him to identify the Lowlands with his father and the Highlands with his mother. The challenge at this level was not merely intellectual: it involved the whole of Miller's personality. This may be why Miller writes with such feeling in his memoir about the demented Mrs Mackenzie, who lives half in the mundane world and half in the supernatural, and whom he clearly identifies with his mother (pp. 126–30). Because he is writing in the masculine idiom, he cannot fully approve of her, but he appears to be reaching out to her in instinctive sympathy.

Miller resolves brilliantly the problem of how to talk about the Highlands. He takes one of those little incidents on which he loved to base general arguments, and holds our attention until we see just what he is about. Miller and a companion, needing a labourer to help them, approached the best-kept among some nearby cottages.

My companion who from the acquaintance with the Gaelic, was best fitted to take the lead, stepped up to the door; and bending his head to accommodate himself to a lintel raised nearly four feet above the soil, he plunged into a gulph which, unseen in the darkness, yawned behind the threshold, and immediately disappeared. He had fallen into the dunghill, which, according to the laudable custom of this part of the country, lay entrenched behind the door. We spent about half a minute in this singular antechamber, groping for the inner opening, which we at length discovered by the bursts of smoke which issued from it. The threshold was raised to the level of that of the outer door. We climbed up, stooped and entered. In the centre of the floor there smouldered a large peat fire, from whence eddied huge volumes of smoke, that at the height of about four feet spread over the whole apartment, – forming a ceiling as smooth, and apparently as tangible as one of plaster. On one side of the fire and dimly discovered by the light there sat a strong looking, red headed, red bearded man, and opposite to him his wife, the mistress of the mansion – a woman of dark, pale complexion, but a rather agreeable expression of countenance, who was busied in spinning on that primitive implement, the distaff and spindle. My companion stepped forward and introduced himself to the High-lander; who received him with a courtesy peculiar to his country, and then turned to me; but as we spoke no common language our conference was summed up in a nod and a smile. In half a minute we were seated by the fire on a large settle, and when my companion was em-ployed in opening to our host the cause of our visit I was occupied in transferring to my memory by minute observation, a picture of the apartment . . . When I had finished my survey I turned to the speakers, and observed that the tone of their conversation had considerably changed. It was no longer that of business, but deep and sympathetic, and it struck me that I myself was the sub-ject of discourse. The woman, who had hitherto been silent, now joined in the dialogue with exclamations of the tenderest pity. 'O,' said my companion, addressing me, 'if you only knew how much you are obliged to these kind people.' 'For what?' 'For their sincerest pity.' 'And what makes me its object?' 'Why, what but your being a Lowlander, and your ignorance of the Gaelic: – are there other circumstances think you that could give you an equal claim!' (pp. 177–8)

This important incident in Miller's life 'first furnished [him] with a key for laying open a principle in the Celtic character' (p. 179). Such generalising, in turn, enabled Miller to edge away from his mother's fireside and bring to bear on her values the impartial rhetoric of the Enlightenment.

The Highlanders, Miller argues, represented a distinctive system of values with which all Scots must come to terms.

The rude Celt, amid all his privations, is contented with his condition, and in consequence his chief pleasure does not consist in acquirement. He is respectful [to persons of higher social standing], because he feels none of that jealousy of wealth and power (a consequence of discon-tent) which constitutes the Whiggism of the lower class

in great towns; and he is hospitable because, according to
the remarkable language of Revelation, he deems it more
blessed to give than to receive. (p. 181)

The problem was how to think about Highlanders in the
abstract. Should they be compared to American Indians or to
the Aboriginals of Australia? Should they be compared to children, as suggested by the theory that human societies pass
through a life cycle, just as do individuals? In other words, did
his father – as he believed – belong to a higher form of culture
than his mother?

Miller was clearly attracted to the notion that societies have
life cycles. Unexpectedly, however, he does not use the typology
to the disadvantage of the Highlander, whom he sees as making
up in youthful, uncorrupted vigour what he lacks in intellectual
development. (The Highlander is also superior in the, admit-
tedly condescending, sense that he makes a more revealing
object of study). Miller's case is most concisely set out in
his memoir and in an exactly contemporary letter to Isaac
Forsyth:

States like individuals decay as they advance in years,
and they at length expire. Their progress from youth to
age includes two extremes and a medium. But in one
respect bodies politic differ from bodies natural; for in
the several members of the former there may be different
degrees of age. In this country there are districts peopled
by men who have not yet reached the medium lines, and
there are others whose inhabitants have gone beyond it.
Of the former kind are the Highland districts; of the latter
are the greater number of those of the Lowlands, – especially such of these as contain large towns. But it is only
among the lower classes that the differences of the several
stages are discernable; for the people in the upper walks
of society bear almost the same character all over the
kingdom. And it is perhaps only by an observer who is
placed on the same level with the former, and who
from this circumstance becomes intimately acquainted
with their manners, habits, and modes of thought, that at

least the minuter differences can be discerned. By such a person, however, if the theory be a just one, a tour through Scotland may be regarded not merely as a journey through various places, but also as an extended existence through different ages. (pp. 175–6)[134]

Miller claimed that this argument was founded on his own observations and had never been proposed before.[135] About the particular version he presents he is probably right, but earlier writers, notably Giambattista Vico in his *Scienzia Nuova* of 1725, had argued that all nations and cultures pass from birth and adolescence through maturity to old age and dissolution.[136] Miller's argument is unusual in suggesting that different segments of the population of a given state can be at different points in the life cycle.

Miller is anxious not to be misunderstood to imply that Highlanders are inferior in every sense. Everything has the fault of its qualities: the Lowlander, further along in the life cycle, is better off materially, more enlightened, more civilised, but also more depraved. The Highlander is socially backward:

It is indisputable that the inhabitants of the Highlands have not yet reached the proper medium of civilization; and it is obvious that they must in consequence be marked by some of the peculiarities characteristic of the rude and early extreme of Society. (pp. 182–3)

But the Highlander is also, according to Miller (certainly influenced by the images of noble Highland clan life conjured up by Scott), 'in general happier and more virtuous' (p. 186). Moreover, he has the advantage that a people 'advancing towards the proper medium of happiness and virtue are in a better condition than those who are retrograding from it' (p. 186).

How then to reconcile Highland and Lowland? Mere mixing of the two will not do: '[t]he least interesting, least virtuous people of the Highlands are those who inhabit the districts that border on the Lowlands' (p. 186). Nor did transplanted Highlanders fare well in the Lowlands. (Was he thinking of

those who attended the Gaelic chapel in Cromarty?) The means
of reconciliation seemed to lie in seeking the 'golden mean'.

> But by the philosopher virtue whereever found, & hap-
> piness whereever enjoyed is not deemed other than virtue
> and happiness. – Perhaps the proper medium of civiliza-
> tion cannot be better defined than as that middle state in
> which the virtues & pleasures natural to the ruder stages
> of society are mingled with those peculiar to the stages of
> refinement. – And the exertions which are directed to
> hasten the advances of a people towards this state are
> truly philanthropic. (pp. 183–4)

In other words, the Highlanders needed more education and
material prosperity, the Lowlanders more virtue and attention
to things of the spirit.

Classes

Following his own advice, Miller attempted but failed to reconcile his father's values and his mother's. The Lowland and the
Highland dwelt side by side in him in perpetual tension.

Having elaborated a binary model of Scottish culture, Miller
appears to have succumbed to the temptation to see polar
contrasts all around him, dividing everything in two the better
to grapple with it. 'There are but two classes in the world'
expresses a typical sentiment of Miller's, whether he is distin-
guishing speculators from helots, small farmers from gentlemen
farmers, the Popish from the Puritan, employers from the employed or men from women.[137] Bifurcation was for Miller a
means of finding a central principle within a complicated
system through a process of redactive elimination. In some instances, the result is forced and crude, but the application of
an organic analogy to the society and culture of Scotland
works very well indeed. The analogy to gender is, for its part,
striking and imaginative.

Working men as a class aroused mixed feelings in Miller. He
continued to the end of his life to think of himself as a working
man, but recognised that other working men were less God-
fearing and prudent than himself. He wanted working men to

have better living and working conditions (and saw nothing wrong in collective bargaining), but was not optimistic that they could achieve them. He was willing to support strikes in principle, but saw in them the seeds of their own destruction: some strikes destroyed the livelihoods of those who participated in them, others of whole industries. And all strikes were liable to be subject to a circular process:

> We had to record in one brief paragraph, a few numbers since, the flight of two delegates of the Preston movement, – the one with twenty-five pounds of the defence fund in his possession, – the other with one hundred and sixty. And such are too generally the sort of men that force themselves into prominence in these movements. Inferior often as workmen, low in the moral sense, fluent as talkers, but very unwise as counsellors, they rarely fail to land in ruin the men who, smit by their stump oratory, make choice of them as their directors and guides. Too little wise to see that the most formidable opponent which any party can arouse is the moral sense of a community, violence and coercion form invariably the clumsy expedients of their policy. . . . We find in strikes, as they ordinarily occur, the disastrous working of exactly the same principle which has rendered the revolutions of the Continent such unhappy abortions. Who can doubt that the revolutions, like some of the strikes, had their basis of real grievances? But their leaders lacked sense and virtue; their wild license became more intolerable than the torpid despotism which it had supplanted; and in the reaction that ensued, the sober citizen, the quiet mechanic, the industrious tiller of the soil, all the representatives of very influential classes, found it better, on the whole, again to submit themselves to the old tyranny, than to prostrate themselves before the new.[138]

The origins of Miller's prejudices are apparent in his memoir. His experiences working in the south of Scotland had convinced him that the 'profligate mechanics of a large town' were simply barbarians, outside the pale of civilisation:

An almost total want of foresight is . . . common to the
extremes of both savage and civilized life. The Caffer or
Hottentot feasts in the evening on the game which he has
entrapped or run down during the day, and the spareness
of his meal, or the depth of his debauch is in proportion
to the scantiness or abundance of his prey. There is no
thought with him of the morrow, and his life is accordingly spent in the extremes of gluttony and starvation. –
The town mechanic receives his wages at the close of the
week, carries them to the tavern or bagnio, and seldom
returns to his employment until the whole is squandered.
When residing in the vicinity of Edinburgh almost every
week brought instances of this kind under my notice. On
a Saturday evening three of the Niddry workmen after
having received a fortnights wages, which in all
amounted to more than six pounds, went to Edinburgh,
and there spent the night in a house of bad fame. Next
morning they hired a coach, and accompanied by three
women of the town set out for Roslin on a jaunt of pleasure. They came back to Edinburgh in the evening, passed
the night, as they had done the preceeding one, and
returned to Niddry on Monday without a single shilling.
This piece of madness was much applauded as a frolic
that shewed no ordinary spirit. It brought to the remembrance of the other workmen exploits of a similar
character with the details of which they regaled one another for several days after. I was told of an Edinburgh
mechanic, a mason, who on the death of a relative received a legacy of about eighty pounds. He was no sooner
paid the money than he carried home his tool chest, and
shoved it under his bed. He then commenced a new
course of life. He bought an elegant suit of clothes; hired
a hackney coach by the week; attended all the fashionable amusements of the place; and regularly once every
day called in his carriage on his brother workmen. In six
weeks the whole of his money was expended. He then
took out his tool chest from under his bed and returned to
his former employment. (pp. 213–14)

This passage contains a good deal of sound sociological observation, as well as of prejudice. The underlying point that different social classes have different standards, not merely of behaviour but also of time, is a very interesting one. Interesting, too, is the development in *Scenes and Legends* of the idea of layers of belief, with those tales nearest in time having more creditworthiness than those dating from remote, perhaps pre-Christian days.[139] Alas, Miller does not elaborate. His Calvinism seems to choke off his sociological enthusiasm, and even the sense of fun he shared with his workmates. Whereas Highlanders emerge from his narrative as something more than ordinary men, workingmen fall below the line. The golden mean was for Miller an exacting standard.

MILLER AND GEOLOGY

As would anyone who spent his days amongst the caves and hills of Cromarty, and walked attentively along the beach and across the rocks, Miller as a child acquired an interest in geology. While learning his trade, he undoubtedly speculated about the rocks with which he worked, and cracked open nodules to find fossils. But the 'geology' he embraced as a young man turns out on closer examination to amount to little more than a poetic interest in the wonders of nature. In two autobiographical articles published in 1838 in *Chambers's Edinburgh Journal* under the title, 'Gropings of a Geologist', Miller quite wrongly implies an acquaintance with the science from the time he first became a stonemason, in 1820 (see Appendix IV). Miller described these articles in a letter as 'a sort of history of the rise and progress of geology in one solitary mind, furnished with abundant opportunities of observation, but cut off from all intercourse with minds employed in the same tract with myself, and unacquainted with books'.[140] Nor does this testimony square with *My Schools and Schoolmasters*, which associates Miller's discovery of geology with a great storm that blew down thousands of trees on the hill of Cromarty towards the end of 1830, exposing the underlying geological formations.[141]

The Old Red Sandstone is much nearer the truth of the

matter. There Miller makes it clear that he effectively discovered geology in 1834, only four years before publishing the
articles in *Chambers's Edinburgh Journal*. By the summer of
1834, Miller was already well known as a source of local information, and some of the many queries that came his way
were partly geological: an invitation to contribute the Cromarty section to the *New Statistical Account of Scotland*, requests
to guide visitors interested in geology, and a request to look
for fossils for his friend John Swanson. But Miller's reading
seems to have had a greater influence than the 'book of nature'
in directing him towards geology. He first came to grasp geology
as the result of reading a guidebook published by George and
Peter Anderson of Inverness in 1834, *Guide to the Highlands
and Islands of Scotland, Including Orkney and Zetland, descriptive of their Scenery, Statistics, Antiquities, and Natural
History*.[142] In *The Old Red Sandstone* Miller pays a generous
tribute to the fifty-page geological appendix to the Andersons'
Guide, his 'first assistance from without', which introduced
him both to 'the highest geological authorities' and to the
fossils of the north of Scotland.[143] By September 1834, though
he still disclaimed all technical knowledge – 'The entire province of Geology is a *terra incognita* to me' – Miller was trying
his hand at geological description.[144]

Even with the Andersons' manual to help him, however,
Miller still preferred to go his own way. As he ruefully confessed
to George Anderson in September 1834, this method was not
very satisfactory:

> Whatever may be the value of my [geological] specimens,
> and I am afraid they are very rarely of any [use] — my
> discoveries almost always turn out discoveries at second
> hand. I see it is a great matter to be acquainted with
> what has been done by others. I have spent week after
> week in arriving at a knowledge of facts which I could
> have acquired in a few minutes from the pages of a geo-
> logical catechism, had I but known that I might have
> looked for it there: – I have formed theories too at some
> little expense of thought, only to find that some more

fortunate speculator had built them up much more neatly, and long before. Sir Thomas D. Lauder, for instance, has anticipated my theory of the formation of the great Caledonian valley, and Mr Murchison in my hypotheses regarding the erection of the Sutors.[145]

Even so, he continued to follow his own line of enquiry, and by the beginning of 1838 felt himself sufficiently advanced to publish his articles in *Chambers's Edinburgh Journal* explaining how he had taught himself geology. These articles find Miller trading in some very broad speculations. Indeed, he used exactly the same method of generalising from particulars that he used in his sociological observations on the Highlands.

A new feature of the articles was that they were directed specifically towards working men. Miller was now a happily married bank accountant, anxious to encourage his former fellow-workers to follow his example. He adopts a suitably didactic style, in striking contrast to that of the memoir, which is almost entirely free of preaching. Miller's 'Gropings of a Geologist' are couched in the idiom of self-help (which was also to be the style of the introduction to *My Schools and Schoolmasters*). This stylistic shift was probably prompted by the journal in which it appeared as well as by Miller's own tastes. The object of William and Robert Chambers' magazine, was to 'better' the reading public by offering improving papers on scientific and literary topics, as well as on the just 'Formation and Arrangements of Society'.[146] The tone of the weekly was cheerful and bright but principally educative, and Miller's encouraging tale of self-education was well suited to it.[147]

The speculations in these two articles exemplify Miller's passion for theorising, as well as his characteristic use of binary oppositions to stimulate his thinking. The articles also reveal that even by 1838 Miller was not able to handle geological questions with any confidence; nor had he acquired much more than a rudimentary knowledge of the science. There were some good geological passages in the *Scenes and Legends*. Some important Cromarty fossils were circulating among geologists. And Miller had put together several small collections of

specimens – one in his own home, another in his friend John
Swanson's, a third in the Inverness Institution. But Miller as a
geologist had still to make his mark. It is characteristic that
he pursues this goal by trying to get the biographical record
straight. The articles represent an attempt to integrate his
new-found enthusiasm for geology into the rest of his thinking.
They thus combine his preoccupation with establishing the
psychological unity of his own life with his habit of generalised
speculation. They were Miller's way of preparing himself to
take the next big step, which was to compete with the leading
contemporary geologists on their own ground.

As is clear from these two articles, the geology that Hugh
Miller encountered in the mid-1830s was a very wide-ranging
science. One branch of geology concerned itself with the origin
of the physical world, addressing questions raised in the late
eighteenth century, particularly in Scottish geology, about the
degree to which the shape of the earth had been determined
by fire (volcanoes) and by water (glaciers).[148] Geology also
encompassed enquiry into the changing roles of living creatures
on the earth: the history of species, including the study of
hereditary transmission, natural history (zoology and botany),
and the vexing question of man's origins and place in nature.
The two approaches were linked methodologically by their
mutual dependence on investigation of the fossil remains of
living creatures. This was the great age of the fossil-collector.

Geological breakthroughs in the first thirty years of the nineteenth century brought about the overthrow of the notion of a
static universe. By the 1830s it was no longer possible to look
on the beauties of nature as the once-and-for-all creation
of a beneficent God. Sir Charles Lyell was essentially correct
(though not all of his contemporaries agreed) when he compared geologists to astronomers whose investigations had
opened up new worlds:

> The senses had for ages declared the earth to be at rest,
> until the astronomer taught that it was carried through
> space with inconceivable rapidity. In like manner was
> the surface of this planet regarded as having remained

unaltered since its creation, until the geologist proved
that it had been the theatre of reiterated change, and was
still the subject of slow but never ending fluctuations.[149]

Of comparably monumental significance was the geological
finding that man was a relative newcomer to the earth. The
fossil remains of many strange creatures had been found, but
no fossilised man. Man, it seemed, could no longer be regarded
as the centrepiece of creation.

The energies of geologists in the 1830s were largely directed
towards construction of a timeline of geological history. A
rough classification of geological periods had been compiled by
William Smith as early as 1799 and published in his pioneering
'Geological Map of England and Wales with Part of Scotland'
(1815) and his subsequent geological atlas of England and
Wales[150]. But Smith's classification scheme was rough and
ready, based on limited data. As Lyell's *Principles of Geology*
makes abundantly clear, very little was known even in the
1830s about the earlier geological ages. When Lyell published
his own classification scheme in 1833, the leading geologists
were hard at work trying to learn more: Adam Sedgwick and
Roderick Impey Murchison were both concentrating on strata
of rocks older than the Old Red Sandstone – what they called
the Cambrian and Silurian systems respectively. While Sedgwick and Murchison attempted to shed new light on the dawn
of geological history by describing rock formations, Louis
Agassiz in Switzerland was approaching geological history from
a new direction in his five-volume study of fossil fish.[151] Agassiz
had had to invent a brand-new system in order to classify
fossil fish, and his system inevitably involved a reappraisal of
existing geological classifications.

Luck and Cunning

Hugh Miller was in several respects lucky in the timing of his
turn towards geology. For one thing, the subject was arousing
great public interest in Britain. Societies opened their doors to
the newly fashionable science, newspapers and magazines carried reviews and reports on geology, and thousands of good

folk set off across the country to scan, pick, hammer, dig,
draw, and survey the land. Local and national collections
were assembled to exhibit fossils, rock and mineral specimens,
and other curiosities drawn from the earth, and the fantastic
remains of giant prehistoric reptiles were disinterred to general
astonishment. Almost everyone seemed hungry for information
about the revealed wonders of the earth.[152] According to Harriet
Martineau, writing in the 1840s (doubtless with some exaggera-
tion) 'the general middle-class public purchased five copies of
an expensive work on geology to one of the most popular
novels of our time'.[153]

Geology was not just popular throughout the land, it had
acquired immense prestige amongst the scientists of Europe
largely as a result of the contributions of Scotsmen. Indeed,
there arose in the early nineteenth century a distinctive 'Scottish Geological School' which as David Forbes put it 'once
made Edinburgh famous'.[154] Such figures as James Hutton, 'the
father of geology', Robert Jameson, Sir Charles Lyell, Sir Roderick Impey Murchison, and Leonard Horner made geology pre-
eminent amongst the sciences in the country.[155]

Miller was also lucky in turning his hammer to the Old Red
Sandstone, for this group of rocks was eliciting considerable
interest among geologists. Sedgwick and Murchison needed to
know more about it in order to relate it to their own systems.
Agassiz wanted to know about its fossil fish, which were virtually unknown. Living atop the Old Red, which is exposed at
Cromarty, Miller was in a position to make a scientific break-
through; what was wanted was simply more information. This
Miller set out to supply in the form of boxes of fossils sent to
Murchison and Agassiz. Almost all his fossil finds were new to
science, and one of them, named *Pterichthys Milleri* by Agassiz,
became famous for its beauty and importance. An anxious
period ensued before Agassiz pronounced Miller's fossils to be
fish rather than other prehistoric creatures. But it then became
clear, all of a sudden, that the Old Red Sandstone had been
populated by a numerous and remarkable tribe of fossil fish,
to which Agassiz assigned names. Formally one of the least
known of geological strata, the Old Red Sandstone became very

quickly one of the best known.[156] And Hugh Miller's *The Old Red Sandstone*, when it appeared in 1841, was eagerly welcomed by geologists.[157] Richard Owen described it as 'the most fascinating book ever written on a geological subject', Gideon Mantell, called it the most 'fascinating volume on any branch of British geology', geologists as renowned as Adam Sedgwick, Archibald Geikie, and Charles Lyell claimed to have been inspired by it.[158] The book was also a popular success and Miller had the satisfaction of discovering that the many amateur geologists he met on his rambles regarded it as he had regarded the Andersons' work of 1834 – as their basic guidebook. During a visit to Cromarty, recorded in *The Cruise of the Betsey* (1858), Miller was delighted to find the town a centre of scientific activity:

> The vessels in which the Crown Prince of Denmark voyaged to the Faroe Isles had been for some time in the bay; and the Danes, his companions, votaries of the stony science, zealously plied chisel and hammer along the Old Red Sandstone of the coast. A townsman informed me that he had seen a Danish Professor hammering like the tutelary Thor of his country among the nodules in which I had found the first Pterichthys and the first Diplacanthus ever disinterred; and that the Professor, ever and anon as he laid open a specimen, brought it to a huge smooth boulder, on which there lay a copy of the 'Old Red Sandstone', to ascertain from the descriptions and prints its family and name. Shall I confess that the circumstance gratified me exceedingly?[159]

Miller was also lucky that geology was the centre not merely of scientific but of theological controversy. That once-famous book, *Vestiges of the Natural History of Creation*, published in 1844, started off a controversy which seemed exactly to suit Miller and the *Witness* – he always knew when to seize the opportunity. In his last work, a revised version of a series of public addresses called *The Testimony of the Rocks*, Miller took up the challenge of reconciling the Biblical account of the creation of the world with the evidence of geology. This was just such a theme as to attract the readers of the *Witness*, who had watched Miller grapple with the topic month by month and year by year. At first Miller accepted the Mosaic account of a six-day creation as factual. But he soon came to regard the Mosaic tradition as poetically rather than factually true, and to think of creation as extending 'over mayhap milleniums of centuries'. 'Nature', he wrote, 'is a vast tablet, inscribed with signs . . . and becomes poetry in the mind when read'.[160]

Hugh Miller's individual achievements in geology lay in the field of description. He recognised, as did few other geologists, the importance of bringing to life the remote eras that geologists were exploring, which not only helped to make geology accessible but also encouraged scientists to pose probing, and rewarding, questions. Miller set out to master in his imagination the life captured in the Old Red Sandstone. He endeavoured, in essence, to bring his fossil fish back to life, and to paint a verbal picture of the lands and waters they inhabited. Every fossil fish introduced in *The Old Red Sandstone* was described in compelling and memorable images. 'Imagine the figure of a man rudely drawn in black on a gray ground; the head cut off by the shoulders . . .' introduces Miller's specimen of *Pterichthys*. The figure of *Coccosteus* is compared to a boy's kite, the tail-flap of the *Cephalaspis* to a Highlander's kilt, and *Glyptolepis* to the handle and bristles of a brush. Here, in full swing, is Miller describing the fins of the *Cheiracanthus*:

> The anterior edge of each, as in the pectorals of the existing genera *Cestracion* and *Chimera*, is formed of a strong large spine. In the *Chimera Borealis*, a cartilaginous fish of the Northern Ocean, the spine seems placed in front of the weaker rays, just, if I may be allowed the comparison, as in a line of mountaineers engaged in crossing a swollen torrent, the strongest man in the party is placed on the upper side of the line, to break off the force of the current from the rest. In the *Cheiracanthus*, however, each fin seems to consist of but a single spine, with an angular membrane fixed to it by one of its sides,

and attached to the creature's body on the other. Its fins are masts and sails, – the spine representing the mast, and the membrane the sail; and it is a curious characteristic of the order, that the membrane, like the body, of the ichthyolite, is thickly covered with minute scales.[161]

Miller's strong visual sense is apparent in the beautiful drawings in his manuscripts, and in the wonderfully clear engraved plates that illustrated his geological works. He could envisage his fossil fish as active living things far more vividly than most contemporary geologists. 'Fossil species', wrote a critic in the *Athenaeum*, 'however long extinct, live again in Mr Miller's pages . . . His fossil fish swim and gambol as if they were creatures of today.'[162] His skill at bringing the past to life through imaginative reconstructions made Miller stand out on the geological landscape of his day. (Readers today, like some 150 years ago, may find the prose too richly embroidered and contrived).[163] Murchison, for example, according to his biographer possessed barely any imaginative power and literary skill. Not surprisingly, he admired – and was not a little envious of – Miller's abilities.[164] So too did Lyell and Owen, while Buckland, a capable writer, declared that he 'had never been so much astonished in his life by the powers of any man as he had been by the geological descriptions of Mr Miller', and added that he would 'give his left hand to possess such powers of description as this man.[165]

GHOSTS AND HEROES
Loss and Recovery

Hugh Miller's widow and his biographer Peter Bayne both regarded his suicide as the key with which to unlock the secrets of his life. Bayne, like a modern psychologist, saw Miller as suffering from an identity crisis whose origins lay in his childhood. His whole life came to turn, according to Bayne, on the loss of his father for he had sought to model his life on his father's, and felt that he had failed.[166]

From all accounts Miller's father seems to have been a remarkable man, who rose from ship's boy to master and owner

of a fine sloop only to lose the ship at sea and begin all over.
By the time he died, he had built a fine house (entitling Hugh
to the franchise on the passing of the Reform Bill) and established himself as a prominent figure in Cromarty, renowned
for his physical strength, courage and honesty.[167] At the time
of his father's death, according to Bayne, Hugh Miller was at
a stage of development (which Freud would later term Oedipal)
in which his father dominated his life:

> He was only five years old when Hugh Miller, the elder,
> perished at sea; but he had already learned to love his
> father with an affection stronger than is common in
> childhood, and 'long after everyone else had ceased to
> hope', he might be seen on the grassy knoll behind his
> mother's house looking wistfully out upon the Moray
> firth.[168]

The image of young Miller gazing out to sea is touching. He
has left his home in spirit, and is poised to become the outdoor
boy and truant of the memoir and mature autobiography.
Only out of doors can he emulate his father. At home, as he
has already found during his father's absences, a different set
of values holds. As Erik Erikson observed about such homes:

> Where mothers dominate households the boy can develop
> a sense of inadequacy because he learns at this stage that
> while he can do well outside in play and work, he will
> never boss the house, his mother, or his older sisters.[169]

Hugh Miller may have looked to his father not merely as an
ideal but as his one hope of escaping from the bonds of maternal
dominance, so that when his father was taken from him he
felt doomed to perpetual inferiority. It is difficult to resist
interpreting Miller's subsequent aggressiveness and exaggerated
masculinity – evident in his demeanour as well as his writing
– as attempts to work through deep-seated feelings of inad-
equacy. Miller's hero-worship and attraction to powerful men
lend credibility to this interpretation. As Miller declared in a
letter to Baird in 1829, 'My curiosity is never more active than
when it has the person of a great man for its object.'[170] He

lived, it is true, in an age that celebrated great men – Thomas Carlyle elevated hero-worship into a kind of religion in the 1840s – and one should be correspondingly careful not to over-interpret Miller's hunger for heroes.[171] Even in his own time, however, Miller's hyper-masculine behaviour and preoccupation with heroism, his own and others, was striking and drew comment.[172]

Bayne also notes the discrepancy in age and talent between Miller's father and mother:

> Hugh Miller's father was at the time of his birth a man of forty-four; mature in every faculty; of marked individuality and iron will. His mother was a girl of eighteen, who had been brought up at her husband's knee, and had learned to revere him as a father before she accepted him as a lover. Throughout life she displayed no special force of mind or character.[173]

Clearly his father's death meant for Hugh Miller the loss of light and life from his home, a narrowing of range from hearty talk of seafaring voyages to the claustrophobia of a closed household. No wonder, Bayne seems to suggest, that young Miller escaped into the fields on long solitary walks; no wonder he used to watch for his father's sloop with its two square top sails.[174]

Miller's mother did not marry again until 1819, when Hugh was sixteen. Though he later claimed to have had 'no particular objections to the match', at the time it provoked in him 'much disgust'.[175] Disgust? The word recalls Hamlet's reaction to his mother's hasty remarriage. By remarrying, Miller's mother must have seemed to him to be betraying his father, whose image was still incandescently alive in his mind.

In discussing why it mattered so much to Hugh Miller that his father and mother were quite different, Bayne offers a startling revelation:

> Hugh Miller's mother was evidently one who, in the jargon of the spirit-rapping fraternity, would be called a good medium. Interpreted into the language of persons

who are neither knaves nor fools, this will mean that she was one who, having long permitted fantasy to be sole regent of her mind, had fallen into the habit of mistaking the pale shapes and flitting shadows of its ghostly moonlight for the substantial forms of noon-day.[176]

Miller's mother also wielded a very powerful influence over him, of which both Bayne and Miller's widow disapproved. Bayne elaborates:

> Her belief in fairies, witches, dreams, presentiments, ghosts, was unbounded, and she was restrained by no modern scruples from communicating either her fairy lore, or the faith with which she received it, to her son. Her faith in her legendary personages was inextricably involved with her belief in the angels and spirits of Scripture, and to betray scepticism as to apparitions and fairies was in her view to take part with the Sadducee or the infidel.[177]

A number of Bayne's stories about Miller's early childhood demonstrate that he shared some of his mother's fantasies, even to the extent of seeing the ghost of his ancestor John Feddes. Until the end of his life, Miller continued to enjoy 'a sustained intensity of mental vision, a creative power of fantasy' that Bayne regards as unhealthy.

> Not powerful enough to overbear or to pervert the scientific instinct with which it was associated, it had a pervasive influence on his mental operations; the feeling, belief, impression on his mind, had for him a substantive reality; and there was an antecedent probability that, if the steadiness of his intellectual nerve were shaken by disease, or by excess of mental toil, some fixed idea might obtain the mastery over him and hurl his reason from her throne.[178]

Bayne makes it plain that his information comes from Miller's widow, quoting a couple of passages she had written in such a way as to suggest that he was simply paraphrasing Lydia Miller.

Particularly telling is this passage about the trauma of Miller's childhood:

> Such was the powerful influence to which little Hugh was subjected for the first six years of his life – a kind of education the force of which he himself could scarcely estimate. Add to everything else that much of his mother's sewing was making garments for the dead. Fancy that little low room in the winter evenings, its atmosphere at all times murky from the dark earthen floor, the small windows, the fire on the hearth which, though furnished with a regular chimney, allowed much smoke to escape before it found passage. Fancy little Hugh sitting on a low stool by that hearth-fire, his mother engaged at a large chest which serves her for a table on which stands a single candle. Her work is dressing the shroud and the winding-sheet, the dead irons click incessantly, and her conversation as she passes to and fro to heat her irons at the fire is of the departed, and of mysterious warnings and spectres. Suddenly, as the hour grows late, distinct raps are heard on this chest – the forerunners, she says, of another dissolution. Her tall thin figure is drawn up in an attitude of intense listening for these signs from the unseen world. The child has been surrounded and permeated with the weird atmosphere. Then a paroxysm of terror supervenes and he is put to bed, to that bed in the corner, in a recess in the wall, where he can still see the work proceed, and hear the monotonous click-click of those irons, till his little eyes close, and the world of dreams mingles with that of reality. I have no doubt that the overpowering terror of those early times, the inability to distinguish between waking and sleeping visions, returned in his last days, stimulating the action of a diseased brain. The peculiarity of his mother's character told against him. There was plenty of affection, but no counter-balancing grain of sense of a kind which would qualify these tremendous doses of the supernatural. He did not learn to read so

early as most children – though, as he has told me, he
learned his letters first when almost in arms, off the sign-
boards above the shop-doors – so that, until after six, the
marvellous in its lighter and more harmless forms, as in
Jack and the Bean-stalk, &c., did not mingle with its
darker and stronger shadows.[179]

Miller's mother outlived him, and her preoccupation with the
supernatural lasted to the end. Bayne quotes Lydia's description
of her response to her son's death:

She told me that on the night of Hugh's death, suspecting
no evil and anticipating no bad tidings, about midnight
she saw a wonderfully bright light like a ball of electric
fire flit about the room, and linger first on one object of
furniture and then on another. She *sat up in bed* to watch
its progress. At last it alighted, when, just as she wondered, with her eyes fixed on it, what it might portend, it
was suddenly quenched, – did not die out, but, as it were,
extinguished itself in a moment, leaving utter blackness
behind, and on her frame the thrilling effect of sudden
and awful calamity.[180]

Everything suggests that Lydia Miller's interpretation of his
suicide would also have been Miller's own. Whenever he was
in low spirits and poor health, as in the year of his death, the
simple direct manliness of his father (with overtones of the
manliness of Christ) was apt to be overpowered by a dangerous
species of delusion derived from his mother. Indeed, his suicide
note suggests of a struggle with demonic forces that even the
name of Christ is not strong enough to disperse. It is as if he
were overcome by the return of horrid childhood fantasies
that can no longer be brushed aside:

My brain burns. I *must* have *walked*; and a fearful dream
rises upon me. I cannot bear the horrible thought. God
and Father of the Lord Jesus Christ, have mercy upon me.
Dearest Lydia, dear children, farewell. My brain burns as
the recollection grows. My dear, dear wife, farewell.[181]

Night Demons

In 1856 it was not merely remarkable for a man to be driven to suicide by demonic fantasies: it was bizarrely anachronistic. Miller's doctor, Professor James Miller of the University of Edinburgh, set down as carefully as he could the nature of Miller's fantasies:

> What annoyed him most . . . was a kind of nightmare, which for some nights past had rendered sleep most miserable. It was no dream, he said: he saw no distinct vision, and could remember nothing of what had passed accurately. It was a sense of vague and yet intense horror, with a conviction of being abroad in the night wind, and dragged through places as if by some invisible power. 'Last night', he said, 'I felt as if I had been ridden by a witch for fifty miles, and rose far more wearied in mind and body than when I lay down.' So strong was his conviction of having been out, that he had difficulty in persuading himself to the contrary, by carefully examining his clothes in the morning to see if they were not wet and dirty . . .[182]

Miller believed that he had been, literally, hag-ridden. Even in his Edinburgh home, having achieved prominence as a newspaper editor and proprietor, he was haunted by the folklore of the north of Scotland. There, as in other regions of Europe and North America where folk traditions were still strong, the motif was a familiar one.[183] A man wakes up in the morning exhausted; he has been ridden all night by a witch. The commonest denouement involves the bridling of the witch by another man, who rides her until she is exhausted. In other stories the witch is taken to a blacksmith and shod; the next morning a prominent woman in the neighbourhood, typically the minister's wife or an employer's wife, is found with horseshoes on her hands.

These stories share a simple theme: the witch is the woman-in-authority who has overstepped the natural role of woman by dominating (bridling) grown men. The conclusion restores the woman to a subordinate sexual role, compensating for the sense of impotency she invokes in the man in everyday life. The story is, indeed, one of the plainest expressions of male sexual frustration in folklore. Miller's wife had been partially paralysed some two years before his death, and there is every reason to suppose that his conjugal life was frustrating. (He and Lydia slept in separate rooms, and appear to have done so since 1839, if not earlier.)[184] But, of course, if all the men in the world who were sexually frustrated in 1856 had killed themselves, there would have been a sad thinning of the human race.

Sexual rejection may, however, have been combined in Miller's case with another type of rejection. The little we know about Miller's last years suggests that he and his wife, a noted writer of children's stories, had become estranged over matters of religion. Mrs Miller seems to have been a very intense, high-strung and intelligent woman. Her religion was of an orthodox evangelical variety, apparently much closer in tone than Miller's to the commonplace evangelicalism of the day. In doctrine she seems to have been a fundamentalist, and it is clear that she was unwilling to follow Miller in his abandonment of the literal truth of Genesis. The evidence is sparse but there is enough to suggest that Miller believed his wife to have rejected both his geology and his religious beliefs, as well as the mystic streak he had acquired from his mother. In view of the end of their marriage, there is a particular poignancy in a message Hugh Miller wrote to his wife not long before they were married:

> However diverse in our tastes, however different in our opinions, however dissimilar in our philosophy, let us at least desire, my own dearest Lydia, to be at one in our religion.[185]

The weight of Miller's sense of rejection may be deduced from a curious passage in another letter that Miller wrote to Lydia while they were still engaged. The theme is friendship, but the entire passage is framed in explicit sexual terms. Miller seems determined to emphasise that as a youth he was particularly drawn to boys with a softer nature than his own; the rather effeminate William Ross and Alexander Finlay, and even his lifelong friend John Swanson, are cast in feminine roles. The only truly masculine figure he allowed into his affections was his father.

> Friendship (if I may venture the metaphor) is a kind of ball and socket connexion. It seems to be a first principle in its economy that its agreements be founded in dissimilarity; and you have but to look round you to be convinced of the fact. Observe the sexes, – they were formed for each other by the Deity himself; – but how? By being made entirely *alike*? No quite the reverse, – by being made entirely *unlike*. They piece together like the two halves of a hinge, and fit because they were made, not to resemble, but to correspond with each other. There is not an asperity or hardness in the character of the one but there is some little soft spot in that of the other on which that hardness or asperity may repose. Truly there is philosophy as well as religion in the text which assures us that husband and wife are but *one* flesh. It is the union that completes the man, and the individuals are but halves apart.
>
> In applying this principle (a principle devised by Infinite wisdom) I remark that there is something analogous in friendship to the connexion of the sexes. It is a marriage of souls . . .
>
> The scale of friendship is as progressive, – as minutely graduated I should rather say, – as that of character; and the same individual may be a *female* friend to one person and a *male* one to another. J[ohn Swanson] would have been the latter to William Ross, to me he is but the former. Indeed I have never met with one among the living whom I think I could regard as a *male* friend; nor often among the dead with that massiveness of character which I deem the pre-requisite.[186]

It is hard to resist interpreting this passage in simple homosexual terms, and suggesting that Miller's problem was simply passive, or repressed, homosexuality. This interpretation would square with his childhood circumstances, with the male youthful excursions described in the memoir, and with his repeated and rigid refusals to allow men to express affection to him. It might also – here we venture further than academic caution normally permits – shed some light on Miller's suicide note.[187] 'My brain burns', Miller writes twice. A literal reading would invoke cranial pain; the post-mortem found 'diseased appearances' in the brain, and Miller had spoken of 'a burning sensation on the top of the brain . . . as if a stiletto was suddenly, and as quick as an electric shock, passed through my brain from front to back'.[188] Such pain, and the observed softening of the brain, could have arisen from tertiary syphilis – an interesting suggestion, but one for which no evidence exists.[189] References to burning also recall Freud's colourful speculations linking sensations of burning and, more particularly, efforts to put out painful fires, to the suppression of homosexual desire.[190]

But there is an alternative and less tortured explanation. As a boy, Miller found refuge from his internal tensions in active outdoor pursuits and in the company of boys who never questioned his leadership. The confidence he gained from their loyalty enabled him to go on. In his twenties, Miller sought confidence in writing books rather than in friendship. When he met his future wife, however, he again reverted to the old pattern. Even before they were married, Lydia adopted what he considered an appropriately feminine and dependent role, as Miller emphasised to her the fragility of her mental and physical temperament.[191] It was a debilitated role imposed on an intelligent and intense woman, and she seems later to have reasserted herself in opposition to him. Whenever they were separated (notably during the first few months of his editorship of the *Witness*), Miller was unhappy and ill at ease. As the strains of editing the *Witness* grew, and as his religious beliefs began to be undermined by the evidence of science, Miller needed his wife's sympathy and backing more desperately. Yet precisely at this juncture she withheld – or could not in conscience provide – the support he needed. At the last, Miller found himself struggling alone with all those problems

that had beset him for years, and the strain proved too great
to bear.

A Man o' Fragments

As the crowds gathered in Edinburgh to watch Miller's funeral
procession, the gossips claimed to have foreseen the end and
to have long known that Miller was more than a trifle mad.
Some talked about his preoccupation with ghosts, others about
his pistols, and a select few about his conversation.[192] The
best story was that of Robert Dick, the Thurso baker-naturalist,
whom Miller had visited some years before. As Dick told an
inquisitive visitor:

> 'I am not at all astonished at the way it ended. His mind
> was touched somehow by superstition. I mind,' he con-
> tinued, 'after an afternoon's work on the rocks together at
> Holborn Head, we sat down on the leeside of a dyke to
> look over our specimens, when suddenly up jumped
> Hugh, exclaiming, "The fairies have got hold of my
> trousers!" and then sitting down again, he kept rubbing
> his legs for a long time. It was of no use suggesting that
> an ant or some other well-known "beastie" had got there.
> Hugh *would* have it that it was "the fairies"!'[193]

What this anecdote reveals is not that Miller was mad but
that in congenial company he was sometimes prepared to talk
the language of the imaginative world he inhabited rather
than that of journalism and science.

We began by asking, 'Who was Hugh Miller?'. That Miller
was in his lifetime – and remains today – an elusive and
paradoxical figure is certain. All that a biography or autobiography can offer is an alluring, but finally deceptive, sense of
rapprochement with the subject. A 'real' historical personage
is always elusive, because of what William James called 'the
breach between two minds'. To make matters more complicated
(and more interesting), Miller was not one person at all, but
several. The characters crowded within him were inventions
of his own, imaginative adaptations that equipped him to
encounter new challenges and situations. The autobiographical

writing he embarked on in 1828 with this memoir became essential to his own self-fashioning, a means to make sense of his own character and place in the world. The memoir, like his other autobiographical writings, is not always truthful. Autobiographies always lie to varying extents, mostly by presenting a public self that is autonomous, coherent, relatively independent and free willed. Miller too presented himself in this light, and his life as a path chosen by him and him alone. But he knew enough about character – the study of which he described repeatedly as one of his 'favourite amusements' – to realise that public image and private experience can be radically dissonant.[194]

Less than twenty years after Miller had sent his memoir to Principal Baird, Charles Baudelaire published a famous definition of modernity in an essay on the painter Constantin Guys. Modernity, Baudelaire wrote, is the experience of life lived in fragments, of the swift pace of change deforming our sense of unity.[195] Baudelaire welcomed the opportunity to experience what lay beyond the walls of the solid, the permanent, the declarative. As for Miller, everything we know of his life and his death suggests that he lived just the kind of fragmentary life that, according to Baudelaire, heralded the modern. But if the autobiographical impulse so persistent in his work tells us anything, it is that he yearned for a return to stability, to some (illusory) place and time in which nothing changed.

The frustration we feel at having no satisfactory answer to the question 'Who, finally, was Hugh Miller?' was shared most piercingly by Hugh Miller himself.

NOTES

1. The *Witness*, 31 December 1856. References to the *Witness* henceforth appear as *TW*.
2. See George Rosie, *Hugh Miller: Outrage and Order. A Biography and Selected Writings*, Edinburgh, 1981, pp. 82–3.
3. For further information, see Roy Porter, 'Miller's Madness', in Michael Shortland (ed.), *Hugh Miller: New Essays*, Oxford, 1995.
4. *TW*, 27 December 1856.
5. See George Rosen, 'History in the Study of Suicide', *Psychological Medicine*, 1, 1971, 267–85, p. 273.

6. For general attitudes towards suicide at this time, see B. T. Gates, *Victorian Suicide: Mad Crimes and Sad Histories*, Princeton, NJ, 1988 and O. Anderson, *Suicide in Victorian and Edwardian England*, Oxford, 1987.

7. Quoted in A. Alvarez, *The Savage God: A Study of Suicide*, London, 1971, p. 178.

8. *TW*, 27 December 1856.

9. *TW*, 27 December 1856.

10. Peter Bayne, *The Life and Letters of Hugh Miller*, 2 vols, London, 1871, II, p. 482.

11. Bayne, *Hugh Miller*, II, p. 482.

12. Porter, 'Miller's Madness'.

13. The *Times*, 26 December 1856.

14. Rosie, *Hugh Miller*, p. 85.

15. See Rosie, *Hugh Miller*, p. 84; Thomas Carlyle, 'The Death of Hugh Miller', *New York Times*, 29 April 1871. The book seems, in fact, to have taught Carlyle little. Reverting to form, his annotations in the copy of *Testimony* Lydia sent to him refer to Miller's 'very idle work' and end wearily: 'Poor Miller; died so miserably, writing this!'.

16. Rosie, *Hugh Miller*, p. 86.

17. Miller, *The Headship of Christ, and the Rights of the Christian People*, Edinburgh, 1861, p. 1.

18. Miller, *Letter from One of the Scotch People to the Right Hon. Lord Brougham & Vaux, on the Opinions Expressed by his Lordship in the Auchterarder Case*, Edinburgh, 1839, p. 1.

19. For details, see Miller, *My Schools and Schoolmasters; or, The Story of My Education*, Edinburgh, [1910], pp. 546–7; p. 406 of James A. Wylie, 'Hugh Miller', in *Disruption Worthies: A Memorial of 1843*, 2 vols, Edinburgh, [1881], pp. 405–12 (continuous pagination); and p. 463 of [Lydia Miller Mackay], 'Mrs Hugh Miller's Journal', *Chambers's Journal*, Sixth Series, V, 1902, pp. 305–8, 369–72, 461–4, 513–16.

20. *TW*, 9 July 1851, 13 January 1844, 11 June 1853, 9 February 1853.

21. John Clive, *Scotch Reviewers: the Edinburgh Review, 1802–1815*, London, 1957, p. 52.

22. *TW*, 24 March 1852.

23. Page 290 of Anon., 'Hugh Miller', *Annual Register*, 1856, pp. 288–90.

24. It is common to find his name omitted from histories of science, of Scotland and of the Church of Scotland. When he does appear, it is often in an unrecognisable guise. A recent study of Scottish literature manages to misspell his name, while historians some years earlier had him strutting the streets of Edinburgh years after his burial in one of that city's main graveyards (Roderick Watson, *The Literature of Scotland*, London, 1984, p. 287 [referring to 'Hugh Millar']; M. I. Newbigin and J. S. Flett, *James Geikie: the Man and the Geologist*, Edinburgh, 1919, p. 150).

25. Anon., 'Hugh Miller's Life and Letters', *London Quarterly Review*, 36, 1871, pp. 439–61.

26. See James Moore, 'Geologists and Interpreters of Genesis in the

Nineteenth Century', in D. C. Lindberg and R. L. Numbers (eds), *God and Nature*, Berkeley, CA, 1986, p. 340.

27. Moore, 'Geologists', p. 340.
28. Richard Milner, *The Encyclopedia of Evolution*, New York, 1990, p. 306.
29. John M. Clarke, 'The Centenary of Hugh Miller', *Science*, n.s. 15, 1902, p. 631.
30. A classic, and disputed, celebration of Scotland's democratic 'social ethics' is G. E. Davie, *The Democratic Intellect: Scotland and Her Universities in the Nineteenth Century*, Edinburgh, 1961.
31. See Jenni Calder (ed.), *The Enterprising Scot*, Edinburgh, 1986, and Gordon Donaldson, *The Scots Overseas*, London, 1966.
32. See pp. 90–1 of Robert Anderson, 'In Search of the "Lad of Parts": the Mythical History of Scottish Education', *History Workshop*, 19, 1985, 82–104, and *Education and Opportunity in Victorian Scotland: Schools and Universities*, Oxford, 1983, pp. 1–26.
33. Adam Smith, *The Wealth of Nations*, 2 vols, London, 1967, II, pp. 269–70.
34. On Scottish literacy, see the classic account in T. C. Smout, *A History of the Scottish People 1560–1830*, Glasgow, 1972, pp. 424–32; see also his *A Century of the Scottish People, 1830–1950*, London, 1986, pp. 209–19. A recent reappraisal of literacy levels appears in Rab Houston, 'The Literacy Myth?: Illiteracy in Scotland, 1630–1760', *Past and Present*, 96, 1982, pp. 81–102. See also R. A. Houston, *Scottish Literacy and the Scottish Identity: Illiteracy and Society in Scotland and Northern England, 1600–1800*, Cambridge, 1988.
35. Samuel Smiles, *Robert Dick, Baker of Thurso: Geologist and Botanist*, London, 1878, and *Life of a Scotch Naturalist: Thomas Edward, Associate of the Linnean Society*, London, 1876.
36. See Laurence J. Saunders, *Scottish Democracy 1815–1840*, Edinburgh, 1850, pp. 251–8.
37. Burns, like Robert Fergusson, developed substantial links with the polite culture of England and Scotland, suggesting not only the possibility of mobility, but also more traffic between 'high' and 'popular' culture than has been acknowledged, for example, in David Craig, *Scottish Literature and the Scottish People, 1680–1830*, London, 1961. On Burns, see C. McGuirk, *Robert Burns and the Sentimental Era*, Athens, GA, 1985; on Fergusson, see F. W. Freeman, *Robert Fergusson and the Scots Humanistic Compromise*, Edinburgh, 1984.
38. This paradox may account for historians' varied interpretations of the impact of Scottish urbanisation, despite agreement on the scale and speed of town growth between 1760 and 1830. See, for contrasting views: Anthony Slaven, *The Development of the West of Scotland, 1750–1960*, London, 1975, p. 145 and Smout, *A History of the Scottish People*, p. 260. These references are from p. 27 of T. M. Devine, 'Urbanisation', in Devine and Rosalind Michison (eds), *People and Society in Scotland. I: 1760–1830*, Edinburgh, [1989], pp. 27–52.

39. For comparative estimates of Scottish urbanisation, see J. de Vries, *European Urbanisation, 1500–1800*, London, 1984, pp. 39–84.

40. David Hogg, *Life of Allan Cunningham, with Selections from his Works and Correspondence*, Dumfries, 1875; J. A. Fairley, *Allan Cunningham*, London, 1907.

41. See, for examples, his 'Beautiful Edinburgh' and 'The Beautiful City of Perth' in James L. Smith (ed.), *Last Poetic Gems of William McGonagall*, London, 1915.

42. Hugh Miller's anonymously published *Letters on the Herring Fishing in the Moray Firth*, Inverness, 1829, charts the dwindling of Cromarty 'into a place of no importance' (p. 7). By 1846, Lewis could describe herring fishing locally as 'almost discontinued' (Samuel Lewis, *A Topographical Dictionary of Scotland . . . with Historical and Statistical Descriptions*, 2 vols, London, 1846, I, p. 278).

43. William Hanna, *Memoirs of the Life and Writings of Thomas Chalmers, D.D., LL.D*, 4 vols, New York, 1857, IV, p. 83.

44. Miller to Andrew Williamson, 15 June 1854, National Library of Scotland MS 7527, 52 (pasted in). In a letter to Louis Agassiz, Miller speaks of Cromarty as a place 'in which the people has scarce at all been affected by the cosmopolitanism which has been gradually modifying and altering it in the larger towns' (Elizabeth Cary Agassiz, *Louis Agassiz: His Life and Correspondence*, 2 vols, Boston, 1885, II, p. 471).

45. See David Alston, 'The Fallen Meteor: Hugh Miller and Local Tradition', in Shortland, *Hugh Miller*.

46. Bayne, *Hugh Miller*, I, p. 7. For contradictory testimony from Miller about the climate and geography of Cromarty, compare his 'Parish of Cromarty', *The New Statistical Account of Scotland* [1836], 15 vols, Edinburgh, 1845, 15, pp. 1–18 (p. 2) with his letter to his mother, [May 1840], National Library of Scotland MS 7527, 38.

47. Miller, *Scenes and Legends of the North of Scotland; or, the Traditional History of Cromarty*, Edinburgh, 1835, pp. 177–8.

48. See [Hugh Miller Williamson], 'Life of Hugh Miller' (c. 1872), National Library of Scotland, MS 7527; 'Hugh Miller', *New York Times* 14 January 1857; *Biographie universelle ancienne et moderne*, 45 vols, Paris, 1854–65, 28, p. 297.

49. Miller offers biographies of several in *Scenes*, pp. 407–19.

50. See National Library of Scotland MS 7524, 1–15 and MS 7518, 50–5.

51. [Miller], *Poems Written in the Leisure Hours of a Journeyman Mason*, Inverness, 1829, p. 9.

52. *Poems*, p. 262.

53. 'Inscription Cutting on Stone', *Inverness Courier*, 23 July 1828; see also 'Hugh Miller in Inverness', *Inverness Courier*, 24 January 1908.

54. Miller, *My Schools*, p. 444.

55. Miller to John Strahan, [January 1830], in Hugh Miller's *Letterbook*, Library of New College, Edinburgh, item 13. Further references to letters in the *Letterbook* appear as, for example, *LB*, 13.

56. *Poems*, p. 266.
57. Miller to mother, 1 August 1828, National Library of Scotland MS 7527, 13.
58. For example, 'Antiquities at Cromarty' (*Inverness Courier*, 29 April 1829), 'A Noble Smuggler' (*Inverness Courier*, 13 May 1829), and 'Gipseys' (*Inverness Courier*, 23 September 1829).
59. Miller to Miss Dunbar of Boath, 25 October 1834, *LB*, 114.
60. D. B. Horn, *A Short History of the University of Edinburgh*, Edinburgh, 1967, p. 102.
61. For more about Baird (1761–1840), see Alexander Grant, *The Story of the University of Edinburgh during its First Three Hundred Years*, 2 vols, London, 1882, II, pp. 270–1.
62. Miller to Mrs Allardyce, 12 February 1830, *LB*, 15.
63. *My Schools*, p. 448.
64. Baird to Miller, 4 November 1829, *LB*, 2.
65. Miller to Baird, 9 December 1829, *LB*, 5.
66. Baird to Miller, 4 November 1829, *LB*, 2.
67. Baird to Miller, 6 January 1830, *LB*, 9.
68. Baird to Miller, 14 February 1832, *LB*, 44.
69. Miss Dunbar to Miller, [January/February 1833?], *LB*, 51.
70. Miller to Miss Dunbar, 12 March 1833, *LB*, 52.
71. Bayne, *Hugh Miller*, I, p. 17.
72. E. P. Thompson, *The Making of the English Working Class*, Harmondsworth, 1977.
73. The variety and number of working-class autobiographies is indicated by the first volume of John Burnett, David Vincent, and David Mayall (eds), *The Autobiography of the Working Class: an Annotated Critical Bibliography*, 3 vols, Brighton, 1984–9.
74. Pages 149 and 164 of [James Lockhart], 'Autobiography', *Quarterly Review*, 35, 1827, pp. 149–65
75. The same year that Lockhart's review appeared, John Jones, a 'poor, humble, uneducated domestic', wrote to Southey seeking encouragement for his poetry. Southey not only responded immediately but arranged to publish Jones' verses and autobiography, and studies of other working-class poets, including the shoemaker James Woodhouse and 'the milkwoman of Bristol', Ann Yearsley. See John Jones, *Attempts in Verse . . . with an Introductory Essay . . . by Robert Southey*, London, 1831, pp. 1 and 171–80.
76. Page 81 of [T. H. Lister], 'Attempts at Verse', *Edinburgh Review*, 54, 1831, pp. 69–84.
77. Bamford's *Passages* appeared in parts between 1840 and 1844 before publication in two volumes in 1844; his *Early Days* was printed in 1848–9.
78. G. L. Craik, *The Pursuit of Knowledge under Difficulties; Illustrated by Anecdotes*, 2 vols, London, 1830–1.
79. Smiles claimed to have been greatly influenced by Craik's book. See his *Autobiography*, London, 1905, pp. 325–6. On the popularity of *The Pursuit of Knowledge* and its many editions, see David Vincent's brilliant work, *Bread, Knowledge and Freedom: A Study of Nineteenth-century Working Class Autobiography*, London, 1981, p. 144.

80. In radical circles, too, working men were enjoined to create a literature of their own, to help them acquire social and economic justice, as well as cultural recognition. See Martha Vicinus, *The Industrial Muse: A Study of Nineteenth Century British Working-class Literature*, London, 1974.

81. William Gifford (ed.), *The Satires of Decimus Junius Juvenalis*, London, 1802; John Nichols, *Illustrations of the Literary History of the Eighteenth Century, Consisting of Authentic Memoirs and Original Letters of Eminent Persons*, 6 vols, London, 1817–31, 6, pp. 14–28.

82. Anon., 'Gifford's Translation of Juvenal', *Monthly Review*, 40, 1803, 1–21, p. 2.

83. See Alexander Finlay to Miller, 14 August 1836, *LB*, 173 and Miller to Finlay, 15 October 1836, *LB*, 174.

84. *My Schools*, p. 326.

85. Leaflet issued by William P. Nimmo, Miller's Edinburgh publisher, c. 1869.

86. Miller to Baird, 9 December [1829], *LB*, 5.

87. Miller to Miss Dunbar of Boath, [March 1833], *LB*, 56.

88. Several collections are preserved in the National Library of Scotland, for example, 'Juvenile Poems' (MS 7520) and 'Poems' (MS 7519).

89. *My Schools*, p. 151; see also p. 558.

90. *My Schools*, pp. 141–3, 367.

91. *Scenes and Legends*, p. 410.

92. *My Schools*, pp. 143–4.

93. *My Schools*, pp. xiii–xiv.

94. See p. 38 of Christopher Harvie, 'Industry, Religion and the State of Scotland', in Douglas Gifford (ed.), *The History of Scottish Literature. Volume 3: Nineteenth Century*, Aberdeen, 1988, pp. 23–41.

95. 'The English [church] contained the *elite* of the place – all its men of property and influence, from its merchants and heritors, down to the humblest of the class that afterwards became its ten-pound franchise-holders; whereas the Gaelic [church] people were . . . simply poor labourers and weavers' (*My Schools*, p. 479).

96. Ibid., p. 492; see also W. Anderson, *The Scottish Nation . . . and Biographical History of the People of Scotland*, 3 vols, 3, Edinburgh, 1869, p. 160.

97. *TW*, 30 May 1856.

98. *My Schools*, pp. 155–7.

99. *TW*, 22 September 1841; Miller, *Essays Historical and Biographical Political and Social Literary and Scientific*, Edinburgh, 1875, p. 200.

100. See *TW*, 17 June 1854; *Essays*, p. 145; *My Schools*, pp. 190–2, 202–5, 289.

101. *My Schools*, p. 154; Miller to John Strahan [c. November 1830], *LB*, 34.

102. *My Schools*, pp. 141–7.

103. On Miller's relationship to literature, see Miller, *First Impressions of England and its People*, London, 1877, p. 122; *Scenes,*

p. 1; *My Schools*, pp. 88–92; also [W. Keddie] 'Miller, Hugh', *The Imperial Dictionary of Universal Biography*, London, n.d., 3, pp. 371–2.

104. See Miller, *Tales and Sketches*, London, 1876, p. 108; Thomas N. Brown, *Labour and Triumph: the Life and Times of Hugh Miller*, London, 1858, p. 30.

105. See J. H. Raleigh, 'What Scott Meant to the Victorians', *Victorian Studies*, 7, 1963, pp. 7–34.

106. Samuel Smiles, *Character*, London, 1910, p. 87; William Chambers, *Memoir of William and Robert Chambers*, Edinburgh, 1884, p. 206.

107. See Brown, *Labour and Triumph*, pp. 80–2; Miller, as we have seen, 'sauntered for whole hours opposite the house of Sir Walter Scott'.

108. See *TW*, 19 August 1840.

109. Richard M. Dorson, *The British Folklorists*, Chicago, 1968, p. 142.

110. Samuel Smiles, *Duty: with Illustrations of Courage, Patience, and Endurance*, London, 1880, p. 412.

111. See Norman Vance, *The Sinews of the Spirit: the Ideal of Christian Manliness in Victorian Literature and Religious Thought*, Cambridge, 1985; and Mark Girouard, *The Return to Camelot: Chivalry and the English Gentleman*, London, 1981.

112. Nancy Moore Goslee, 'Witch or Pawn: Women in Scott's Narrative Poetry', in Anne K. Mellor, *Romanticism and Feminism*, Bloomington, Indiana, 1988, pp. 115–36.

113. See, on this, A. Welsh, *The Hero of the Waverley Novels*, New York, 1968.

114. Miller wrote several articles on witchcraft for the *Inverness Courier*, for example on 11 November 1829 and 17 February 1830; and the article in *LB*, 17.

115. Miller, *Scenes and Legends*, pp. 189–90.

116. Miller to Chambers, October 1837, *LB*, 183.

117. Robert Chambers to Miller, 13 March 1838, *LB*, 188.

118. See my essay, 'Hugh Miller's Contribution to the *Witness*, 1840–56', in Shortland, *Hugh Miller*.

119. Bayne, *Hugh Miller*, II, p. 191.

120. Ibid., II, p. 246.

121. Ibid., II, p. 278.

122. Miller, *Headship of Christ*, p. 33.

123. Prospectus of the *Old Whig* included in Miller to Alexander Dunlop, 3 October 1839, *LB*, 225.

124. *TW*, 22 September 1841; Miller, *Essays*, p. 200.

125. *Scenes and Legends*, p. 406.

126. Miller to Miss Dunbar of Boath, [March 1833], *LB*, 56.

127. Bayne, *Miller*, II, p. 64.

128. Miller, *My Schools*, p. 372.

129. See, for example, *TW*, 24 December 1851.

130. See, for example, Miller, *The Testimony of the Rocks, or, Geology in its Bearings on the Two Theologies, Natural and Revealed*, Edinburgh, 1869, pp. 160–8.

131. Miller, *The Cruise of the Betsey; or, A Summer Ramble Among*

the *Fossiliferous Deposits of the Hebrides*, Edinburgh, 1858, p. 92. Swanson brought up his children as Gaelic-speakers (ibid., p. 114).

132. Some samples of Miller's writing on the Highlands are collected in his *Essays*, pp. 187–99, 207–17, 231–5. Chapter 13 of *My Schools* is devoted to the sociology and economics of the region.

133. Miller collected commonplaces about the Highlands in notebooks he kept as he worked in *Scenes and Legends*; see National Library of Scotland MS 7527 for example.

134. Miller to Isaac Forsyth, 12 February 1830, *LB*, 15.

135. Ibid.

136. See *The Autobiography of Giambattista Vico* (trans. Max Harold Fisch and Thomas Goddard Bergon), Ithaca, NY, 1963, pp. 91–6. The first English historian to acknowledge indebtedness to Vico, Thomas Arnold, argued that 'states, like individuals, go through certain changes in a certain order, and are subject at different stages of their course to peculiar disorders'. Arnold proposed the analogy between states and individuals – soon to become a commonplace in Victorian letters – in an essay published in 1830, very shortly after Miller completed his memoir (see Lionel Trilling, *Matthew Arnold*, London, 1939, p. 50).

137. For some examples of Miller's approach, see *TW*, 1 January 1850, 13 May 1854; *Tales and Sketches*, pp. 61–2, 368–9; *My Schools*, p. 467; and Miller to Miss Dunbar of Boath, 12 March 1833, *LB*, 52.

138. *TW*, 21 January 1854; see *Essays*, pp. 178–9.

139. *Scenes and Legends*, pp. 58, 70, 161. On this, see Dorson, *British Folklorists*, 150; and W. M. Mackenzie, *Hugh Miller: a Critical Study*, London, 1905, pp. 69–70.

140. Miller to Dr John Malcolmson, 2 April 1838, *LB*, 190.

141. *My Schools*, pp. 463–6.

142. George and Peter Anderson, *Guide to the Highlands and Islands of Scotland, Including Orkney and Zetland, descriptive of their Scenery, Statistics, Antiquities, and Natural History: with Numerous Historical Notices . . . With a Very Complete Map of Scotland*, London, 1834.

143. *Old Red Sandstone*, p. 137.

144. Miller to George Anderson, 15 September 1834, *LB*, 110.

145. Ibid.

146. See Trevor Royle, *The Macmillan Companion to Scottish Literature*, London, 1983, p. 65.

147. Joan Milne and Willie Smith, 'Reviews and Magazines: Criticism and Polemic', in Gifford, *The History of Scottish Literature. Volume 3*, 189–201, pp. 198–9.

148. See R. S. Porter, *The Making of Geology: Earth Sciences in Britain 1660–1815*, Cambridge, 1977, pp. 149–56; A. Hallam, *Great Geological Controversies*, Oxford, 1987; Dennis R. Dean, *James Hutton and the History of Geology*, Ithaca, NY, 1992.

149. Sir Charles Lyell, *Principles of Geology: Being an Attempt to Explain the Former Changes of the Earth's Surface, by Reference to Causes Now in Operation*, 3 vols, London, 1830–3, I, p. 73.

150. The proper and full title of Smith's long-awaited map is *A Delineation of the Strata of England and Wales, with Part of Scotland; Exhibiting Collieries and Mines, the Marshes and Fenlands, Originally Overflowed by the Sea, and Varieties of Soil According to the Variations in the Substrata, Illustrated by the Most Descriptive Names*.

151. Louis Agassiz, *Recherches sur les poissons fossils*, 5 vols, Neuchâtel, 1833–44.

152. See pp. 1–3 of Michael Shortland, 'Darkness Visible: Underground Culture in the Golden Age of Geology', *History of Science*, 32, 1994, pp. 1–62.

153. S. F. Mason, *A History of the Sciences*, New York, 1977, p. 411.

154. See Archibald Geikie, *Scottish Reminiscences*, Glasgow, 1904, p. 374, and *The Life of Sir Roderick I. Murchison, Based on his Journals and Letters with Notices of His Scientific Contemporaries and a Sketch of the Rise and Growth of Palaeozoic Geology in Britain*, 2 vols, London, 1875, I, pp. 101–3.

155. See pp. 445–6 of [David Brewster], 'Hugh Miller's *Footprints of the Creator*', *North British Review*, 12, 1850, pp. 443–81.

156. See Louis Agassiz, 'Hugh Miller', in Hugh Miller, *Footprints of the Creator: or, the Asterolepis of Stromness*, Boston, 1869, iii–xxxvii.

157. Parts of the book first appeared in the *Witness* on 15 April 1840; 9, 12, and 16 September 1840; 3, 10, and 17 October 1840; and 16 December 1840.

158. Horace B. Woodward, *History of Geology*, London, 1911, p. 109; Gideon Mantell, *The Medals of Creation; or, First Lessons in Geology, and the Study of Organic Remains*, 2 vols (continuously paginated), London, 1854, p. 612; John Willis Clark and Thomas McKenny Hughes, *The Life and Letters of the Reverend Adam Sedgwick*, 2 vols, Cambridge, 1890, II, p. 89; Archibald Geikie, *A Long Life's Work: an Autobiography*, London, 1924, p. 18; Charles Lyell to Miller, 21 October 1840, National Library of Scotland MS 7528, fo. 30 (referring to the first three articles on the Old Red Sandstone appearing in the *Witness*); see also Lyell to Miller, 2 November 1846, National Library of Scotland MS 7528, ff. 32–4.

159. Miller, *Cruise of the Betsey*, p. 169. The book appeared in serial form in the *Witness* from March 1845 until March 1849.

160. Miller, *Sketch-book of Popular Geology; being a Series of Lectures Delivered Before the Philosophical Institution of Edinburgh*, Edinburgh, 1859, pp. 86–7; *Testimony of the Rocks*, p. 133; see Tess Coslett (ed.), *Science and Religion in the Nineteenth Century*, Cambridge, 1984, p. 135.

161. *Old Red Sandstone*, pp. 108–9.

162. See p. 432 Anon., '*Testimony of the Rocks*', *Athenaeum*, 4 April 1857, pp. 429–31.

163. Charles Darwin, a keen reader of Miller's work, found the scenic descriptions too elaborate and wished for a 'little less geologic eloquence' (*The Correspondence of Charles Darwin*, Cambridge, 1981, 4, p. 81).

164. See Geikie, *Murchison*, II, pp. 345, 122, 316; see also Lynn

Barber, *The Heyday of Natural History 1820–1870*, London, 1980, p. 191.

165. See K. M. Lyell, *Life, Letters and Journals of Sir Charles Lyell, Bart.*, 2 vols, London, II, pp. 134 and 205; Richard Owen to Miller, 3 October 1849, National Library of Scotland MS 7516, pp. 225–7; Rosie, *Hugh Miller*, p. 70.

166. Bayne, *Hugh Miller*, I, p. 10.

167. See [Brewster], 'Hugh Miller's *Footprints*', p. 447; Brown, *Labour and Triumph*, p. 17.

168. Bayne, *Hugh Miller*, I, p. 9.

169. Erik H. Erikson, *Identity, Youth and Crisis*, New York, 1968, p. 117

170. Miller to Principal Baird, December [1829], *LB*, 5. See also *Tales and Sketches*, p. 68, and *First Impressions*, p. 240.

171. Carlyle's *Hero-Worship and the Heroic in History* (1841) offered a transcendental admiration of great men. See H. G. Schenk, *The Mind of European Romantics: an Essay in Cultural History*, Oxford, 1979, p. 184, and Basil Willey, *Nineteenth Century Studies: Coleridge to Matthew Arnold*, Cambridge, 1980, p. 102.

172. See [F. Close], *Hugh Miller's 'Testimony of the Rocks': or, God in His Word and in His Books. A Lecture*, London, [1858], p. 32.

173. Bayne, *Hugh Miller*, I, p. 11. See also *My Schools*, pp. 495–8.

174. See *My Schools*, pp. 21–3.

175. Bayne, *Hugh Miller*, I, p. 53.

176. Ibid., I, p. 17.

177. Ibid., I, p. 16.

178. Ibid., I, p. 15.

179. Ibid., I, pp. 16–17. The dead irons presumably clicked as they became cold while ironing the winding-sheet.

180. Ibid., I, pp. 17–18.

181. Ibid., II, p. 481.

182. Ibid., II, p. 473.

183. See Ernest W. Baughman, *Type and Motif Index of the Folktales of England and North America*, The Hague: Mouton & Co., 1966, pp. 239, 246; and Stith Thompson, *Motif-Index of Folk Literature . . . and Local Legends*, Bloomington, IN: Indiana University Press, 1932–6, 6 vols, III, p. 294. Good versions of the story appear in Katharine M. Briggs, *A Dictionary of British Folk-Tales in the English Language*, 2 vols, Bloomington, IN: Indiana University Press, 1970–1, II, pp. 623–65, 715, 749–50.

184. Bayne, *Hugh Miller*, II, p. 119; Thomson, *Eminent Scotsmen*, III, p. 144; Mackay, 'Mrs Hugh Miller's Journal', p. 513.

185. Miller to Lydia Fraser, undated, *LB*, 101.

186. Miller to Lydia Fraser, August or September 1833, *LB*, 67. See also Miller, *Tales and Sketches*, pp. 80–1.

187. Such suggestions prompt the further speculation that Miller's dream might have been that he himself was being 'ridden' sexually by a man.

188. Bayne, *Hugh Miller*, II, p. 470.

189. The suggestion is made by Neal Ascherson in his 'Introduction' to Rosie, *Hugh Miller*, p. 10.

190. See *The Standard Edition of the Psychological Works of Sigmund Freud*, 24 vols, London, 1966–74, 22, pp. 185–93; 21, p. 90; 9, p. 175.

191. Miller to Lydia Fraser, [early 1829], *LB*, 128.

192. A rich variety of observations appears in obituaries of Miller. See, for some examples, *Annual Register*, 1856, 288–90; *Eclectic Review*, 40, March 1857, 335–46 (which includes the two obituaries from the *Witness* and edited versions of those from the *Scotsman, Edinburgh Advertiser, Scottish Guardian, Edinburgh Express*, and *Edinburgh Courant*); *Edinburgh Evening Courant*, 28 December 1856; *Gentleman's Magazine*, 202, 1857, 244–6; *Inverness Advertiser*, 30 December 1856; 6 January 1857; 13 January 1857; *Inverness Courier*, 25 December 1856 and 30 December 1856; *Proceedings of the Royal Physical Society of Edinburgh*, 1854–8, 1, 223–5; and *Scotsman*, 25 December 1856 and 29 December 1856.

193. Samuel Smiles, *Robert Dick*, p. 235.

194. Miller to Baird, 9 December 1829, *LB*, 5; Miller to John Strahan, [January 1830], *LB*, 13; Miller to Isaac Forsyth, 12 February 1830, *LB*, 15.

195. See Anthony Giddens, *The Consequences of Modernity*, Oxford, 1989.

THE MEMOIR
OF HUGH MILLER

NOTE ON THE TEXT

This memoir comprises two letters written by Hugh Miller to George Husband Baird, Principal of the University of Edinburgh. The first is dated 'Cromarty Oct. 1829', the second (which begins on p. 110) is undated, but was evidently written in late 1829 and early 1830. The letters appear in Hugh Miller's *Letterbook* (*LB*, 1 and *LB*, 23), in the Library of New College, Edinburgh.

Miller's occasionally eccentric punctuation and spelling have been retained; all footnotes are supplied by the editor.

THE MEMOIR
OF HUGH MILLER

When about a twelvemonth ago I determined on coming before the Public as a writer of verses it was with a mixed feeling of solicitude and indifference.[1] If it be decided, thought I, that I am no poet, I shall have an excellent opportunity of proving myself at least a practical philosopher. I am much mistaken if I have anything to fear from the evils of success, and as for those of its contrary, as I have been battling with them all life long, 'I shall go forth against them even as at other times.' It is with no such mixed feeling that agreeable to your request, I now take up the pen to relate under what circumstances my habits of thought were first formed, and to describe the manner in which I have attained my little, imperfect skill in the art of writing. I cannot be indifferent, Sir, to your approbation, for I regard it as one of those few things that are truly valuable; and I am aware that I do not come before you as I did before the Public merely as a writer. The history of what I may term my education is also that of my life; and though it were no great matter though the Public should have to say of me 'This mason writes ill,' I would deem it a truly serious one should Principal Baird have to say of me 'He has lived ill.'

I was born in the town of Cromarty on the 10th of Oct. 1802. My father, whom I barely remember, was master and owner of a small trading sloop.[2] Towards the close of the year 1807 he left Cromarty on a voyage to the western Highlands for a cargo of kelp, and on his return his vessel was driven by stress of weather into Peterhead. From that port he wrote my

mother the last letter she ever received from him; for on the
day after he sailed from it there arose a terrible storm in
which many seamen perished, and he was never heard of.
Nearly fifty years prior his father and two of his uncles (one
of the latter sailed round the world with Anson) experienced
a similar fate. It is a singular circumstance that nearly a
century has elapsed since the body of a male relative was
deposited in the burying ground of the family.

At the time of my fathers death, though the eldest of three
children, I had only completed my fifth year. The two others
were girls.[3] My mother, who had married young, and was not
yet twenty five, was tolerably skilful as a seamstress; and
when she had somewhat recovered the stroke which deprived
her of a kind husband, she applied with singular industry to
the needle.[4] By her earnings in this way, joined to a yearly
income of twelve pounds, which was derived from a small
property of my fathers, she provided for herself and her family
in such a manner that though we often endured much privation,
we never suffered from positive want. Young as I was at the
time the difference in the economy of our household from
what it had been formerly struck me very forcibly, and I remember setting my mother a crying by enquiring of her why it was
that she wrought so much later at night now than before, and
why those ship-masters who when my father was alive used to
stroke my head and fill my pockets with halfpence, never now
took any notice of me, or gave me any thing.

My mother had two brothers, James and Alexander Wright.[5]
They were Whigs of the old school; – men who had they lived
in the days of Cameron would have attended field meetings
and fought the battles of the Covenant. The one was a saddler,
the other a carpenter. They lived together, for they never
married, with their aged father; and as they were industrious
and their desires moderate, their circumstances were easy. I
was oftener with them, especially at meal times, than at home,
and one of my sisters lived with them altogether. James, the
saddler, was naturally acute and shrewd, fond of reading and
possessed of a fund of anecdote. I never knew a man more
rigidly just in his dealings, or who regarded every species of

meanness with as perfect a contempt. In my father, who was a man of no common mould, he had found his beau ideal of character; and I was a great favourite with him fully as much from the reverence in which he held his memory as from his affection for my mother. When I had learned to read, which I did when very young, I would sit by him in his workshop whole hours every day, either reading little storybooks to which his remarks and explanations served me instead of a dictionary and commentary, or listening to his anecdotes of my father. The latter interested me much and left deep impressions on my mind. My father's whole life had been spent in a war with fortune, – in rising by a singular perseverance from circumstances the most depressed, and in falling to the old level in consequence of unforseen disaster. He had sailed over almost every ocean, he had fought both by land and sea, and he had suffered from famine, tempest and ship-wreck.

My uncle Alexander, who still survives (the other I have lost) indulged like his elder brother, James, in an early taste for reading, possesses equal powers of thought, and acts upon similar principles, but his mind is of a cast entirely different. James had a turn for humourous anecdote and repartee, and thought and narrated like a historian. Alexander on the other hand is grave and serious, and though he never wrote a single couplet his conformation of mind is decidedly poetical. He served seven years aboard a Man of War; and it so chanced that there was little either suffered or achieved by his countrymen during the eventful period which immediately preceded the short peace of 1802 in which he had not a share. He sailed with Nelson, witnessed the meeting at the Nore, fought under Admiral Duncan at Camperdown, and Sir John Borless Warren off Loch Swilly. He assisted in capturing the Generoux and Guilliam Tell [sic], two French ships of the line; he was one of the seamen who in the Egyptian expedition were draughted out of Lord Keith's fleet to supply in the army the lack of Artillery men; he had a share in the dangers and glory of the landing in Egypt; he fought in the battle of the 13th March, and in that which deprived our country of one of her best and most popular generals. He served too at the siege of Alexandria.

I was as much a favourite with him as with my other uncle. His narratives to which I have listened in the long winter nights from twilight until bedtime, and which when he had concluded I would urge him to begin again were in the highest degree interesting. They were not mere dry, matter of fact stories, but animated transcripts of human life and human passion, and full of pretty little strokes of poetry.

Before I had attained my tenth year my mind was filled by these stories with ideas of what could be seen and done in foreign parts; and I wished myself big enough to be a sailor that I might go and see burning mountains and fight battles. My hours of play were frequently spent at this time aboard the ships in the harbour, or in tracing on the maps of an old Geographical Grammer the track of vessels to and from the several countries which had been visited by my father and uncle. Among my mothers books there was an odd volume of Cooks voyages which I read over with a delight which I cannot now derive from the perusal of any work whatever; and I borrowed from a neighbour the voyages of Anson, Drake, Raliegh [sic], and Captain Woods Rogers. Of poetry as an art I had not at this time the most distant idea, but on reading one of those ballads that are termed *sea garlands* I was particularly struck by the manner in which it was written, and for months after I had perused it I was in the habit of quitting my school companions for the sea shore, where I would saunter for whole hours, pouring out long, blank-verse effusions (rhime was a discovery of after date) about sea fights, storms, ghosts, and desert islands. These effusions were no sooner brought to a close than forgotten; and no one knew anything of them but myself; for I had not yet attained the art of writing, and I could only compose when alone. My predilection for a sea life, which still continued to strengthen, distressed my mother, who anticipated for me the fate of my father and grandfather, and she attempted, but in vain, giving my mind a different bent. This, however, was accomplished by the perusal of a single book.

My uncle James had procured for me the loan of a common stall edition of Blind Harry's Life and Adventures of Sir William

Wallace, but as it did not treat of ships or sailors it lay by me for several weeks unopened.[6] My uncle urged me to the perusal, and I was at length induced to read the first four chapters, when I became interested in the story, and read on with increasing astonishment and delight. I was quite intoxicated with its narratives of lofty devoted patriotism and astonishing prowess; and though hitherto I had scarcely had any ideas of country, or had merely prided myself on being born near the edge of one of the finest harbours in the world I now gloried in that I was a Scotchman, and the countryman of Wallace and Sir John the Grahame.[7] My very dreams were of these heroes. I have wept over the pages that described their death, and have longed for a war with the Southron that they might yet be avenged. All I had formerly read and heard of foreign parts and modern battles appeared in comparison tame and uninteresting; and I never more worried my mother by wishing myself big enough to be a sailor.

Both my uncles (particularly James) in the opinion that I possessed superior natural parts, were bent on fitting me by a classical education for one of the learned professions. My mother was poor and unable either to keep me at school or to procure for me the necessary books, but uncle James whose singular industry was wealth, did both. I entered with something like ardour, for the study was new to me on the Rudiments of the Latin Tongue, but after hammering at its lessons for about three days I concluded it to be the dullest book I had ever seen. It contained no thought, it detailed not narrative, it was a perfect contrast to the Life and Adventures of Sir William Wallace, or to even the voyages of Cook and Anson.[8] In short I determined to bestow as little labour upon it as I possibly could; and this as the schoolmaster was an easy, though excellent man, and was of opinion too that my uncles had much over-rated my natural abilities, proved to be little indeed. I became an egregious trifler; and during those hours in which my schoolfellows were busied with their tasks, I was to be found by every one, except the master, engaged in reading some story book, which I had brought to school among my other books, and which I relished all the better from the circumstance of my being compelled to peruse it by stealth. I was at this time acquainted with almost every tradesman in town who had the command of a few books, and was on such terms with many of them as to be allowed the privilege of ransacking every dark corner in their houses where the dust and wisdom of past ages were sleeping together. There were five other boys in the class with me. None of them were by any means naturally bright, but I would soon have been distanced by the very dullest of them had I not fallen upon the means of making them all as careless of their lessons as myself.

One day after our tasks had been recited to the master in a manner tolerably creditable to all the members of the class except one, who occupied as usual the lowest place in it, I began narrating to the lad who sat next me some of the adventures of Sir William Wallace. I possessed at the time a memory uncommonly tenacious, my imagination had a wild activity, and the subject was one in which I was much interested. The lad was quite delighted; and next day when the other members of the class were set down to their lessons, and I to the perusal of Gulliver's voyage to Lilliput, he tapped me on the shoulder, and besought me to tell him another story. Pleased to find one as idly disposed as myself I complied with his request, and the result was that the master was considerably puzzled (a thing which had not happened before) to decide whether my companion or myself was the worse scholar, or deserving of the lower place. To affront the former he gave me the preference. Next time the school met I was called upon for another story, and I now kept two of my classfellows, the boys upon either hand, as idle as I before had kept one. In a short time my narratives had charmed even the very shadow of diligence out of the class. Every meeting demanded a new one, and in a few weeks my whole stock was exhausted. What was to be done! My classfellows might have returned to their tasks as before, and I to my storybooks; but alas! though I relished storybooks as much as ever, my classfellows had lost all inclination to their tasks. They urged me to try whether I could not remember one other story, and so to satisfy them, though without letting them into the secret I set myself to try whether I could not invent one. I succeeded beyond expectation, and my class-fellows were hugely delighted. Each of my other stories had a beginning, a middle, and an end; – this one was middle alto-gether. Each of the others had but one character peculiar to itself; – this one had half a dozen. The hero of it was such a warrior as Wallace, and such a voyager as Gulliver. He was the sworn foe of magicians, and not very much afraid of ghosts. Like Philip Quarle he lived at one time in a desert island where he had to contend with wild beasts and wild men, and at another he resided in a huge old castle which had as many subterraneous passages winding through it as there are veins in the human body.[9] This wild tale was the first of an endless series; for I never after had to complain that my stock was exhausted.

To the east and south of Cromarty there is a large wooded eminence which, from its summit having been in former times the scene of baronial executions, is termed (a name common in Scotland) the Gallow-hill. It slopes gently towards the north and west, and the slope is laid out in corn fields; but on the south and east the declivity is abrupt and precipitous, skirted by the sea shore, and in many places hollowed into deep cav-erns. My holidays were frequently spent on this hill; and I prided myself on being better acquainted with its caves and precipices, its glades and thickets than any other boy in school. There were some curious traditions connected with its scenes, and these I occasionally introduced into my school narratives. There were wild berries too and fine flowers to be found among its cliffs, and pretty stones on its shores. My oft repeated descrip-tion of this hill awakened the curiosity of my schoolfellows, and during the holidays some of them accompanied me in my excursions to it. As I thought it one of the finest places in the world, and was jealous of its honour, I was not a little piqued to find that most of my companions deemed it a wild savage place, too far from home, and too solitary to be a proper scene of amusement. The very track along its summit in which accord-ing to tradition Wallace had driven before him the broken remnants of an army of *Southron*, and in which I have marched for whole hours, beating down every tall weed that sprung in

the way (thistles excepted) with a sabre of lath, they regarded
as nothing other than a piece of barren moor. Their indifference
vexed me to the heart. One of them, however, an interesting
lad, who had scarcely any thing in common with the others
became nearly as much attached to the scenes to which I
introduced him as I was myself; and for more than a twelvemonth after almost all my hours of play were spent with him
in the woods of the hill, or among its rocks.[10] Though much
superior to me as a scholar, and both shrewd and sensible, he
was my junior by nearly two years, and this circumstance
added to my knowledge of books, and my peculiar cast of
character which was decided and cool, gave me considerable
influence over him. My example had not the effect of making
him a more diligent scholar, but as he possessed an active and
powerful mind, it did not operate so unfavourably on him as
on some of my other schoolfellows. He afterwards bore away
at one of the Aberdeen Universities the first prize in Mathematics, and the second in Natural Philsophy [sic]; and I owe to
him the correction of several false opinions which I held not
many years since, and which had no tendency to encourage
the more pleasing moods of thought, and no legitimate connexion with the more excellent principles of action.

On a pleasant spring morning he and I left our respective
homes for a stroll through our favourite hill. As we went I
described to him a singular cavern, the haunt of rock pigeons,
which I had visited alone a few days before, and we agreed on
exploring it. The place is only accessible during the ebb of
spring tides, and at this time the tide was a very low neap;
but as we were more bent on reaching the cavern than inclined
to deliberate how it could be quitted were we once there, we
proceeded to examine the precipice which projecting into the
sea, like a huge mole barred us out of it. A narrow shelf which
winded round this cliff we deemed practicable, for we were
both expert climbers; and in a few seconds we had scrambled
on it to the other side, where it terminated abruptly about
twelve feet above the beach. Leaping had long been one of our
favourite amusements, and though twelve feet was a rather
hazardous leap for two little fellows of eleven and thirteen

years, we ventured on it; and were soon though without once dreaming of the matter, in a similar predicament with the fox in the well. The cave proved a mine of wonders. We found it of great depth, and when at its furthest extremity the sea and opposite land appeared to us as they would if viewed through the tube of a telescope. We discovered that its sides and roof were crusted over with a white stone resembling marble, and that it contained a petrifying spring. The pigeons which we disturbed were whizzing by us, through the gloom, reminding us of the hags of our storybooks, when on their night voyages through the air. A shoal of porpoises were tempesting the water in their unwieldy gambols, scarcely an hundred yards from the caverns mouth; and a flock of sea gulls were screaming around them, like harpies round the viands of the Trojan. To add to the interest of the place we had learned from tradition that in *the langsyne* this cave had furnished Wallace with a hiding place, and that more recently it had been haunted by smugglers. In the midst of our engagements, however, the evening began to darken; and we discovered that our very fine cave was neither more nor less than a prison. We attempted climbing round but in vain; for the shelf from whence we had leaped was unattainable, and there was no other path. 'What will my mother think!' said the poor little fellow whom I had brought into this predicament, as he burst into tears, 'I would not care nothing for myself, – but my mother.' The appeal was powerful, and had he not cried I probably would; the sight of his tears roused my pride, and with a feeling which Rochefoucault would have at once recognized as springing from the master principle, I attempted to comfort him; and for the time completely forgot my own sorrows in exulting with all due sympathy over his. Night came on both dark and rainy, and we lay down together in a corner of the cave. A few weeks prior the corpse of a fisherman, who had been drowned early in the preceding winter, had been found on the beach below. It was much gashed by the sharp rocks, and the head was beaten to pieces. I had seen it at the time it was carried through the streets of Cromarty to the church, where in this part of the country the bodies of drowned persons are commonly put until the cofin [sic] and grave be prepared; and all this night long, sleeping or waking, the image of this corpse was continually before me. As often as I slumbered a mangled headless thing would come stalking into the cave, and attempt striking me when I would awaken with a start, cling to my companion, and hide my face in his breast. About one o'clock in the morning we were relieved by two boats, which our friends, who had spent the early part of the night in searching for us in the woods above, had fitted out to try along the shore for our bodies; they having at length concluded that we had fallen over the cliffs, and were killed. One of my first essays in written verse detailed this adventure.[11]

My companion and I continued for several weeks after this unlucky incident as inseperable [sic] as before, when another still more untoward, had the effect of breaking off our intimacy. By some means or other he had procured a large cannon-cartridge of gunpowder, which having stored in a box, he secreted under his bed. I was of course, let into the secret, and allowed a share of the treasure; and I very gratefully proposed that as I was less under control than he, I should take upon me the risk of being deemed the owner of the powder, and the sole projector of all our fireworks. This agreed to we began to mine and countermine with much perseverance and no little ingenuity. Our squibs and volcanos were suberb [sic] and the little accidents which took place so long as we remained together were mere matters of course; but after parting for the night my poor friend when going to bed, opened the box to survey his treasure, and by a spark from the candle the whole contents exploded. He was so terribly scorched as to be blind for several hours after, and for more than a fortnight he was confined to his room. It was not until ten days had succeeded the accident that I summed up resolution enough to visit him. He received me, as I thought, with great coldness; and suspecting that he had made a rather ungenerous use of our late treaty, for the explosion had not been one of its anticipated consequences, I took my leave of him in high dugeon; without once hinting, for pride restrained me, how much more honourable it would be for him to act up to the spirit than to the letter of our agreement. My suspicions wronged him; for as I afterwards learned he stoutly denied that I had any share in the powder; but such was their effect that more than two years elapsed, though during that period our hearts beat thick and high every time we accidentally met, before we exchanged a single word. I was too proud to ask an explanation, and he too much offended by my suspicions to give one unasked.

In the interim I chanced to fall in with a French work on Fortification.[12] I knew nothing of the language in which it was written, but by dint of poring over the prints assisted by the second volume of Baillie's Dictionary, I acquired pretty correct notions of the art.[13] My leisure hours were now occupied in building huge fortresses of sand either on the sea shore or on a bank to the east of the town. As my friends knew nothing of the book I studied they regarded my new amusement as rather childish for a boy of thirteen; and some of my old companions when I was busied with my work would stand hooting at me from a distance. Still, however, I continued to persevere, and consoled myself by reflecting that neither my friends nor companions knew any thing of bastions, orillions, or lunettes or knew that a regular fortification could only be constructed on a regular polygon. I soon discovered that as both the shore and bank were sloping planes, neither of them afforded a proper site for a fortress; and I determined on building one else where which would be impregnable even to Vaubans method of attack. After a due survey, I pitched upon a grassy knoll, and with much labour removed to it vast quantities of sand. I drew a circle in which I inscribed a pentagon. I constructed on the angles *secundem artem* five bastions; connected them by curtains, and shielded the curtains by ravelins, horn-works, and tenailles. Never did general feel more elated on the unconditional surrender to his arms of some fortress before deemed impregnable, than did I on the completion of mine. I shouted for very joy. Observing, however, a small eminence in the vicinity of my fort on which a very annoying battery could be erected I determined on taking possession of it by a redoubt, and was busied in carrying sand for the building, when the overseer of the farm upon which my works were

constructed made his sudden appearance. Like other great tacti-
cians I had at the time no very distinct ideas of the right of
private property; but when the man rated me for spoiling his
grass in a manner so wantonly mischievous I had not the
power even to reply. The works I had deemed impregnable
proved of no manner of use in repelling his attacks and so
piqued was I at the rencounter that I never after constructed
a single bastion.

Soon after dismounting from off this hobby I mounted another. A work on Chemistry fell in my way, and I became a
chemist. My experiments, however, were wofully [sic] unfortunate. I next tried painting, and daubed in varnish and colour for
nearly a week. When engaged in boiling oil, which somehow
found its way out at the chimney, I succeeded in producing a
sublime fire scene, and then flung away the pallet. A few weeks
after I became a founder of leaden images. The bust of a neighbour whose features were rather singular than agreeable was my
last production in this art; for the bust though ugly in the extreme being sufficiently striking as a likeness to be recognized,
my ingenuity gained me so severe a reprimand that I flung my
casts into the fire. I next attempted making a piece of mosaic
work, and failing as might be expected, I applied to the fashion-
ing of watch seals. When I had worn the points of my fingers
with cutting and polishing until the blood appeared, I forsook
the grindstone, threw away the graver, and betook myself to
reading. A little old book on natural magic, palmistry, and
astrology, which I stumbled upon by accident wonderfully delighted me, and I applied to these studies; but as the last could
not be prosecuted without an acquaintance with astronomy
and the mathematics I was unwillingly compelled to give up all
thoughts of gaining that insight into the future which it promised; and the two first though of easier attainment proved after a
slight examination rather strong for my credulity. I forget by
what train of reflection I was led to conclude it absurd to suppose that a man's future history was shewn forth by hiero-
glyphic on the palm of his left hand, and yet rational to believe
that it was written among the stars; but I remember discovering
by a rather singular process that the whole after course of my life

was to be strangely eventful, and that after many vicissitudes it was at length to terminate on the scaffold. I was to be hung for sedition. To these occult studies the writing of verses succeeded. Verse in turn gave place to prose, and prose to a third sort of composition which imitated the style of Macpherson's Ossian.[14] I remember reading about the close of this period Drydens character of Zimri, and it was with no little complacency that I recognized in it the transcript of my own.[15]

I had other amusements of this time from which I derived much pleasure, though like some of the ones I have described they laid me open to the ridicule of my companions. About half a mile from the town of Cromarty there is a large horse pond to which on holidays the schoolboys resort to sail their little smacks and schooners. The edge of this pond was one of my favourite haunts. From the perusal of books of voyages and history I had become acquainted with a great many different modes of navigation, and instead of borrowing the model of my little vessels from the ships which frequented the harbour of Cromarty, I used to keep in exercise the risible faculties of all the mimic navagation [sic] of the pond, with slim, fish-like boats of barks, like those of North American Indians, awkward high pooped galleys, like those I had seen in the prints of an old edition of Dryden's Virgil, two keeled vessels, like the double canoes of Otaheite, & wall-sided, half vessels, like the proas of the Ladrone islands. Nor could I derive, like my companions, any pleasure from the merely mechanical operation of plain sailing. I had a story connected with every voyage, and every day had its history of expeditions of discovery and cases of mutiny and shipwreck. But my chief amusement of this period was after collecting great quantities of the variously coloured little shells of the sea shore, to draw upon the sand the map of some country, which I would people with these shells, and then imagining myself its king design on it towns and roads, canals and harbours, and all other works of men. I have ruled my little kingdoms by every different scheme of government I had read of in Guthries Grammar, and attacked or defended them by every stratagem of war with which books or my uncles had brought me acquainted.[16]

In the space between my thirteenth and fifteenth years I was a wild reckless boy the hero of my schoolfellows and the plague of the master. I became the leader of a band of the boldest and most intelligent lads in school, who from their acquaintance with me had grown nearly as romantic, and as fond of enterprize and adventure as myself. Perforating one of the steepest precipices which skirt the southern base of the hill of Cromarty there is a deep dark cavern. In this cavern during the harvest vacation I and my band have spent whole weeks, not quitting it each day until late in the evening, and returning to it often before daylight. From the steepness of the precipices above and the roughness of the shore below the place is nearly inaccessible, and we were seldom disturbed by visitors. The shore supplied us with limpits [sic] and perwinkles [sic], the cliffs with hips and brambles, the fields through which we passed on our way, and which we had learned to consider as much our own as the shore and cliffs, furnished us with potatoes, and the wood above with fuel. A lad of the party contrived to bring away undiscovered one of his mothers pots, and another furnished us with a pitcher. In short our household was amply stocked. The time not employed in cooking or in procuring victuals we spent in acting little dramatic pieces, of which I sketched out the several plans, leaving the dialogue to be supplied by the actors. Robbers, buccaneers, outlaws of every description were the heroes of these dramas. They frequently, despite of my arrangements to the contrary, terminated in skirmishes of a rather tragic cast, in which with our spears of elder and swords of hazle [sic] we exchanged pretty severe blows. We were sometimes engaged too in conflicts with other boys, in which, as became a leader, I distinguished myself by a cool, yet desperate courage. Nor was I entitled to the rank I held from only the abilities which I displayed in framing plays and in fighting. I swam, climbed, leaped, and wrestled better than any other lad of my years and inches in the place.

Some of my exploits of this period were of a rather disreputable cast. I loved dearly to be actively employed in a good cause either in doing or suffering; but just causes of exertion or endurance are not often presented, and I thought it hard to be debarred being a hero through mere lack of opportunity. As I could not in the course of my errantry find giants to encounter, I became a giant myself; and my boys to whom I was both thought and impulse, were taught rather how to blend courage with caution, than a principle of justice with either. One of our adventures well nigh effected the dissolution of our society. There is a large orchard in the vicinity of the town of Cromarty which we had to pass and repass in our way to and from the cave. When looking into it from an eminence, one of our number chanced to remark that the very tempting fruit which we saw shinning [sic] through the leaves would make excellent deserts to our banquets of shell fish and potatoes. The thought was one with which we were all familiar, but this expression of it set our wits to work. During the day we deliberated, and fixed upon a plan for robbing the orchard; and after nightfall a select party of which I was leader was despatched from our head quarters to make an invasion on it. We went to work with great coolness, made as may be supposed, considerable havoc, and came off undiscovered. We had left behind us, however, no faint vestiges of our inroad, the robbing was traced to us through the imprudence of one of the party, and we were threatened with immediate incarceration. As the emergency was one of no common character a council extraordinary was held in the cave, where we agreed that the parties implicated should leave town, and live until the offence was forgotten in a wild sequestered cavern about half a mile south of the one we frequented, which though both solitary and difficult of access we considered as too accessible and too generally known. The other could only be approached at low water and had the reputation of being haunted. Preparations were accordingly made both for subsistence and defence. To serve us for beds we piled up withered grass and dried fern in the recesses of the cave, and the entrance we nearly blocked up with brushwood for fuel. For food we depended on the fields and the shore. As we determined to defend ourselves manfully in the event of our retreat being discovered and attacked, we provided ourselves with arms. One of the party brought along with him a large horseman's pistol, I swaggered an old bayonet, and the others armed themselves with bludgeons. It is true the bayonet was much ragged at the edges and all over rust, but it was a formidable weapon notwithstanding; and as for the pistol, though unfurnished with a lock, it was evidently calculated to do great mischief by the fire side. All these preparations, however, as the proprietor of the orchard did not urge matters to the threatened extremity, came to nothing; and though the recollection of what we had felt on the occasion had the effect of rendering our future exploits more prudent and a little less immoral, so bent were we on bringing this one to a different issue that there was not one of us who did not feel disappointed.

My friends grieved that I should squander my time in a manner so useless and disreputable attempted recalling me to application and regularity, and this by the gentlest methods. Force they had already tried, but it had only had the effect of exasperating my native obstinacy to such a pitch that for some time I carried about with me a long clasp knife as a weapon of defence. Notwithstanding my wildness my uncle James was much attached to me and he was scarcely more ready to chide me for my irregularities than to make apologies for them to others. Nothing could convince him that the schoolmaster had formed a proper estimate of my capacity in regarding me as the dullest boy in school. He would tell me when he detected me playing the truant, how certainly in after years I would regret my carelessness and want of attention. He would tell me I was neglecting the culture of talents which if properly cultivated would raise me to distinction; and that I was squandering the only season of life in which a proper foundation of at least book knowledge could be laid in; for that season once unprofitably spent, even were I afterwards to apply to learning, I could only expect to gain that late imperfect education which rather shows a man his deficiencies that supplies them. I was wild and reckless and neither his censures nor advices had any effect. My other uncle took higher ground in dealing with me; – he appealed to the code of morals inculculated [sic] by Christianity; and my poor mother, despairing of a reformation in my

conduct gave me up altogether, and suffered her hopes and
her affections to rest on my two sisters, who were interesting
little girls, and both docile and intelligent. Alas! in the winter
of 1816, when the one was in her tenth and the other in her
twelfth year, they were both seized at nearly the same time
by a malignant fever, then raging in the place, and died within
a few days of each other. The stroke made a considerable
impression on me, for I was not destitute of affection. I remember being wrung to the heart by overhearing my mother remark
how different her condition would have been had it pleased
Heaven to have taken her son from her, and left one of her
daughters. It was bitter for me to think, and yet I could not
think otherwise, that she had cause of sorrow both for those
whom she had lost, and for him who survived; and I would
willingly have laid down my life could the sacrifice have restored to her one of my sisters. These feelings, however, produced no lasting effect. A particular way of thinking, a peculiar
course of reading, a singular train of oral narration had con-
curred from the period at which I had first thought, read or
listened, in giving my character the impress it then bore and
it was not in the power of detached accident or effort to effect
a change. In a few weeks after I was again at the head of my
band.

The school at which, though I commonly played truant
three weeks out of every four, I still occasionally attended,
was not the only one in the place. There was another kept by
a man who had the character of being severe and a good
teacher; and my uncles in the hope that his authority would
prove an overmatch for my obstinacy and negligence, placed
me under his care. Latin, in which it was seen I would
make no proficiency whatever, was given up for Arithmetic.
I acquired the first few rules in nearly the common time and
this satisfied my new master, for he rated my natural abilities
rather lower than the former. This I soon discovered, and
content barely to justify his estimate, I began to crawl over
my *Hamilton* at a much slower rate than any other boy in
school.[17] Two thirds of every day I squandered in pursuing my
old favourite amusement, light reading, or in one of more

recent date, the composition of verses. I here renewed my intimacy with the friend with whom I had quarreled about two years before, and in a short time we again became inseparable. His character was in almost every respect the reverse of mine, but we loved each other none the less on this account. He was better acquainted than I with men and things in their real modes of existence; from his diligence and ability as a scholar he was a great favourite with the master; and was as superior to most of the other scholars in soundness of judgement as I excelled them in strength of imagination. When these faculties of judgement and imagination, however, come in contact, the less excellent, and I have since wondered how it could be so, proved the more powerful; for during the continuance of our second intimacy I exerted over him an almost uncontrolable [sic] influence; and he entered into all my wild schemes as readily, and seemingly with as little power to think for himself as his less gifted companions.

At this school what I did I was compelled to do well, and so I was gaining a little, – occasionally a rule in Arithmetic, or the just pronounciation of a word, when the master in consequence of indisposition was obliged to relinquish his charge, which was taken up by a singular, eccentric man, who lax and rigid by turns was by no means so competent as a teacher. Such as he was, however, had I been placed under his care five years sooner he would have made me a scholar; but by this time I had got beyond the reach of all human instruction. The only school in which I could now be taught was that which awaited me, – the school of experience where toil and hardship were the teachers. My new master discovered, what the others did not, that I had considerable influence over my schoolfellows, and he accordingly set me down for being possessed of talents of some kind or other. In examining my copy and Arithmetic books he found many pages scrabbled [sic] all over with verses, which he took the pains of deciphering; and though they were rude and ungrammatical, and nearly as obscure as the prophecies of the antient Sibyls, he deemed them to display considerable powers of thought and imagination. I shared in consequence much of his attention; but jealous of the friendship of one who would expect me to become a scholar I continued as negligent as before and invincibly sullen. He must have regarded my character as anomalous in the extreme; for while he perceived by my verses that I could both think and feel, he found me the most impenetrably dull of all his pupils, and apathetically indifferent to either praise or censure. After finding that kindness had no effect on me, he changed his method and tried severity, but all that he inflicted I endured with a patience similar to that which the Cherokee Indian exhibits at the stake, and I proceeded with my lessons at exactly the same pace as before.

There was a mulatto lad, a native of the West Indies, who sat at the same form with me. He was older and stouter than I, and much dreaded by the other boys for a wild, savage disposition which is, I believe, natural to most of his countryfolks. He was famed too, as an expert and ready combatant; and once or twice when on the eve of being overmatched by stouter boys than himself he had with his clasp knife overawed and chased off his opponents. One day, upon some slight difference arising between us, he struck me, and a quarrel ensued. I was fast gaining the battle, when he stepped back, opened his knife, and aimed it at my breast. Though much startled, for this species of warfare was new to me, I recollected that my reputation for courage was at stake, and instantly armed myself with a similar weapon. From standing on the defensive I soon became the assaulting party; and as I was more agile than he, and perhaps more in earnest, our conflict ended by my stabbing him in the thigh. The mulatto was terribly frightened, and not a little hurt, but conscious that he had been the aggressor he did not accuse me to the master; though I rather think an incorrect and exaggerated account of the exploit afterwards reached him. At any rate he suddenly changed about this time his manner of dealing with me, and seemed rather to measure me as a formidable opponent, than to regard me as a backward pupil. He showed a determination too, by the occasions he sought of quarreling with me, to have me expelled the school. A favourable opportunity soon offered. On my committing some slight offence he called me up for chastisement, when instead of using the lash in the common

way, he laid hold on me, and attempted throwing me down.
This, though he was a tall robust man, and I a mere stripling,
he found no easy task, for wrestling had been one of my favourite exercises, and I resisted him to the utmost of my strength
and skill. After maintaining the struggle for several minutes I
was at length floored;· and as from the unexpected opposition
he had met with, his passions were much excited, he beat me
unmercifully. On escaping out of his hands I laid hold on my
cap, and marched out of school. Before night I had written a
satire upon him entitled the Pedagogue, which, as his eccentri-
cities gave me ample scope, occasioned a good deal of laughter;
and thus terminated my course of school education.

For some months after this luckless incident I was perfectly
free; but though hitherto I had invariably associated the idea
of freedom with that of happiness, I now found the connexion
not necessary, for I was not perfectly happy. I was haunted by
thoughts of the future, – by anticipations of the life of toil
which I knew awaited me. My companions too, (I still headed
a party) seemed like myself conscious of being in the last
stage of boyhood; and we one day determined on constructing
a something, we knew not what, that would serve as a monument to recall to us, in after years the recollection of our
early pastimes and enjoyments. After deliberating on the subject, I proposed that in some remote corner of the hill of
Cromarty we should dig a subterraneous chamber, like one of
those we had read of in our storybooks, and deposit in it our
arms and the utensils of our cave. I sketched out the plan of
an apartment which could only be entered by a trap door; &
having chosen a solitary spot nearly hid by a large bush, as a
proper site, I set my lads to dig. As the task was one which
required considerable labour and time, all my influence over
them was exerted to keep them at work; and as I had formerly
amused them by telling stories, I now encouraged them by
drawing pictures. 'Only imagine,' I have said, 'how happy we
shall feel in after years when we meet in our dark apartment
and there embody into reality what in other places will appear
to us to be but vague unsubstantial dreams of the past. On the
rude damp walls which will then be reddened by the glare of

our torches, shall hang the brown, rust eaten dagger and wasted pitcher of our frays and banquets. Remember the story I have told you of the Persian shepherd who when raised by his sovereign to the second place in the kingdom experienced his highest pleasure in contemplating the pipe, the crook, the coarse habiliments which reminded him of his juvenile employments. We are now purchasing for our after years enjoyments similar to his, and this too by spending a few days rather in amusement than labour.

Feeding on such imaginations, day after day saw us engaged in our new employment, and at length we had dug in the hard soil a pit eight feet in depth and nearly as much in length and breadth. One morning when on the way to the scene of our labours we were pertinaciously followed by a numerous horde of young fellows whose curiosity had been excited by the tools we carried. As it was essential to the very existence of our cave of mystery that none should know of it but ourselves, we had recourse to every expedient to shake them off; – we besought, we remonstrated, we ran, we doubled, but all to no purpose, our pursuers were staunch as bloodhounds; and what made the affair desperate, we saw that were we to provoke them to fight with us there was no chance of our coming off with the victory. The emergency roused me to display my skill as a tactician. I stepped up to the stoutest of our pursuers, and in the hearing of both parties challenged him to fight me. The suddeness of the manoeuvre unmanned him; he hesitated, and without giving him a moment to recover, for fighting was by no means my ultimate object, I turned away contemptously [sic], and challenged another. He also drew back, remarking, however, that he would fight any of the party except myself. I replied to him by calling on the friend whom I have so often had occasion to mention, and who now acted as my lieutenant, to step forward. He came with a leap, and with out speaking a word began to strip; while the challenger kept moving backwards until he had entrenched himself behind his companions, and then declined to fight. Without making a single remark I gave orders to my lads to march forward; and I had the satisfaction of seeing as I had anticipated the others, instead of following us a [sic] before, standing for a few seconds on the place where they had been left, and then turning homewards. The joy afforded us by this bloodless victory was, however, of short duration; – our pit was not destined to form the intended monument. On arriving at it one morning we perceived by indubitable marks that it had been discovered; and when we reached home we found a report current in the place that some malicious persons, for detecting whom a reward was to be offered, had constructed a formidable trap for maiming the cattle of the gentleman who farmed the hill. The secret of these malicious persons was, as may be thought, safe enough in our keeping. After nightfall, with heavy hearts we again returned to the now hopeless scene of our labours, and filled up the cavity with soil and branches of trees. Thus concluded the last of my boyish enter-prizes.

*   *   *

What I have written I may term the first chapter of my life. The second, in the writing of which, when the storms of winter prevent me from pursuing my labours as a mason, I promise myself some amusement, may be of a different character, and will, I trust, better deserve your perusal. In the writing of this one I have been sadly carried away from my first intention. On taking up the pen the wayward incidents of my boyhood appeared huddled together in a little dark corner of the past; but as I walked over them they expanded into size and interest, and at every step new lights of memory were springing up and dancing round them, like elf candles on a morass. Profitless as that portion of the past which they occupied appeared to me, I felt a desire of living it over again, and I have done so in my narrative. And now for the last ten minutes I have been thinking what sort of an apology would best suit me for the egotism it displays. But I shall make use of none. True I address the egotistical story of my boyish waywardness to a gentleman whose single head contains, I am aware, no very minute portion of the collective learning and philosophy of the kingdom. but then is it not enough to be convinced that his heart is warmed with a still ampler share of its entire benevolence. He will

forgive me my egotism from the interest he takes in my humble
fortunes, and pardon me my early carelessness, regarding its
effects as sufficient punishment. – It is a consequence of my
having been so wild and reckless a schoolboy that I am now a
poor journeyman-mason.

I trust Sir that ingratitude is not among the number of my
faults. I am convinced that even on the narrow principle of
the old philosopher Epicurus, it is a man's interest to be grateful.
I have always experienced more pleasure in indulging a proper
feeling towards those by whom I have been obliged than I
have derived from the obligations themselves. And I owe much
to you. It is long since I have learned to consider myself a
debtor to every good benevolent man whose character inclines
me to think favourably of human nature; for my every-day
experience of it justifies such an opinion as inclines me to
misanthropy, and I have yet discovered that one cannot be
both happy and a misanthrope. To the good man of whose
benevolence I myself am the object I feel doubly indebted;
and in the present instance there is a third feeling which at
the very least is not of less influence than any of the others.
My vanity is flattered. It will be long ere I forget that he who
has honoured me by his notice was the friend and correspondent
of Robert Burns, and the generous benefactor of the mother of
Michael Bruce. Besides, Sir, I have already received lessons
from the Critics which show me the value of a friend to whose
judgement I may look up as the mariner to the star of the
Pole. Of these lessons the following is a summary. First, I am
taught that I am a dull correct fellow who has written a book
in which there is nothing amusing and nothing absurd. Sec-
ondly, that I am a man of genius whose poems contain much
that is faulty and much that is interesting. Thirdly, that I
have no chance of being known beyond the bounds of Cromarty,
and that my book exhibits none, or next to none of those
indications which sanction the expectation of better things to
come. And Fourthly, that scintillations of real genius flicker
visibly in almost every page, and that my name shall yet be
classed with those few names which to the ear of taste have
become familiar as household words. On receiving the opinion

of one Editor who has prognosticated that the author of the
Boatmans Tale shall yet become a burning and shinning [sic]
light, I caught myself muttering 'Ah Mr Editor you and he
have shared the same spirit of prophecy, – what a pity 'tis
that there are lying spirits;'[18] and when I found that I had
narrowly escaped being hung up by another as a dreadful
warning to all versifiers of the same class, I could not help
exclaiming 'Hang up the journeyman mason! Why? what evil
hath he done?' The dogmas these gentlemen would have me to
hold regarding myself are sufficiently mysterious. They have
discovered to me that I am both a blockhead and a man of
genius, and that my name is to be at once illustrious and
obscure.

There accompanies this a dozen copies of my letters on the
Herring Fishery;[19] two of which you will oblige me by presenting
to Mr Gordon, a gentleman who has shown me kindness; some
of the others you may perhaps find opportunity of distributing
among your literary friends.[20] A first edition of six hundred
has already been sold off. With many faults, the discovery of
which encourages me to hope I shall one day write more
correctly, my pamphlet has, I believe, one merit. It contains
some information on the subject of the fisheries which lay
beyond the reach of the mere literary man, and some remarks
on character which could only have been made in a peculiar
and unusual point of observation. – I expected to have had
my books boarded and ready for sending you ere now, but my
bookbinder has disappointed me; in the course of a few days,
however, they shall I trust be sent off. Accept my thanks for
the very favourable critique on my poems which appeared in
the *Caledonian Mercury*.[21]

At the close of what I have termed the first chapter of my
narrative I have described myself as in the last stage of boyhood.
Recent experience had taught me that neither ease nor freedom
do of themselves constitute happiness; but their contraries,
toil and restraint, I regarded as positive misery. O the wretchedness, have I said to myself of having no will of ones own; – of
toiling every day merely that one may eat, and eating every

day merely that one may toil. I have since formed a very different estimate of the evils of a life of labour and restraint from what I did then. I have learned that the middle state with its hours of grief and enjoyment, and its whole years of monotonous indifference, is the state assigned to man, and that he can not quit it either by rising higher, or by sinking lower in the scale of external circumstances.

In 1819 my mother after a widowhood of twelve years entered into a second marriage.[22] Both my uncles were averse to the match, particularly James, who had not ceased to cherish the memory of my father. So far as I myself was concerned in the event I considered it unlucky; and I began to perceive the necessity of my immediately applying to some trade. I determined on being a mason, – for it had not escaped me that masons in this part of the country during the winter and spring seasons are commonly unemployed; and I trusted by pursuing this profession to find in the amusements of the one half of each year, a compensation for the labours of the other half. The life of a mason, thought I, is not invariably wretched; It is like one of Jacobs stripped rods checkered white and black alternately.

Neither of my uncles took a similar view of the matter. Though their intention of fitting me for one of the learned professions had come to nothing, for at this time the whole of my school attainments were summed up in reading, writing, and an imperfect acquaintance with the simpler rules of Arithmetic, they still continued to think, so partial were they to me, that Providence could not possibly have intended me for a mere tradesman. James assailed me with ridicule, and Alexander with remonstrance and advice. 'You have not yet,' the latter has said to me, 'completed your seventeenth year. There are instances of men who for even a longer period were wild and careless, who yet by late application became eminent as scholars. Devote to learning the three years in which, as you say, you intend serving an apprenticeship to masonary; – depend upon't it will avail you more; and if you feel uneasy at home come and live with your uncle and me.' 'When you were a little boy,' uncle James has said, 'among other stories

you have told me of one Hercules who was doing much good
in the world, and gaining himself a great name, when all at
once he took it into his head to become a spinner of yarn. I do
not remember of your having told me that he became very
expert in his new trade; but at best he could only have tri-
umphed in it over a few old women. You are going to play the
fool in exactly the same manner; – to cromp over the distaff
powers that evidently were given you to wield the club.'

So bent was I on accomplishing what I purposed that neither
advice nor remonstrance had any effect. Though I had no
predilection for any of the occupations of masonry the long
seasons of leisure which the profession afforded made me deem
it superior to any other; and though a course of study might
probably have proved less irksome to me that a series of employments which engaged only the bodily and mechanical powers,
I saw that when pursuing such a course I could not be other
than dependent. A sister of my mother's was married to a
mason who on a small scale contracted for village and country
buildings.[23] He generally kept two apprentices and employed a
few journeymen. With him I agreed to serve three years; and
early in February 1820. I commenced work in one of the Cromarty quarries; – my master uniting as is common in this part
of the country, the professions of the mason and quarrier.

My first six months of labour presented only a series of
disasters. I was at the time of a slender make and weak constitution; and I soon found I was ill fitted for such employments as
the trundling of loaded wheelbarrows over a plank, or the
raising of huge blocks of stone out of a quarry. My hands were
soon fretted into large blisters, my breast became the seat of a
dull oppressive pain, and I was much distressed after exertion
more than usually violent by an irregular motion of the heart.
My spirits too were almost always miserably low; and I was so
wrapped up in a wretched, apathetical absence of mind that I
have wrought for whole hours together with scarcely a thought
of what I was doing myself, and scarcely conscious of what
others were doing around me. My master pronounced me the
most awkward of all his apprentices, and remarked that I did
not seem possessed of capacity enough to make even a common

mechanic. His estimate vexed me, but I had no power to shake off the apathetical mood which I was aware occasioned it; and which had otherwise the effect of adding to my miseries. At one time I barely escaped being crushed to pieces, through inattention, by a falling bank; at another my right toe was flattened by a large stone, and during the first six unfortunate months of this year I lost at different times the nails of no fewer that seven of my fingers. To add to these sufferings I had several sharp fits of sickness which compelled me to suspend my labours for whole weeks together. Still, however, pride enabled me to bear up. My uncles had predicted that I would deal by my trade just in the manner I had already dealt by the school, a prediction which I determined to falsify; and so I obstinately pursued my employments, despite of petty accidents, low spirits, bad health, the ridicule of my companions, and the gibes of my master. I discovered, however, when treated with my brother workmen to a glass of liquor, that the ardent spirits of the dram shop were much greater luxuries than I had formerly accounted them; and it is probable that the want of money alone prevented me from indulging at this period in the low vice of dram-drinking. I deem the spring and summer of this year the gloomiest seasons of my life. The autumn I passed more pleasantly; for all of a sudden I became as expert a hewer as my master or any of his journeymen; and so flattered was my vanity by the respect which they paid me on this account, and such satisfaction did I derive from emulating them in what they confessed the better department of their profession that the coming winter, to which a few weeks before I had looked forward as good men do to the pleasures of another state of existence, was no longer an object of desire. When it arrived, however, I congratulated myself on my being once more at liberty to pursue my inclinations, and I began to look around me for amusement.

My early companions had all either left the place or had been indentured to trades which, unlike the one I pursued could be plied in winter. My friend of the cave had gone to London, and was there apprenticed to a grocer. I had no one with whom to associate, and though occasionally when in a particular mood I could enjoy solitude even more than society, I found that in my common, everyday frame leisure without friendship was a thing rather of endurance than of enjoyment. I sought after some one whom I could regard as a friend, and I learned in the search that the men best fitted for carrying on the common business of life, feel as if by rule, and think as if by precedent, and have no sympathy for thoughts and feelings of the kind which I had been accustomed to cherish,. These people, thought I, are the wheels and pinions, the pins and axes of the great machine of society. When united they form a whole, but they are useless apart. My friend must not be one of these pieces, – one of these useful fragments; – he must be detached from the machine and independent of it; and though he should be tiny and profitless, even as a butterfly, he must, like that insect, be a thing both of life and enjoyment.

Early in this winter I found the friend I sought in a house-painters apprentice, a thoughtful looking, reserved young man of about two and twenty. I first became interested in him when I found that no one was intimate with him, but that every one accounted him clever. 'He is skilled in music,' said his master, 'he plays beautifully on the flute, draws admirably, and has an elegant taste in poetry; but he is quite a hermit and has no relish for society.' This description quite enchanted me, and I sought opportunity of becoming acquainted with him. In a few days we had grown intimate, in a few weeks inseparable, and our friendship continued until his death.

William Ross a man to whom time for at least the last half of his life presented only a succession of sorrows, but who I firmly trust is now happy in the enjoyments of eternity, was born in the year 1798. His father, a common labourer, was weak of intellect and careless of his children; his mother though more affectionate, was equally weak. The people who affirm that the soul is material and owes, as the schoolmen express it, its lineage to parental traduction, would, I should think, find it difficult to account for the fact of two such persons being the parents of a man of superior understanding and fine genius. He lived from his fifth year until he was indentured to a master with his grandmother and a maiden aunt, two excellent women who supported themselves by keeping a school for children in the country parish of Nigg. They soon discovered that William was unlike all the other boys that attended their school. He outstripped his classfellows almost without effort, and soon became a much better scholar than either of his teachers; for they only taught him to read and write, and to these acquirements he himself added Grammar, Arithmetic, and Geometry. He never joined in the amusements of his schoolfellows, but when released from his studies he would retire to a thick wood, at the edge of which his grandmother's cottage was situated; and there would he saunter for hours together, indulging in the wild dreams of a powerful imagination. His animated descriptions of these reveries have appeared to me the transcripts of my own. 'In these woods,' he has said, 'I always forgot my circumstances but never myself. In doing or suffering I was always my own hero. At one time I have imagined myself a warrior deserted by his followers, and left alone to cut his way through a whole host of enemies; at another I have fancied myself the sole inhabitant of a desert island. I have been the leader of a victorious army; – I have been a martyr chained to the stake.' Such perhaps is an epitome of the general history of that department of fiction which relates the exploits of generous courage and devoted patriotism. Its details are as certainly the offspring of self love as of creative genius. The poet first glories over the achievements which as the noblest of heroes and the most devoted of patriots he has wrought in his own ideal world before he transfers them to some fictitious personage.

My friend though fond of reading after he had perused the few volumes which belonged to his grandmother, had no opportunity of procuring books. He applied to other amusements. He copied the prints which were pasted on the walls of the schoolroom, and then drew from nature. He wrote Scripture paraphrases in imitation of the psalms of our common metrical version, and long narrative poems in the style of Chevy-Chase and the Babes in the Wood. He constructed flutes and fifes of young shoots of elder, with which, as he had a delicate ear he contrived to make an agreeable music. He afterwards studied the gamut, and was reckoned one of the best flute players in this part of the country. 'The years,' he has said to me, 'in which I was thus engaged were the happiest of my life; for as my standard of excellence in any of the fine arts was far from high, I suceeded in whatever I attempted, and so considered myself as one of the most talented persons in the whole world.' But these days were soon to have an end. My friend in his sixteenth year, when undetermined what profession to pursue, was advised by some relatives to make choice of that of the housepainter, as one in which his skill in drawing could be turned to account; and he accordingly came to Cromarty where he was indentured to a master for the term of seven years.

He exchanged when he quitted the country for the town the society of people who loved and admired him for that of people who were no way interested in his welfare; and who neither regarded his attainments as admirable in themselves or as the earnests of future excellence. He had opportunities, however, which he did not formerly enjoy of seeing good pictures and reading the works of our classical English poets. The favourable effect of the new ideas imparted to him by the study of the former was soon visible in his drawings; for he acquired a minute knowledge of the rules of perspective, and the other principles of art which assist the genius of the painter; but his acquaintance with the latter did not improve his verses. His early pieces were sweet simple things in the old ballad style, or rather in that of the more pleasing compositions of the patriotic Marvel;[24] while those he wrote latterly were comparatively stiff and unnatural. The ground work of his poetry was still simple as before, but it was 'broidered over with sounding epithets, and lines which imitated, and that not skilfully, the artful structure, and compressed energy of thought of those of Dryden and Pope. He soon became conscious of this defect, and losing all taste of poetical composition through a despair of attaining the skill of the poet, he flung aside the pen, and never again resumed it.

The portion of leisure time which he had formerly devoted to this amusement he now spent in the study of Architecture and Anatomy. His acquaintance with the latter art was acquired from books, and limited to that department the knowledge of which is reckoned essential to the painter and statuary. He also studied the principles of music, and became, as I have said before, one of the best flute players in this part of the country. Music is the most generally beloved, and consequently the most popular of all the fine arts; and the skill which my friend acquired in it brought him more local celebrity than all his other attainments; but even this circumstance did not prevent him from neglecting it as he had done the study of poetry. He went to Edinburgh in the Spring of 1822, where he resided about five years. On our first meeting there, which took place in 1824, there was a young lad in company with us, with whom my friend had lived in the closest terms of intimacy for nearly two years, and who for the greater part of that time had lodged with him in the same apartment. I asked him whether he yet continued to improve in music; he told me in reply that he had given it over altogether. What followed was characteristic of the man. 'Robert,' said he, turning to his companion, 'you will be surprised to learn that I who never hum an air or handle an instrument, was once reckoned a tolerably skilful musician.'

During the seven years of his apprenticeship he attained a command of the pencil, and a knowledge of the rules of painting possessed by few, except professors of the art; and for nearly a year after the term was completed he still continued to improve, but from the time he quitted the country for Edinburgh, though he occasionally amused himself by making black lead sketches, he did not finish a single drawing. His pencil shared the same fate with his flute and his pen. Latterly he made a few attempts. in painting; but they were unsuccessful as first attempts usually are, and he was at the time of a mood too diffident and apathetical to persevere. When at Edinburgh his genius involuntarily [sic] betrayed itself to one of his employers. His master surprised by the unusual neatness of style in which he finished pieces of common work assigned to him the execution of a central ornament in a ceiling designed to represent a richly embossed stucco patrass. It chanced that the gentleman his master's employer, was married to the daughter of an eminent painter and was himself an amateur. He was so much struck by the boldness and delicacy of style in which my friend completed the piece, and the singular knowledge of light and shade which it exhibited that he called upon his wife to come and admire it, remarking to her that could this north country mechanic rival the works of nature as successfully as those of the Architect, no painter of the present day would excell him. His master for the time he afterwards remained in his service employed him exclusively in works of a similar description; and a few months before his death he was reckoned one of the best workmen in the south of Scotland. Almost his last journey, one from Glasgow to Ireland was taken for the sole purpose of finishing the ceiling of an apartment in the Bishop of Lononderry's [sic] Palace.

The moral character of my friend was of a cast not less decided than his genius; but its influence as manifested in his conduct was much more happy than that which the latter exercised over his fortunes. The whole of his life was virtuous, and his end was pious. Though weak of body, and of a sickly constitution he was possessed of personal courage; and together with this of a chivalrous and somewhat romantic disposition, which while it prompted him to forgive the person who had wronged or insulted himself, incited him to avenge an injury done to any of his few friends. 'It is both my duty and my pleasure,' I have heard him say, 'to forgive my enemies, but to forgive the enemies of my friends I have neither right nor inclination.' He had a female cousin to whom he had been early attached for when children they had lived under the same roof and had been companions in amusement. She quitted the country when only ten or twelve years of age, and returned to it an agreeable looking young woman of about two and twenty, – of gentle and pleasing manners, and not quite unaccomplished. My friend renewed his intimacy with her, and formed a favourable, though as it afterwards proved not a just estimate of her character. A young man, an ensign in the army, who had known her previous to her return dropped in company some injurious insinuations respecting her which reached the ear of her kinsman. With a spirit not very common in men of his condition he sought an interview with the officer, and expostulated with him in such manner that the latter deemed it prudent to retract what he had asserted. When at Edinburgh he joined a society of mechanics, who convinced of his ability and honour requested him to undertake the management of their funds. There was a salary attached to the office; but aware that the business of it would interfere with his amusements, he declined it. The manager afterwards chosen proved unfaithful. Partly through negligence, partly to conceal his frauds, he involved the affairs of the society; and it was quite on the verge of ruin, when my friend voluntarily assumed the guidance of it; and in a few weeks he not only restored it to a prosperous condition, but he had also now modelled it on such principles as rendered its management much less an office of either trust or difficulty than before. He then resigned his charge, refusing to accept of any compensation from his grateful constitutents [sic]. He was particulary [sic] mindful of his poor parents, and frequently sent them small sums of money. One of his last acts of this character I deem peculiarly affecting. He died of consumption, and his companion the same whom I saw with him in Edinburgh, was suffering at nearly the same time from the same disease, though accompanied by different symptoms. In the latter who had been a healthy young man of a florid complexion and sanguine temperament, and who had scarcely any previous acquaintance with sickness, its progress was sudden; and his sufferings were so acute that for several months before his death he was incapacitated from pursuing the labours of his profession. The whole life of my friend had on the contrary been a protracted disease which affected him less in its latest than in many of its earlier stages; and as his employments required, as Bacon expresses it, rather the finger than the arm he continued to prosecute them not more for himself than for his companion; for he shared his earnings with him until the latter died. A few months after he wrote me the last letter I ever received from him; – he was in his grave before I perused it. From the style & manner in which the greater part of it is written it is evident the mind of the writer was unfixed by delirium; towards the close, however, he seems to have regained his accustomed command of thought and language. 'This,' he writes, 'is to all human probability my last letter; but the thought gives me little trouble; for my hope of salvation is in the blood of Jesus. – Farewell my sincerest friend.'

I trust this digression stands in no need of an apology. It is the only record of one whom I have both loved and regretted, and whose memory I still delight to cherish. The varieties of the human character form, it is acknowledged, one of the noblest subjects upon which philosophy can find employment; and that particular variety of character of which my friend may properly be considered an example is not one of the least interesting. He was a man of genius, – one of that singular class whom the a priori speculatist might rationally suppose sent into the world to delight and instruct their brethren of mankind, and to enjoy happiness themselves; but who alas! in very many instances achieve little and suffer much. – Philosophy, however, has its seat in the head not in the heart; and I cannot survey the character of my friend through so cold a medium. There is much that is unamiable in the heartless speculations of the man whom a modern poet has happily described as

> One that would peep & botanize
> Upon his mother's grave.[25]

I spent the winter of this year (1820) very agreeably in the society of my friend. As I was vain of my drawings and my verses I submitted them to him that he might praise them. He was too skilful not to discover their faults, but too good natured to point them out; for he feared lest he should destroy my confidence in myself; and he knew from experience that the particular species of conceit in which I indulged was both harmless and conducive to happiness. I have since thought with regard to our intimacy how excellent a doctrine it is which teaches men to recognize a benevolent Providence directing their affairs and ministering to their comforts by timing and regulating their schemes and intentions. When I consider how much pleasure we mutually derived from the intercourse which subsisted between us, I feel convinced that it was owing to that Power who delights in the happiness of his creatures that we became intimate at the only period at which our intimacy could have ripened into friendship.

I frequently accompanied my friend in his moonlight walks; and I learned in them that though he was no longer a writer of verses it was not in his power to cease being a poet. He has pointed out to me what is meant by the winding line of beauty, and defined to me from example the peculiar qualities of the beautiful, the picturesque, and the sublime. In return I introduced him to all the scenes with which my early disposition for rambling had brought me acquainted. There is in the vicinity of the town of Cromarty a beautiful, thickly wooded dell, through the bottom of which there runs a small streamlet. This dell was one of our favourite night haunts. In winter when the trees are bare of foliage, the moonbeams when the moon is at full, find their way to the water, though the steep banks on either side are lost in the shade. The appearance when viewed from some of the overhanging thickets is exceedingly beautiful, and when contemplating it in the company of my friend, I have in the wild extravagance of fancy compared the little moonlight brook to, – I know not how many different objects, – to a pictured flash of pale lightning, – to a stream of lava, – to a rippling strip of the Aurora Borealis. I have termed the little dell a dark oblong mirror, and the bright streamlet in its centre, the reflection of the milky way. I have described the trunks of the trees and the stones which were relieved by the light from the shade behind, as fays and spectres by which the place was tenanted. I have even given a minute detail of the particular expression of their features, and the peculiarities of their attire. On completing my pictures and comparisons my friend would praise what he used to term the wild vigour of my imagination; and as from my having formed a high estimate of his taste and judgement I was not a little vain of any expression of his approbation, the making such pictures and comparisons became one of my favourite occupations. He derived from them, extravagant as they were, so high an opinion of my imaginative faculties, and such a knowledge of the peculiar scope of my mind, that he

began seriously to believe me possessed of poetical genius. Such,
at least, seems to have been the opinion that dictated an advice
which he gave me a few days before we parted for the season.
'Your drawings,' he said, 'have but little merit, nor can I regard
them even as works of promise; – neither by any means do you
write good verses. And why do you think, do I tell you so? – Only
to direct your studies to their proper object. You draw ill
because Nature never intended that you should do otherwise;
whereas you write ill only because you write seldom. You are
possessed of talents which with due culture will enable you to
attain no common command of the pen; for you are an original
thinker, your mind is richly embued with poetry, and though
devoid of a musical ear, you have from Nature something much
better, – that perception of the harmonies of language which is
essential to the formation of a good and elegant style.' Had this
advice flattered me less, it would probably have had less
influence in directing my studies.

When in the company of my friend I frequently have had
opportunity of remarking how much more favourably a poet
judges of such chance strokes of poetry as he may discover in
a simple remark or plain narrative than of attempts made on
it by those who apply to it as an art. I have seen him charmed
by the poetry which he discovered in the traditional stories of
an ignorant old woman, and have heard him ridicule as entirely
prosaic pieces of tolerably smooth verse that were not altogether
devoid of sentiment. I remember being sadly puzzled to assign
a cause for this, regarding it, and I believe properly, not as the
peculiarity of a single individual, but as the characteristic of
a whole tribe. At first I deemed the contempt with which the
poet regards imperfect specimens of his art to be the effect of a
covert jealousy; and the satisfaction which he derives from
chance displays of the spirit of it I attributed to a sympathy
similar to that which exists between corresponding tones of
music. This theory, however, after examination was rejected
for another. In the one case thought I, the poet only considers
the thing conveyed; in the other the manner of the conveyance.
His imagination supplies the deficiencies of the former, and
the image presented becomes in reality his own; whereas his

judgement, rendered acute by its acquaintance with the rules of his art, and by his practice in it, leads him only to detect, not amend the defects of the latter.

When the pleasant weather of the Spring of 1821 called me to employment, I found I had grown considerably stronger than I had been at the opening of the preceding season. Labour I no longer regarded as the wretched thing I had once supposed it; and besides I discovered that there was much positive good to balance against its modified and still diminishing evils. If every morning brought its task every evening furnished its enjoyment. In the latter end of May the pieces of work for which my Master had contracted were finished, and after spending several weeks in doing nothing, a manner of passing the time to which he was much less partial than his apprentice, he set himself to procure work as a journeyman. This he succeeded in securing at Conan-Side, a gentleman's seat so termed from its vicinity to the Conan, a river of Ross-shire, which falls into the sea at the head of the Cromarty frith. As he had procured employment for both himself and his apprentice, I accompanied him to that place.

The evening before I left Cromarty I waited upon my friend to take leave of him. The term of his apprenticeship was within a few days of its expiration; and I found him in a state of extreme dejection, – strongly possessed by the idea that he was in imminent danger of starvation. 'Had I but the means,' he said, 'of quitting this part of the country for some place where I would be unknown, and where there would be none to insult me with either pity or assistance I would be careless of what my fate might prove; but here I shall be exposed both to want and to pity.' My friends natural constitution of mind inclined him to melancholy, a disposition which his habits of solitude, and the indulgence of a hopeless passion tended to deepen. With the details of the latter I am unacquainted, for we were never the depositaries of each others secrets. I had nothing to entrust him with which I would not have imparted to almost any one; he on the other hand had been so long accustomed to lock up in his breast whatever rendered him solicitous, that he could not make that use of a friend which my Lord Bacon recommends. Friendship proved to him no opener of the heart, for he could impart nothing until it had ceased to interest him. It is a consequence of this disposition that I am unacquainted with the particulars of one of the most interesting passages of his singular history. He cherished a hopeless romantic attachment for some female whose station in life was considerably above his own, and his disappointment in this affair had the effect of deepening the melancholy natural to his constitution of mind.

On the day after our arrival at Conan-side my master and I were dispatched to a place about five miles farther up the country to build a jointure house for a widow lady; & at this building we were employed for about four weeks. There were two other masons with us. We ate in the kitchen of the family mansion, which the lady still occupied, and slept in an adjoining outhouse. There were two young girls, servants of the lady; and the two stronger masons amused themselves by assuming before them each the character of the other; though they were quite the reverse of each other both in disposition and circumstances. One was a lowlander, and married, the other a Highlander and single. The unmarried man though scarcely turned of twenty and miserably deficient in English assured the girls that he had a wife and several children, and that being a Lowlander he could neither speak nor understand Gaelic; while the other who had been married for 14 or 15 years insisted to them on his being yet single, and made an indefatiguable display when in their company of all the gallantries of courtship.

I became acquainted when at this place with an elderly woman, a Mrs Mackenzie, from the study of whose character I derived something more than mere entertainment. Her brother who at this time had been dead for several years, had been a Highland Clergyman of great worth and respectability, and of a powerful though somewhat eccentric genius. His fame in this part of the country even at the present day fully equals that of any of the champions of the covenant. By the more judicious he is celebrated as an excellent man who was nearly allied in genius, and almost equal in the management of allegory to the ingenious author of the Pilgrims Progress; by the common people, who are unable to appreciate the merits of even good men, and who are prone to exaggerate, he is famed as a prophet. My new acquaintance seemed to have been originally possessed of equal powers of mind with her brother, and was perhaps of a similar cast of character, but for more than twelve years prior to this time her life had been spent in alternate intervals of madness and melancholy. When first seized by the malady she deserted her husband and family, and took up her abode in a solitary hovel in which she continued to reside, and which at this time reminded me of the ruinous cottage of Wordsworths Margaret.[26] I became acquainted with her in a manner somewhat singular and not quite unpoetical.

On a pleasant evening after my companions had gone to bed, I remained leaning over the window of the room where I slept. Fronting the window there is a low, long moor, which terminates in lofty sweeping hills, the first of a chain that runs quite across the island. The furthermost boundary of the moor and the base of one of the hills is covered by a little wood of dwarf birch and hazle, near which there is a small burying ground and the ruins of a chapel. The scene is solitary and Highland; and I had heard from the girls of the house singular stories of the chapel which associated well both with ideas of solitude and with the habits of the early Highlanders. It had once, it was said, been set on fire and burnt to ashes, together with the people it contained, who were of the clan Mackenzie by a party of Macdonalds, whose piper continued to play a gay warlike air all the time the conflagration lasted. The other traditions connected with it were of wild unearthly shrieks, spectres, and death lights. The evening was perfectly calm and still, and so beautiful that I continued leaning over the window until midnight. Suddenly I saw emerging from that part of the wood which bordered on the chapel a light clear and distinct as that of a candle. It moved towards the ruin. It hovered awhile in the centre of the Churchyard, appearing and disappearing by intervals, as if carried around the building; then returning by the same track which it had followed on leaving the wood, it was again lost in the foliage. I

was much surprized by an appearance so singular, and was
deliberating whether I should not awaken my companions,
when my attention was again excited by a distant frightful
noise, apparently occasioned by a continuous screaming. I
sprang from the window to the bed side of my master, but the
sounds ceased on my quitting it, and I again returned to it
and listened. The noise began, louder than before, and so
distinct that I could discover it was not that of a continuous
screaming, as I had at first imagined but that it was caused by
some one singing at the full pitch of a very powerfull [sic]
voice. Soon after I saw the light emerging from that part of
the wood which skirted the moor, and then proceeding over
the latter in a straight line towards the house from whence I
observed it. A loud knocking at the door of our apartment
accompanied by an alarmed and hurried voice urging the inmates to rise soon solved the mystery. 'Rise,' exclaimed the
voice without, which I knew to be that of one of the girls,
'Mrs Mackenzie the madwoman is coming this way with a
lighted candle and may set the house on fire; – rise and assist
in binding her.' The Conan-Side masons rose and went out,
and I accompanied them; when we found the poor woman
already in the custody of two men who were dragging her
towards her cottage. She made no reply to their threats but
continued to sing snatches of hymns and old ballads in a voice
so shrill and powerful that the distant hills were re-echoing
the notes. I followed her to the cottage. It was as I have
described, a miserable hovel. The walls were bulged in several
places, and there were crevices in the roof through which I
could see the stars; but the few pieces of furniture which it
contained were neatly arranged, and there were a great many
little fantastic ornaments stuck round them which gave to the
place so doubtful a kind of character that one unacquainted
with the tenant would have hesitated to determine whether it
might not be rather the Museum of some village virtuoso than
the hut of a maniac. In the lower part of one of the large
rafters there was a staple to which a chain was attached, and
by this chain the poor woman was fastened down to the damp
earthen floor by a savage looking fellow, who alleged in reply

to my remonstrances and those of one of my companions, that were she permitted either to sit or stand upright she would soon set herself loose. 'Be that as it may,' we replied, 'she must not be bound in that manner.' We then proposed a way which we considered equally secure, and which allowed her the liberty of the whole apartment. The maniac had continued to sing as if regardless of the treatment she received, but on our interference she stopt short in the middle of one of those psalms that are termed condemnatory and repeated in a faint subdued tone of voice the text 'Blessed are the merciful for they shall obtain mercy.' She then began to sing in a low mournful key, an old ballad; and as we left the cottage we heard her voice gradually heightening as we proceeded, until it had at length attained its former pitch and wildness of tone.

Next morning when engaged in hewing at some distance from my companions, I was visited by the maniac. She stood by me for some time without saying any thing, and then began to question me in a coherent and even delicate manner concerning the place of my birth, my education, and the motives which had led me to make choice of a profession so rude and so exposed to hardship as that of the stonecutter. I satisfied her curiosity, and began to ask questions in turn; when I found that the mind of the poor deranged woman had originally been of no common cast. She possessed an astonishing power of poetical description, she had been a minute observer of characters and events, and her reading though not extensive was curious. For the three following weeks she was seldom an hour absent from the place where I wrought; and I was interested to find, which I did from the manner in which she dealt with me, that the warmest feelings of friendship could have place in a mind so entirely ruined. When released in the evening from my occupations I have spent whole hours in her company. She was amazingly quick of perception, & laid hold with surprizing eagerness on every thing that assimilated with the disordered state of her imagination, – whether philosophical theory, fanciful argument, or picturesque description. She had made herself acquainted, by means of some controversial works of the old Divine, with divers singular opinions of the Schoolmen, and she

expatiated upon them with great delight. The information I
derived from her was of a cast both amusing and uncommon.
She could relate traditional stories of chiefs whose names were
no longer familiar to their descendants; and anecdotes and
verses of Highland poets, whose fame had never reached the
lowlands, and now scarcely survived even in the places of
their birth. Among the latter was one Colin Mackenzie, or
Colin the Green, whose songs she said were very popular in
her younger days in that part of the country. The poet, like
some of the Border Minstrels to whom the most eminent of
living authors has introduced the Public, was not at all of the
stamp of Beattie's Edwin.[27] His hand was fully as conversant
with the dirk as with the pen. 'He quarreled,' said my informant,
'with one of his neighbours, a fiery, bold, wicked man; fought
him, left him lying dead in one of his own fields, and fled the
country. It is more than a century ago, and the bard was then
young and robust; but ere he returned again he was old and
worn out, and both his friends and his enemies were worn out
too. My father, who was a boy at the time, saw and conversed
with him, and could repeat a great many of his songs.' Of a
similar character were almost all the narratives of the maniac.
She never failed of becoming eloquent when her brother was
the subject of them. I remarked that all the anecdotes she
related of him, unlike the strange legendary stories which I
had heard of him before were characteristic only of his genius
and piety. The following may be regarded as a specimen.

'Once every year my brother visited his parents, and as he
had an aversion to riding he travelled on foot; generally accompanied by one of his parishioners, who was a great favourite
with him, and who though somewhat rude in his manners,
and not of a decidedly religious character, was warm hearted
and honest. There were two classes of persons whom my brother
respected, – men of fortune who did not presume on their
being such when in the company of men of sense who were
poor, – and men of sense who though poor maintained an
independence of sentiment when in the company of men of
fortune. His companion was of the latter class; but my brother
used to allege that no sooner had he take a dram than from

being simply independent he became opininative [sic]. The parish of —— [sic] like most Highland parishes is extensive; and the first day of their yearly journey was spent in going from house to house, in a zig zag course, visiting the people and baptizing their children. My brother's companion on occasions of the latter kind procured the water, and held out the vessel which contained it; and the sole fee of his office was a dram. One day, as they were proceeding towards the lowlands, they visited a house on their way and baptized a child. The Highlander got the accustomed dram; and as the father of the child and he were old acquaintance, the minister had no sooner turned his back than he got other two. All that afternoon he was unusually argumentative, and singularly unhappy in the choice of his subjects. He at length became angry, and lagged behind, barely keeping his companion in sight. At a sudden turn of the road, however, he found my brother standing before him, with his eyes fixed on one, of the strongest looking trees he had ever seen, and apparently lost in thought. The lower part of the trunk twisted and winded in almost every direction, somewhat in the manner of a corkscrew; but it was straight and taper towards the top. 'Well Murochy,' he said, 'is not this a very singular tree! – come, tell me what it most resembles?' 'Truly Mr L—' said the man, 'if you allow me to take off that straight unmenacing piece above I shall readily find out a resemblance – would it no be real like the worm of a whisky still?' 'Very ingenious,' replied my brother, 'but I cannot allow you to lop off the upper shoot; – the tree serves my purpose much better as it is. You have heard of the life of the Christian! His early progress is slow and interrupted; for on every side there are temptations which retard it. The desire of pleasure draws him to oné extreme; – the force of a passionate zeal impels him to another; – but there is a principle within him which combats continually with sense and with passion, – it strengthens as these decay; and so the early part of his course is not more like the twisted trunk of that tree than its latter period resembles the upper extremity: – he shoots off heavenward in a straight line.'

It was not without regret I parted from this singular maniac, whose ravings were fraught with wit and poetry, and who delighted me in her lucid intervals with pleasing stories and superior sense. In her moments of excitation she strongly resembled one of the striking conceptions of the author of Waverly [sic], – the Ulrica of Ivanhoe, or what I regard as nearly the same character, a little changed by differing habits and circumstances, the Meg Merilees [sic] of Guy Mannering.[28] Her ravings have at one time reminded me of the terrible war song of the exasperated Saxon, at another the mysterious predictions of the enthusiastic gipsy. Prior to my acquaintance with her I had heard the philosophical remark that the idiotical draw wrong conclusions from right principles, and the insane on the contrary right conclusions from principles that are false. With an eye to this remark I have attended to her ravings, and those of other mad people, occasionally too to the talk of idiots; and the result of my observations has been that the rule implied in it is one of many exceptions.

My master had initiated me before leaving Cromarty into all the usages of country masons employed at a distance from their homes. Some of these are sufficiently curious. Each squad or party form a kind of little republic governed by laws which have been constituted such by the sanction of custom, and which may be divided into two opposite classes: – the laws of the one class tending to the preservation of order, – those of the other subversive of it but pregnant with mirth. These laws are enforced by a kind of mutual compact, and award to offenders two different kinds of punishment of a description singularly whimsical and which are termed 'ramming' and the 'law.' The latter, which is the more severe, is a species of bastinade, in which blows are dealt to the culprit with two small rules used in hewing, according to the number of syllables in a rude unmeaning rhime which is repeated slowly and distinctly by the accuser. – The minor punishment I shall have almost immediate occasion to describe. Some ruinous kiln or deserted cowhouse in the vicinity of the building at which the masons are employed, serves as a barrack to the party; – it is procured for them by the contractor, who sometimes also supplies them with fuel, and their stapple [sic] article of food oatmeal. They cook, bake, and make up their beds for themselves, each one of the party officiating in turn as servant to the whole. Their rude furniture is also of their own workmanship, beds, tables, seats, &c and as it is merely necessary that these serve for a few months, they are of course not strikingly neat, and in most instances not exceedingly convenient. There is a primitive rudeness, – a kind of Robinson Crusoe style observable in every thing connected with a mason's barrack, from the mechanic its inmate who is quite a different person when inhabiting it from what he is when at home, to the clumsy deal settle upon which he seats himself to enjoy his rough fare. Of the barrack itself a tolerable idea may be acquired, if what I have said already has failed of producing one, by the mere statement that a proprietor of the north when charged with bad taste for suffering a crazy old building to remain standing near some neat modern offices apologized for the house and himself by remarking that he found it extremely useful as a kind of caravansary every time his speculations brought either a drove of pigs or a squad of masons to his farm yard.

I returned to Conan-Side on a Saturday evening. Some of the masons were lounging in the front of their barrack. A highland shepherd, who seemed not a little perplexed and angry was attempting to drive his flock along a road which passed the door; but he was baffled in every attempt by a stout fellow who stood directly in the way shaking his leathern apron at the animals. Every time he succeeded in driving them back his companions greeted him with a shout of laughter. From the interior of the building there proceeded a confused noise of voices which reminded me of the hum of a bee-hive. One of the inmates began to sing in a sweet plaintive voice; silence immediately ensued, and the mason who had annoyed the poor shepherd leaped through the sheep towards the barrack door, to listen to the singer, leaving the way clear. In a few minutes the song was interrupted, a noise of uproarious contention ensued, and out bolted one of the inmates followed by about ten others, the pursuers yelling out 'a ramming, a ramming.' The men who were lounging outside, starting into sudden activity joined in the chase and the cry. The aggressor was captured, carried back to the barrack door, charged with having wantonly disturbed the singer, and sentenced to be punished after the minor form enjoined by the barrack code. He was first thrown on his back on the ground; his companions clustered round him, and seizing him by the head, arms, and legs, they raised him up and poizing him in the manner of an antient battering ram they drove him endlong thrice several times against the wall. He was then released and the punishment pronounced complete. I followed the horde into their barrack. It consisted of one large apartment. Along the wall, and across one of the gables there was a range of beds rudely constructed of outside, slab deals, and filled with straw, which bristled from beneath the blankets, and from between the crevices of the frames in a manner much less neat than picturesque. At each bedside there were two chests, which served not only the purpose originally intended but also for chairs and tables. Suspended by ropes from the rafters about there hung at the height of a man's head from the ground several bags filled with oat meal; which by this contrivance was secured from the rats with which the place was infested. Along the gable further removed from the door there was a huge wood fire; above it there were hung several small pots, enveloped in smoke, which for lack of proper vent, after filling the whole barrack escaped by the door. Before the fire there was a row of stones, each of which supported an oaten cake. The inmates, who exceeded twenty, had disposed of themselves after the recent affair of the 'ramming' in every possible manner. Some were lounging in the beds, others were seated on the chests. Two of them were dancing on the floor to the whistling of a third. There was one employed in baking, another in making ready the bread. The chaos of sounds which reigned among them was much more complete than that which appalled their prototypes, the builders of Babel. There was the gabbling of Saxon, the sputtering of Gaelic, the humming of Church-music, the whistling of the musician, and the stamping of the dancers. Three of the pots on the fire began to boil together, and there was a cry for the cook. He came rushing forward, pushed the man engaged in baking from out his way with one hand, and drawing the seat from under the one employed in making ready the bread, with the other, he began to shout out, so as to drown their united voices, for meal and salt. Both were brought him, and in a few minutes he had completed his task. He was then sentenced to a ramming for the confusion he had occasioned.

As I was disgusted rather than amused by scenes so savagely rude, I kept as much aloof from the barrack as possible. The country round Conan-Side is strikingly beautiful; and I spent the long summer evenings in wandering to its more pleasing scenes, in writing verses in a little rocky recess on the edge of the Conan, or in practicing when unseen some of the exercises in which, a few years before, I had excelled my juvenile companions. There is not an old castle, burying ground, or cairn within five miles of the barrack which I have not visited, nor a precipice of the hills nor a pool in the river where I have not climbed and swam. I have scaled the cliffs above Brahan Castle, among which according to tradition, an ingenious blacksmith of the olden time discovered a rich vein of silver ore, which he wrought by stealth until he had filled one of the apartments of his cottage with bars of the precious metal. The treasure, it is further added, was betrayed to the Mackenzie through the unfortunate vanity of the mechanic, who was deprived of his life that the other might become his heir; and since his death no one has been found sufficiently skilful to convert the rude stone into ingots of silver. I have swam across a black pool of the Conan, which Superstition has tenanted with two of her most singular creations, – a huge demoniac eel covered over with long yellow hair, and a malignant water-wraith that has frequently appeared to the evening or moonlight traveller, in the form of an old, and very tall woman habited in a green shroud. Before the erection of the bridge which was built on the river about twenty years ago, scarcely a winter passed without some person being drowned in attempting to ford it, and either the wraith or the eel was charged with having caused the accident.

Strathpeffer, one of the finest vallies [sic] in this part of the country, lies within five miles of Conan side. My walks occasionally extended to it; and I still retain a vividly-pleasing recollection of its enchanting scenery, with the more pleasing features of the scenes through which I passed in my way to it. There is in its vicinity a beautiful little lake which contains a wooded island. Along the banks of this lake I have sauntered for whole hours; and from the green top of Knock-ferril, one of the hills by which the valley is bounded I have seen the sun sink behind Ben Weavis, without once thinking that I was five miles from my place of residence. This hill is rendered somewhat famous among antiquaries by the vitrified remains on its summit, and among the people of the strath by the traditional stories with which it is connected. It is pointed out by the latter as the site of a Fingalian fortress, which when the warriors of the tribe were engaged in a distant hunting expedition, was burnt to glass by an incendiary. Their wives and children perished in the flames, and hence the extinction of the race. The few traditions of the Fingalians which I have gleaned during the course of my peregrinations through the Highlands are mostly all of one character. They relate the incredible exploits of a tribe of gigantic savages, who had scarce any thing in common with the gentle high minded warriors of Macpherson. In the bottom of that part of the valley which is opposite to this hill there is an obelisk of rude undressed granite of a shape nearly square, and about seven feet in height. This stone, according to tradition was pitched from the summit of the hill to the place where it now stands; but the honour of the feat is variously attributed, one edition of the story assigning it to a Fingalian, and another to the Devil. The marks of a gigantic finger and thumb are still pointed out on two of its sides.

But I have not even yet summed up the whole of my evening amusements. They were not all equally poetical. The country round Conan-side abounds with wild fruit, and I have feasted among the woods, during my long rambles, on greens, rowans, rasp-berries, and blac-berries with all the keeness of boyish appetite. The fruit furnished me with an ostensible object for my wanderings, and when complemented by a romantic young girl, who had derived her notions of character from the reading of romances, on that disposition which led me to seek my pleasures in solitude, I could remark in reply that I was not more fond of solitude than of rasp-berries.

For the first six weeks after I had come to Conan-side I proved one of the least successful of cooks, and positively the most unfortunate of bakers. My porridge commonly assumed the appearance of leaven, and my leaven as often degenerated into something exceedingly like porridge. I broke the bread which I attempted to make ready, burnt my fingers in turning it to the heat, and once or twice suffered the hook by which I suspended my pot over the fire to drop into the half prepared food. The disasters of one unfortunate day in particular, are worthy of being detailed. My porridge had as usual refused to part from the bottom of the pot; I had placed at the fire a bannock, which divided and sub-divided, like the empire of Alexander, until I was at length fain to carry away the fragments in my apron; and I now set myself to prepare *brochan* for supper.[29] I was fond of this species of food when of a thicker consistence than usual, and so I mixed up in a small earthen dish about twice the ordinary quantity of meal, which as it received only half the proper measure of water assumed the appearance of dough. In consequence when I poured the preparation into the boiling fluid, instead of incorporating with it, it sunk to the bottom and there remained. I attempted mixing it with a spoon, but the fragments which I broke off from the mass always returned to the bottom, and changing my plan of operation, I determined on boiling the whole into a proper consistence. An hours experience convinced me, however, that in the art of cookery, as in every other art, there is little to be acquired from a priori speculation. The mass remained solid as before, and the surrounding fluid though it became much browner did not thicken in the least. My Master coming in I unslung the pot, and laid down before him a dish of the thinner portion of its contents, which in consistence and colour somewhat resembled chocolate. 'What sort of *brochan* is this,' said the poor man, as he refunded the first spoonful, 'do you call this *brochan*?' 'Not so fast Master,' said

I, 'there are two kinds in the pot, and it will go hard if none of them please you.' I then dished up to him one of the pieces, which was also rejected. All my succeeding experiments as a cook were, however, more fortunate, though in the vexation occasioned by even my minor failures, I could not help wishing that our establishment had resembled in simplicity that of a brother mason, one of our barrack companions, when employed some years before in the central Highlands. The whole of his culinary utensils consisted of a hempen sack and the string which tied it, – and the whole of his food in the oatmeal its contents. When hungry he carried the bag to a neighbouring stream, undid the tier, flung with his open palm some of the water on the meal, and then ate all he had rendered moist.

The nights now began to lengthen and gradually abridged my evening walks mile by mile until at length I was compelled to discontinue them altogether. I discovered, however, that I could be amused by the exercise of the mental faculties alone. My master and I slept in a large hay loft above a stable, their [sic] being no room for us in the barrack, and for several weeks every evening after work was over, I regularly retired to this loft, where I would remain for whole hours either seated on my chest or lying above the bedclothes. I have since thought with reference to these evenings, how singular a narrative the history of mind would furnish were all the trains of idea, the reasonings, the imaginings, the remembrances which passes in the course of a few days through a single sensorium (abstracted, as mine was by the darkness, from objects of sense) to be minutely and faithfully recorded. What I write is the history of my education, and there will be nothing digressive in my including in it a chapter of such a narrative. Suppose me seated on my chest in a corner of the loft. It furnishes only one object upon which the eye can rest, – that one a small opening in the wall which appears a square patch of darkness-visible stamped upon utter darkness. The only sounds are those occasioned by the horses in the stable below, chomping and snorting over their food.

A few weeks ago (thus begins the train) I stood upon the summit of Ochiltree (a high hill about six miles from Conan-side.) I was then the centre of a wide circle of more than sixty miles in diameter; and at this moment my imagination retains a vivid picture of the circle in its whole extent. It presents a turbulent, rough edged sea of hills, with the clear blue firmament arching over it. The human imagination, capacious as it is accounted, has not, if I may judge from my own, a more extensive field of space to expatiate in than the human eye. I cannot imagine a wider circle than that which the sight commands from the summit of a lofty eminence; and yet my imagination contains an idea of the entire world; nay of even the solar system. But then, the pictures of the world, the system, and the view from the eminence are all of one size; – the transcript of a mountain district in Scotland, and of the hugh globe in which that district is but a speck, occupy an equal surface of canvass. My idea of the system is only that of an Orrery of about sixty miles in diameter, – my picture of the whole globe with all its oceans and continents, measures no more.

The associative principle connects this subject with another: – I brood over the picture of the solar system with which my imagination has presented me, and contemplate the motions of the planets. I conceive of the satellites as light shallops that continually sail round heavier vessels, and consider how much more of space they must traverse than the orbs to which they are attached. I then regard the whole system in a pictoral aspect. I imagine the space circumscribed by the orbit of Georgium-Sidus to be occupied by an atmosphere like that of the earth, which reflects the light of the sun in the different degrees of excessive brightness, noon-tide-splendour, the fainter shade of evening, and grey twilight obscurity. I preceived that this veil of light is thickest towards its centre; for when my glance rests on its edges I behold the suns of other systems peeping through it. I see Mercury sparkling to the sun with its oceans and rivers of molten glass, and its fountains of liquid gold. I see the ice mountains of Saturn, haar through the twilight; – I behold the earth rolling upon itself from darkness to light, and from light to darkness. I see the clouds of winter settling over one part of it, with the nether mantle of snow shinning [sic] through them: – I see in another a brown dusky waste of sand lighted up by the glow of summer. The ocean appears smooth as a mirror, – another is black with tempest. I see the pyramid of shade which each of the planets casts from its darkened side into the space behind; and I perceive the stars twinkling through each pyramid, as through the angular door of a pavilion.

A new link of association shifts the scene, and one of those uncertainities arise in my mind which so frequently convince me that I am ignorant. I become anxious to know whether a straight line stretched across the diameter of Georgium Sidus and passing through the centre of the sun would also pass through the orbits of all the other planets; or whether it would not form an angle with the orbits of some of them, the point of which would be that centre. I deliberate and a ray of light at length breaks in upon my mind. Huzza! I have found it! If the courses of the planets as seen in the heavens form parallel lines, each with the others, then it necessarily [sic] follows that the supposed line would pass through all their orbits; – and *vice versa*.

I congratulate myself on the discovery. The scene is immediately charged by self love; and I enquire of myself whether I be possessed of one of those capacious minds to which the abstrusest studies appear matters of mere common sense that can be discussed almost without effort. The decision is of course favourable, but I suspect its justice; knowing that independent of the magnifying medium of self love through which I necessarly [sic] survey myself, there is a kind of moral perspective which, like the natural, enlarges whatever is near, and diminishes whatever is distant; and that the powers of ones own mind must always prove the foreground objects of ones view. – I consider how one mind excells another; – nay, how one mind excells a thousand; and I illustrate the subject by the manner of valuing diamonds. A single diamond that weighs fifty carets is deemed more valuable than two thousand each of which only weighs one. The illustration refers exclusively to the native powers but may it not, I ask, bear also on the aquistion of knowledge. Every new idea added to the stock already collected is a caret added to the diamond; for it is not only valuable in itself, but it also increases the value of all the others by giving to each of them a new link of association. The next transition is natural though the connecting link is perhaps somewhat obscure. The minds of men of exalted genius, such as Homer, Milton, Shakespear [sic], seem to partake of the qualities of infinitude. Add a great many bricks together and they will form a pyramid as huge as the peak of Tenerife. Add all the common minds together that the world ever produced, and the mind of Shakespear [sic] will tower over the whole in all the grandeur of infinity. That which is infinite admits of neither increase nor diminution. Is it not so with genius of a certain altitude. Homer, Milton, Shakespear [sic], were men of perhaps equal powers. Homer, it is said, was a beggar; Shakespear [sic] was an illiterate wool comber; Milton was skilled in all human learning. But they have all risen to an equal height. Learning has added nothing to the *illimitable* genius of the one, nor has the want of it detracted from the *infinite* powers of the other. – But it is time that I go and prepare supper.

After many efforts I at length succeeded in shaking of my habits of solitude, and the dread and dislike of society, which grew upon me the more I indulged in them, so far as occasionally to seek amusement among my companions of the barrack. In a short time I became reconciled to the rough humour which had at first disgusted me, and I began to entertain a rather favourable opinion of men in whom a very few weeks before I could see only grossness and vulgarity. This opinion, soon became reciprocal, and I discovered that the less favourable one had been so likewise.

Among the inmates of the Barrack there was one John Mc-ghaol, a native of the Highlands. He was a man of a vigorous imagination, but his judgement was extremely weak and his ideas confused. His master passion was a love of the marvellous, and his chief talent a power of detailing his own adventures in such a manner, and with such additions as to render them as amusing as fairy tales. Almost every evening he was called upon for a story, by his brother work-men, who, as amusement was their sole object, never thought proper to hint at his anachronisms and inconsistences. Of

John Mc-ghaol's narratives John Mc-ghaol was always the
hero. He had failed one season he said in procuring employment
as a mason, and in the beginning of Autumn, as he was bred
about a farm house and skilled in the labours of farming, he
went with other Highlanders to the south of Scotland, to assist
in reaping the harvest. On his return he passed through Edinburgh. When going along the side of one of the streets he saw
a young girl with whom he was intimate, and whom he after-
wrds married, on the opposite side, and he immediately made
up to her; but in stepping across he was struck on the breast
by the pole of a coach that was sweeping along in full speed,
and thrown down. In a few minutes the part injured became
much inflamed; and he found that unless promptly relieved
he would be unable to prosecute his journey on the morrow.
He enquired of his companion, who was well acquainted in
Edinburgh, for the house of a surgeon. 'We are on the way'
said she, 'to a person who can give you more effectual and
immediate relief than any of the faculty.' After they had passed
along a spacious street they turned down a narrow lane, and
were soon in a dark damp cell, lighted by only a large fire.
The sole inhabitant was a very old woman. Mc-ghaol's companion stated to her the cause of their visit; and the woman
pointing to a seat by the fire, motioned him to sit down. She
then by the imperfect light of the place examined the contusion.
'Chuse one of two things,' she said, when she had passed her
fingers over it, 'a cure slow but effectual, or one sudden but
partial.' 'Enable me,' replied the mason, 'to prosecute my journey homewards to morrow, and I care not how partial the
cure may be.' 'But I warn you rejoined the hag that in that
case, I can only postpone the bad effects of the bruise until a
few weeks hence; – you will then feel them perhaps more
severely than if I had not interfered.' 'Ah,' said Mc-ghaol [']post-
pone them for but three weeks; whatever be the consequences;
– ere than I shall be at home and among my friends.' On this
the hag began to pass her fingers over his breast, as if she were
drawing figures on it, and to mutter a charm in a language
that was neither Gaelic nor English. As she signed the pain &
inflammation gradually subsided, until in about half an hour

his breast assumed the appearance which it had presented the moment after he had received the blow. Instead of the huge livid tumor there remained a white circular mark, round which the skin was slightly discoloured. Next morning he proceeded on his journey. His route northwards furnished a series of adventures which he had wrought into the main story with considerable skill. He was attacked by high-way-men, he lost his way in a thick mist, and he encountered a terrible snow storm in a desert houseless district, where he wandered in the midst of drift and darkness for a whole night. At length he arrived at home and applied to his usual occupations. The last evening of the third week came to a close as he was returning from his employment, and the pain of his breast struck him of a sudden with such violence that it was with difficulty he reached home. On opening his waistcoat to the light, the bruise presented the same appearance which it had done before he applied to the woman. He went to bed with a high fever, and more than six weeks elapsed before his health was again established. – This story was not by any means the most wonderful of *Mc-ghaols* narratives. At one time when passing at midnight through a solitary churchyard, he tumbled into an open grave, in which he was imprisoned until morning; – at another he narrowly escaped being carried away by resurrexionists; – he had fought with witches, and conversed with ghosts.

I am convinced that to men of *Mc-ghaols* cast of character we may assign the invention of two thirds of those superstitious narratives which are to be found floating on the current of tradition in every district of the country. These narratives would prove no uninteresting study could there be added to them by way of supplement a detail of the several motives to which they owe their production. The satisfaction derived from the exercise of the inventive faculties (for it is not only the poet and the theorist that are suceptible [sic] of the pleasures of invention) furnished one of the motives of *Mc-ghaol*; – vanity was the other. He was ambitious of attracting the notice of his companions to himself & his adventures, and the latter were either of too uninteresting a character to engage attention, or he wanted, what indeed few possess, the ability of giving

interest to narratives strictly true. This singular mechanic was
unlike common men in more respects than one. Though remarkably deficient in judgement, and unacquainted with even the
simpler rules of Arithmetic as taught in schools, he was yet
skilful in calculation, and could cast up the contents of a
piece of mason work more readily and correctly than most
workmen who have the advantage both of practice and a
common education.' On considering such a fact one may well
exclaim 'How infinite are the varieties of nature, and with
how bold a hand does she in some instances connect circumstances of character which no human imagination would ever
dream of combining. Neither Shakespear [sic] nor Sir Walter
Scott would have dared to represent the half-witted mechanic,
the master of fiction, and the ready calculator as the same
individual.

I have said that I soon became reconciled to the coarse
humour of my companions; I may add that I became more
than reconciled to it; for I learned to admire the wit and
ingenuity of their jokes both verbal and practical. Some of the
latter were ludicrous in the extreme. Though oatmeal and
milk prepared in the simplest manner were the only articles of
food used in the barrack there were some of its inmates exceedingly nice in their eating. Two of the masons were more difficult
to please in this respect than any of the others; – the one
requiring a less than common portion of salt in whatever was
served up to him, and the other a greater. As their food was
prepared in the same pot they were continualy quarreling at
meal times on this account, with each other or with the cook,
who I should have observed was changed every day; – each of
the workmen officiating in turn. One of the men, who was
skilful in managing a practical joke, succeeded when in this
office, in playing off his wit upon them. He made up their
food, and pouring it out on their plates flung a handful of salt
into the one and left the other without any, – placing the
former on the chest of the man who disliked salt, and the
latter on that of him who was fond of it. They had no sooner
eaten each the first spoonful than the one exclaimed 'A ramming to the rascally cook! he had not given me a single particle

of salt,' while the other roared out in a voice like thunder 'A ramming to the wretched cook! he has given me porridge like brine.' 'Comrades' said the cook, addressing himself very cooly to the men of the barrack, 'surely both these fellows deserve to be punished. They have already given trouble enough to us all on this score; and you see to what a pitch they have come at last. Look here, this is the very pot in which I prepared the food they condemn for such opposite faults. Let us give them a ramming.' The motion was immediately carried into effect, the men were rammed, and in a few minutes after the cook explained the whole contrivance.

There was a not less ingenious though more mischievous joke played off against myself this season. I occasionally met in my evening walks a genteel, good looking young girl, a native of the Western Highlands. She was unacquainted with English, and I had no Gaelic; and our customary greeting was an inclination of the head and a smile. When enquiring of some of my companions concerning her, I spoke rather favour-ably of her personal attractions, and the natural grace of her carriage; and in return was charged with being head and ears in love with her, – a charge which I took no pains to rebut. A few nights after I chanced to meet with her, and I was greeted with a smile much kinder than usual; – she spoke to me too a few words in Gaelic which I answered at random in English. For the week following scarcely a day passed without my seeing her, and she always appeared much disposed to be kind. This thought I is coquetry; – what a taste must she have to attempt the conquest of a personage so ungainly as myself! All of a sudden she forsook her accustomed haunts, and nearly a month passed without my seeing her, which when I at length did by accident, she passed by me hanging down her head as if much ashamed. It was not until more than a twelvemonth after that I was furnished with an explanation of the coquetry of the previous meetings and the confusion of the last. I then learned that the poor girl had been told by two of my comrades, each of whom pretended to know nothing of the communica-tion of the other, that I was deeply in love with her, and intended marrying her, could I but gain her consent, when I

had completed the term of my apprenticeship. She was afterwards undeceived, but not until she had transmitted an account
of her conquest to the western Highlands.

To the student of human nature it is interesting to observe
how much the formation of character depends upon things that
are external; and to what a degree of similitude the various
traits which mark different men may be brought by being acted
upon by similar circumstances. It is with the human mind in
this respect, as with the human frame. A military man may be
known by the erectness of his figure, a ploughman by the stoop
in his shoulders, a joiner by a side-long inclination in his gait,
like that which when he is employed, twists him over the bench.
In like manner there is something peculiar in the character and
bend of mind of the members of almost every one of the
mechanical professions. By even a common observer who
attends merely to the more general & striking traits, mechanics
may be divided into two great classes, – the sedentary and
laborious; – and by the nicer judge these may again be
subdivided into a number of distinct tribes, each differing from
the others in their minuter features. The tradesman who pursues
a laborious, out of door employment, is taciturn, and finds
considerable difficulty in expressing his ideas; the sedentary
mechanic on the contrary, is loquacious and has a ready
command of language. The former is imperfectly acquainted
with the affairs of his neighbours, unless these affairs have some
connexion with his own; the latter knows all that is said and
done on every side of him. The former is contented with existing
establishments; for he knows little of the king or his ministers, or
of the ministers of religion except that they are the men whom
fate has appointed to be the rulers or the teachers of others. The
latter on the other hand is a staunch Whig. He would set by the
king, according to Dryden, on motives of pure economy. The
ministers of Government he regards as a gang of conspirators
against that principle in the Constitution which extends to the
poor the protection of the law; and the opinion he entertains of
the ministers of the Church is nearly as unfavourable. The
thoughts of the laborious mechanic, as he is generally ignorant
of what is taught by books, and what is to be learned from the

conversational exchange of sentiments and ideas, are limited to the narrow sphere of his own wants and wishes; but from this very circumstance his conclusions with regard to the points that immediately affect his own concerns, are commonly correct. The sedentary workman is often what is termed a man of information; but he seldom manages his personal affairs better than his more ignorant neighbour. The classes are dissimlar in even their vulgarity. The sedentary mechanic is affectedly vulgar; – he has set up for himself a false standard of politeness, and is vulgar by rule. The laborious mechanic on the other hand is unsophistically blunt, for he deports himself to no standard either false or true. If a new sect which does not owe its origin to either a woman or a priest springs up in a country parish, the chance is ten to one that a few sedentary mechanics are the heresiarchs. If masons and ploughmen are concerned in it, it is as seconds not as principals. In like manner if a Deistical club be formed by the working class of a large town, it will invariably be found that the great bulk of the members consists of sedantary mechanics; for the weavers and tailors of the city are adepts in the philosophy of infidelity in the same way that those of the country are skilled in theological controversy, and acquainted with the history of the church. Their discontent with existing establishments is the same. These are only a very few of the points of dissimilarity observable in the two main classes. – To divide them into castes and tribes, according to the different occupations, and to delineate the character peculiar to each, would be a work rather laborious than difficult. My business at present, however, is only with that class of mechanics to which I myself belong.

In the winter and spring seasons when the country mason is unemployed he lives much in the manner of other mechanics, – enjoying the comforts of home, and the society of his friends; but at the beginning of summer he leaves his residence for some distant part of the country where a house, bridge, or quay, is to be erected, and he straightway enters into a scene of existence different in almost every respect from the one he has quitted. Ease and comfort are succeeded by hardship and privation. One of the effects which follow the change could only be anticipated by the philosophical observer of the phenomena of human nature. The mason's season of comfort is marked by little of either frolic or gaiety compared with his period of hardship. His merriment seems proportioned not to what he enjoys, but to what he endures. The fact wears a singular, but, from a pretty widely concurring experience, not a suspicious aspect. It has been repeatedly remarked that the subjects of a despotic government laugh much oftener than those of a free; that banished criminals and galley slaves are the most recklessly gay of all men; and that scenes of license and riot almost always mingle with those of shipwreck and pestilence. Perhaps the life of a country mason in a barrack is the nearest state to one of comfort, – the first remove towards wretchedness in which this singular phenomenon becomes apparent. It were work for imagination, not philosophy, to trace the principle to its worst extreme. To conceive of the place of final punishment as a hall of terrible revel and frantic merriment would be a flight not unworthy of poetry.

A monotonous course of privation and hardship has almost always the effect of blunting the more delicate faculties of the mind, and of hardening the heart. The gentler affections, – the finer powers of judgement and imagination have no exercise in a state in which there is little to be enjoyed, and much to be suffered. I speak, of course, of only common minds and natures, for it has not escaped me that Burns was a ploughman, and Epictetus a slave, and that there have been men whose hearts have remained warm and benevolent in the midst of much suffering. It is from the rule, however, in this case not from its exceptions that it is proper to reason and conclude; and we are taught by the rule that a state of exclusion from the common comforts of civilized life is unfavourable to rectitude of both understanding and principle. The data which could be adduced to support this, would I am of opinion be satisfactory and curious. It would be supplied by narrative of shipwrecked seamen, such as that of Commodore Byron, by details of protracted sieges, and by the history of countries wasted by famine or impoverished by misgovernment.

This rule applies to even the wild whimsical anarchy of a

masons barrack, and explains a leading trait in the character of the profession. Luckily however there is one circumstance by which the more debasing effects of all the others are much modified. At the close of Autumn the mason returns to his home and his family; and he is subjected for several months to the polishing influences of what may be termed civilized life. Next year he enters anew into the ruder habits of the preceding one, and these habits receive at its close a similar check. Thus the changes which act on his character are to be considered rather as repetitions of the same experiment which lead always to the same result, than to a course of differing and progressive ones in which the result of the last is an effect of the results of all the others. His course is to be compared rather to that of a moving wheel in a fixed engine which revolves on its axis without shifting its place than to that of the wheel of a chariot whose rotary motion conveys it from one stage to another.

For the coarseness of the manners of the country mason a satisfactory cause may be assigned different from any of those already given. More than one half of each year he spends in the society of men only, and without coming in contact with women, – the grand refiners of taste and manners. He speaks without any dread of giving offence to ears more delicate than his own; and he acts without the desire of being admired except as a wit or a humourist. It has been remarked that in countries where either through a jealous fear, or from a low estimate of their worth, women are not permitted to mingle in general society, civilization can perform only half its work; and the rudeness of manners which characterized the people of even the civilized states of antient Greece has been attributed to this cause.

But is there no danger of error in regarding slight and what may be deemed equivocal appearances in human manners, as thus arising out of the established principles of human nature? May it not be improper, too, thus to portray character with a dark shading pencil, – to describe it in no other manner than by enumerating its defects? I have been accustomed to think otherwise. By the poor student of chemistry the iron spoon and tobacco pipe must be often employed in carrying on his

experiments, instead of the retort and the crucible. It is thus
with the student of human nature. He must often judge of
such of the more striking and wonderful phenomena of his
subject as can only be properly displayed in the midst of unusual
circumstances, by minutely observing such of their partial
half-defined lineaments as comparatively common occurrences
render visible. And with regard to the other remark I cannot
avoid being of opinion that human character, whether it be
that of nature, – or (what I have been attempting to describe)
that of manners, and particularly the latter, is better delineated
by enumerating its peculiar aberations from the standards of
reason and morality, than by marking out its points of conform-
ity to these standards. The least striking of all characters is
the living manual and personified argument.

Nearly a month of winter had passed this year before I
returned home. What remained of the season, together with
the greater part of the ensuing spring was spent in profitless
indolence. I neither wrote verses nor drew pictures, but wandered during the day through the fields and woods, and among
the rocks of the hill of Cromarty; and my evenings were commonly spent either in the workshop of my uncle James, where
a few of the more intelligent mechanics of the place generally
met, or in the company of a new acquaintance. My friend
William Ross had left the town (where contrary to his fear, he
had succeeded, after parting from his master in procuring employment) at the beginning of winter; and he now resided
about four miles from it in his mother's cottage. So short a
distance would not have prevented us from frequently seeing
each other were it not that nearly the half of it was sea, – the
frith of Cromarty lying between us.

My new acquaintance was a lad of nearly my own age who
in his tenth year had been siezed by a fever which entirely
ruined his constitution, and deprived him of the use of his
limbs. For eight years before I became intimate with him he
had been bound down in such helpless decrepitude as to resemble the half-man, half-marble prince of the Arabian tale.
He was carried every morning from his bed to his chair, and
every evening from his chair to his bed. His mother, a poor old

woman, was one of those decent, pious paupers, of a spirit above their condition, that are still occasionally to be met with in the north of Scotland. It was curiosity alone that first led me to form an acquaintance with this lad; for on my return from Conan-side I had heard that almost all the young people of the neighbourhood, both male and female, were fond of his company, and that they frequented his mothers house to enjoy it, particularly in the long winter nights; and I was desirous of examining the nature of the attraction. It proved rather curious, than difficult of discovery. The cripple was naturally shrewd and sagacious, and as disease had incapacitated him from pursuing common business and pleasures, he had recourse for amusement to reading and conversation. His mind was in consequence tolerably furnished with idea, and he had attained such a command of language as enabled him to express his thoughts with facility and clearness. Hence his conversations were deemed interesting by the young men of the place; – the young women were attached to him on this and another account. He was discreet and inviolably secret; and as they regarded him from his helpless decrepitude, not as a young man, but as a thing of mind only, – as an abstract intelligence, they made him the confident and adviser of all their affairs of love and courtship. He and I were on exceeding good terms, and we entertained a mutually favourable opinion of each other. I esteemed him as a singularly amusing companion, and he regarded me as an amazingly clever, good tempered fellow. He died about three years after we became acquainted.

Early in the spring of this year (1822) I spent a day with William Ross, in his mothers cottage. I found that his winter had been spent very differently from mine. He had in the leisure hours it afforded him completed an elegant set of drawings of several of the old castles and gentlemen's seats of Ross-shire; and he had besides filled a large portfolio with black lead sketches of rocks, trees, trailing plants and groupes [sic] of men and animals; but his most curious and laborious work had been a second set of drawings, five in number, of three ancient obelisks, two of which are to be seen in the parish of Nigg, the third in Fearn, an adjoining parish. These obelisks

are curious relics of no recent era. Two of them are covered
over on both sides with hieroglyphical figures of men, animals,
instruments of music and war, and an intricate species of fret
work composed by the twisting of myriads of serpents, in a
variety of forms, singularly involved and difficult to be traced,
but yet perfectly regular and mathematical. The two Nigg
stones are still in a state of tolerable preservation; but the
third though apparently more modern, and of a much more
elegant style of sculpture, has been less fortunate; for about
two hundred years ago it was taken down by some barbarous
mason, who converted it into a tombstone by erazing the neat
mysterious hieroglyphics of one of the sides, and engraving
upon it a rude shield and label, and the following singular
incription.

HE. THAT. LIVES. WEIL.

DIES. WEIL.

SAYS. SOLOMON. THE WISE.

HEIR. LYES.

ALEXANDER. DVFF. AND.

HIS. THRIE. WIVES.

My friends drawings of these obelisks were executed in the
best possible manner. His figures were true to the proportions
and style of those of the sculptor, and the fret work was drawn
on exactly the same principles (and it was no easy task to
discover these) with his. There was nothing supplied, amended
or omitted. Some months after he was employed by a gentleman
in making a drawing of a curious piece of sculpture, bearing
date 1651. and executed under the eye of Sir Thomas Urquhart
of Cromarty, the eccentric author of the Jewel, and the first
English translator of Rabelais.[30] From this drawing a litho-
graphic print was taken a few years ago by an Edinburgh
artist, an impression of which was lately presented to the
Inverness Museum. I recognized in it the striking characteristic
fidelity of my friends pencil which like the painters in the
fable rendered to every feature its proper expression; but his
name was not attached to it. That name was deemed too
obscure by even a common mechanic to be affixed to a common

print in connexion with his own. There is only one solitary mind in which it is associated with ideas of taste and of genius.

The working season of 1822 was well advanced before my masters inate aversion to doing nothing more than balanced the lingering hope he entertained of being engaged as a contractor. At length, however, he set himself to seek employment for himself and his apprentice on the terms of the preceding year; and before the beginning of May we were engaged in working as journeymen, at Conan-side. I had determined early this season to conform to every practice of the barrack, and as I was an apt pupil, I had in a short time become one of the freest, and not the least rude of its inmates. I became an excellent baker, and one of the most skilful of cooks. I made wonderful advances in the art of practical joking, and my bon-mots were laughed at and repeated. There were none of my companions who could foil me in wrestling or who could leap within a foot of me; and after having taken the slight liberty of knocking down a young fellow who insulted me, they all began to esteem me as a lad of spirit and promise. But my poor master, though a plain honest man, was by no means so popular. He had when a contractor been accustomed to deliver his opinions somewhat dogmatically, and he was still exceedingly ready to forget that he was now only a journeyman, and that his companions were his equals. This defect of memory was deemed more than unfortunate; and there was another circumstance besides, which prejudized them against him. It was discovered that he was careful in his habits, and he was one day overheard reading me a lecture on my undue predilection for my newly acquired art of baking, – a predilection which as he truly affirmed produced serious effects on the contents of his meal chest. He proposed that for the future I should restrict myself to three cakes per week, – a proposal to which for the sake of present quietness, and in the hope of its proving the occasion of some mirth in the future I immediately agreed. The compact had no sooner become known than the whole inmates of the barrack set themselves seriously to deliberate whether the old man should not be 'rammed' for what they accounted so flagrant a stretch of perogative, but I seriously urged that his age and not very patient temper should serve as his apology, and I insisted that the management of him should be left wholly to myself.

One evening when he had gone out, I set myself to bake a huge bannock on the lid of the largest chest in the barrack. After having brought it to the size of a grindstone I divided it into about twenty parts, and placing an equal number of stones in front of the fire I set up the pieces before them. My companions were divided, when I was thus employed into two parties; – one half of them being engaged with much good will in assisting me in making ready my cake, the other in watching with intense interest the return of my master. His approach was announced by half smothered bursts of laughter and when he entered the door the roar became loud and continuous. He looked round to ascertain the cause of so much mirth. His glance rested on the hearth where he beheld cones and fustrums of cones, rhombs and rhomboids, squares and parallelograms of oaten cake, and the extent and nature of the joke burst upon him at once. He was wise enough, however, to join in the laugh, but he ever after carefully avoided giving occasion to such another. It is Goldsmith, I believe, who remarks that wit generally succeeds more from being happily addressed than from its native poignancy; and that a jest calculated to spread at a gaming table may be received with perfect indifference should it happen to drop in a mackerel boat.[31] On the same principle the practical joke related could perhaps only have succeeded in a mason barrack, – there, however, no joke could have succeeded better.

The foreman of the masons employed at Conan-side was a man of a singularly interesting cast of character. As he neither ate nor slept in the barrack, and was besides reserved and taciturn, I had in the preceding year only known him as a person more than commonly skilful both in the theoretical and practical parts of his profession. This year, however, I shared more of his company and conversation than all the other workmen under his charge put together. He was a man of very superior abilities. Nature in fact seemed to have intended him for a philosopher and a mathematician; and I found that though he owed scarcely any thing to education he was no contemptible scholar; and that though rather severe in his strictures, there were few who could form juster estimates of character. He had not always been so severe. Some of the workmen had known him for more than twenty years (he was now turned of forty) and they described him as having been for the first five or six of these one of the warmest hearted young men they had ever seen. 'We have drunk with him,' they have said, 'for whole nights together; and so pertinaciously generous was he that he would suffer none of us to discharge any part of the reckoning. He had something kind too to say to every one.' All of a sudden, however, he became morose and reserved, and no one could guess why. He never joined as formerly, in the amusements of his companions, seldom took any part in their conversations, and appeared alike unwilling either to receive or confer an obligation. He was of a weak constitution, and subject to severe fits of illness. The workmen have told me that when lodging with him in a barrack he has languished in sickness for whole days, without permitting them to make his case known to the neighbours, or to do any thing for him themselves. He is now dead, and I have lately heard that in his last illness the gratification of this singular dispostion led to a melancholy result. When engaged in the isle of Skye in superintending a party of workmen he was taken suddenly ill, and he requested the men, as usual, when going out to their morning employment, to make no mention of his sickness, – a request with which they unfortunately complied. On their return in the evening he was a corpse.

The feeling with which this man regarded me was of as singular a cast as his character. He spake well of me to the other workmen, and lent me books of Geometry and Architecture; but he was cold as ice; his esteem was a matter of the head only; his very acts of kindness reminded me of the movements of an automaton. He seemed to derive a species of sullen satisfaction from our conversations; but even in this there was something characteristic; for it did not arise either from the consciousness of his exhibiting in them very superior powers of thought to one who could in part appreciate their value, or from that sympathy, which may be be [sic] regarded as friendship in its first stage, and which is almost always elicited by the conversation of two persons of some what more than ordinary capacity who meet by accident, and unexpectedly find, each in the other, a man who has thought for himself, and that justly, on subjects of which common people know nothing. His pleasure was derived simply from the exercise afforded his mental faculties; for he seemed no way desirous of being deemed talented, and he had none of that sympathy which improves into friendship. There were few subjects connected with human affairs on which he had not thought, and few characters, as I have said, of which he could not form an estimate; and yet with all his ability, his own character owed its more striking traits rather to weakness than strength of mind. When a young man he had bent his excellent natural parts to the study of his profession; and he became so skilful in it as to be entrusted with the superintendance of a party of workmen while yet an apprentice. His early proficiency was subject of wonder to his less gifted companions; he was gratified by their admiration, and acquired that appetite for praise which is of so general experience, and which in many instances becomes more keen the more it is supplied with food. He had too much good sense to be open to the direct flatteries of other people, but he was not skilful in detecting his own; and having attained in the limited circle to which circumstances confined him the fame of being talented, he set himself to acquire the reputation of being generous and warm hearted; and this perhaps, for he was naturally of a cold temperament, from that singular weakness incident to human nature, which has so frequently the effect of making even men of reflection derive more pleasure from the praise of the qualities or talents of which they are destitute, than of those which they really possess. When treating his companions he was rendered happy by believing they entertained an opinion of him similar to that with which he regarded himself; and that they would describe him to others as one whose head and heart were the warmest and clearest they had ever met with. A few years experience of the world convinced him that his expectations were miserably unfounded. He saw, or at least thought he did that every man he came in contact with had himself for his centre; and though unacquainted with the maxims of Rochefoucault [sic], he concluded with that philosopher that the selfish principle is the spring of all human action.[32] The consequence of this conclusion was a misanthropy of the most sincere and unaffected kind. So sincere was it that he made no profession of it; – unlike those silly, would-be misanthropes who while they affect a hatred of their kind, take care to inform them of that hatred, lest they should fail of attracting their notice.

I was advised by this man to study Geometry and Architecture. With the latter I had previously been acquainted; of the former I was entirely ignorant. I had not even a single correct idea of it. The study of a few detached hours, though passed amid the distraction of a barrack, made me master of the language peculiar to the science; and I was then surprized to find how wide a province it opens to the mental powers, and to discover that what is termed mathematical skill means only an ability of reasoning on the forms and properties of lines and figures, acquired by good sense being patiently directed to their consideration. I perceived, however, that from the prosecution of this study I could derive only amusement; and that too not of a kind the most congenial to my particular cast of mind. I had no ambition to rise by any of the professions in which it is necessary; and I chose rather to exercise the faculties proper to be employed in it, in the wide field of nature and of human affairs, – in tracing causes to their effects and effects to their causes; in classing together things similar, and in marking the differences of things unlike. The study of Architecture I found more amusing; – partly, I believe, because it tasked me less; partly because it gratified my taste, and exercised my powers of invention. In Geometry I saw that I could only follow the footsteps of others; and that I would be necessitated to pursue the beaten tract for whole years before I could reach that latest discovered extremity of it, beyond which there lies undiscovered untroden regions in which it would be a delight to expatiate. Architecture, on the contrary, appeared to me a field of narrow boundaries. I could see at one glance both over it, and beyond it; – I have found that the grotesque cottage of a Highland peasant, – the hut of a herd boy, – a cavern half veiled over with trailing plants, – an opening in a wood, – in short a countless variety of objects of art and nature supplied me with ideas which though connected with it, had not yet become part of it.

Late in September my master was informed by letter that a contractor was wanted for building a wall and repairing a farm steading at a place within six miles of Cromarty, and that, from his character as a skilful workman and honest man, his estimate would be preferred. He accordingly mentioned the circumstance to his employer who obligingly released him from the engagement which had bound him to work for the season as a journeyman; and when thus released his estimate was drawn up and accepted. Before the beginning of October he and I had taken leave of Conan-Side, and were settled in a barrack as rude as the one we had lately occupied. – The place to which we removed proved to me a new field of observation.

The gentleman who tenanted it was on the eve of ruin, and his steadings bore in their dilapidated condition the marks of negligence which had in part been a cause, and was in part a consequence of this. The barrack in which we lodged, and which was also that of two unmarried farm servants, was a truly comfortless habitation. The roof leaked in many places, and along the ridge it was open to the sky from gable to gable, so that when I awakened in the night I could tell what o'clock it was, without rising out of bed by the stars which appeared through the opening. The approaching ruin of the master was written in as legible characters on his fields as on his premises. The stone fences were ruinous, the palings were broken down and converted into fuel, the hedges were gapped by the almost untended cattle, and sheaves of corn which had fallen from the cart at the close of harvest were still lying among the stubble, – fastened to the earth by the grains having struck their shoots downward and taken root.

There were, I have said, two unmarried farm servants who lodged with us in the barrack. They were both young men; and the life they were almost necessitated to lead was one of the most unfriendly possible to the formation of moral character. All day they were employed in the monotonous labours of the farm. Their evenings, as they had no home, were spent either in neighbouring houses, where young people similarly circumstanced with themselves were accustomed to meet, or in a small village, about a mile distant, where there was an ale-house. Their ordinary pleasures consisted in drinking, and amusements of a low & gross character; their principal enjoyment they derived from what they termed a ball; and scarce a fortnight passed at this season without one being held at the village. It was commonly midnight before they returned to the barrack. The effects of this heartless course of life were apparent in their dispositions and conduct. They were bound by no ties of domestic affection; and though they were never apart, they seemed to have no other idea of friendship than that it was a matter of convenience which substituted the pleasures of society for the horrors of solitude. To a person of a degraded, selfish cast of mind it is misery to be alone; and hence it will almost invariably be found that the more careless a common man becomes of his fellows the less can he live without them. The lads were besides extremely ignorant; they were of a gay reckless disposition; and as they entertained no affection for their employer, and had their moral feelings much blunted the services they rendered him were profitless and inefficient, as those services generally are which are extorted by necessity, and regulated by only a dread of censure. I could not think without regret that they were yet to become husbands and the fathers of families; and at this time I was first led to perceive that the large farm system has been as productive, at least, of moral evil to the country as of physical good. By the discoveries in the art of Agriculture to which it has led the soil has been meliorated and rendered more productive; – but what have been its effects upon men? So far as it has extended it has substituted two classes of character which may be regarded as opposite extremes equally removed from the intermediate line of excellence, for a class which occupied the proper medium. It has given us for a wise, moral, and religious peasantry, gentlemen farmers and

farm servants; – the latter in too many instances a class of de-
based helots of the character described; the former a body of
men too often marked (though certainly with many exceptions) by an union of the worst traits peculiar to the opposing
classes of country gentlemen and merchants, – the supercilious
overbearing manners of the one class, – the unfeeling speculative spirit of the other.

Our employment at this place was of the worst and most
unpleasant kind, 'Wi dirty stanes biggan a dike;' and as the
season was far advanced we wrought from daylight in the
morning until nightfall, 'bating an interval of half an hour in
which we took breakfast. We had for fuel the wood of a dove-
cot which we had pulled down to supply us with stones. It
was fungous and spongy; and in the long evenings as I had no
other light than that which it afforded, it was with difficulty
I could pursue my wonted amusement of reading, – writing I
found altogether impracticable. I had accidentally fallen in
about this time with a volume containing the works of Gawin
Douglas and Will. Dunbar; and I perused it with great interest,
lying on the barrack floor with the page spread out within a
few inches of the fire.[33] It was with considerable difficulty I
mastered the old Scotch, which from its dis-similarity to the
modern of this part of the country was to me nearly as a
foreign tongue. In reading the poems of Douglas I discovered,
or at least believed I did, the cause why common men who
possess that knowledge of the languages which, whether justly
or not, is termed learning, but who are unskilled in criticism,
deem the Greek and Roman writers superior to those of their
own country. When reading a work in the language of the
latter they pass over fine description, high thought and delicate
sentiment, without either catching the meaning, or seeing
with the eye of imagination the scenes or images of the author.
The process of perusal is so sudden compared with the slowness
with which they imagine or understand, that they slide over
the surface of his numbers, or periods without acquiring a due
sense of what lies beneath. But when they peruse the works of
a Greek or Latin author the case is different. They can only
proceed slowly; and they must render the thoughts of the

writer into the language of their own thoughts, before they can understand him. Hence they lose none of his meaning; and not reflecting on the process by which they have entered into it, – nor on the possibility of their having missed the thoughts which from the circumstance of their being conveyed in their native tongue, they deem easily understood, – they contrast the little they gain from a hurried perusal with the much they acquire from a leisurely one, and term the former the poverty of modern writers, – the latter the fertility of the antient. I of course, only speak of common men who in these matters judge for themselves; for I am aware that there are many who pronounce a like sentence either from the ambition of being deemed learned, or because like judges in another department, they determine by precedent.

A heavy shower of rain deprived me of my only amusement; for the decayed spongy wood which we used as fuel became so saturated with water, that though with difficulty I succeeded in making such a fire of it as sufficed to cook our victuals, it defied all my skill to make one by which I could read. My day employments became as the winter advanced more and more unpleasant, and my evenings no longer afforded the accustomed balance of enjoyment. I restricted myself to two meals per day, that immediately after taking dinner I might go to bed; and in a short time this new arrangement became such a matter of habit that I commonly fell asleep every evening about six o'clock, and I did not rise, sometimes not even awaken, until near eight next morning, Since this time I have been accustomed to decide whether I am happy or the contrary (a query of difficulty when one measures ones circumstances by the standards of either hope or fear) by a test extremely simple. I deem the balance to incline to the side of happiness when I prefer consciousness to unconsciousness, – when I consider sleep merely a thing of necessity, instead of regarding it as a refuge from the tedium of waking inanity, or unpleasant occupation. The converse leads me to a contrary conclusion.

These long nights did not in every instance prove blanks in my existence. I had a singular dream at this time which I still sometimes think of with a feeling not quite the reverse of superstitious. It was a prophecy of contingency; – one of those few dreams which according to Bacon, men remember and believe because they happen to hit, not one of the many which they deem idle and forget, because they chance to miss.

I dreamed that I was walking alone, in an evening of singular beauty, over a low piece of marshy ground which lies about half a mile to the north of the place where I wrought. On a bank which rises above the marsh there is a small burying ground, and the ruins of an old chapel. I dreamed that I arrived at the burying ground, and that it was laid out in a manner the most exquisitely elegant. The tombs were of beautiful and varied workmanship. They were of a style either chastly Grecian or gorgeously Gothic; and enwreathed and half hid by the flowers and foliage of beautiful shrubs which sprung up, and clustered around them. There was a profusion of roses, mingled with delicate blue flowers of a species I never saw except in this dream. The old Gothic chapel seemed roofed with stone, and appeared as entire as the day it had been completed, but from the lichens and mosses with which it was covered, it looked more antique than almost any building I remember to have seen. The whole scene was relieved against a clear sky, which seemed bright and mellow as if the sun had set only a minute before. Suddenly, however, it became dark and lowering, a low breeze moaned through the tombs and bushes, and I began to feel the influence of a superstitious terror. I looked towards the chapel, and on its western gable I saw an antique-looking, singularly formed beam of bronze, which seemed to unite in itself the shapes of the hour hand of a clock and the gnomon of a dial. As I gazed on it it turned slowly on its axis until it pointed at a spot on the sward below. It then remained stationary as before. My terror increased, – the images of my dream became less distinct, and my last recollection before I awoke is of a wild night-scene, and of my floundering on in the darkness through the marsh below the burying ground. A few weeks after the night of this dream, one of my paternal cousins in the second degree, was seized by a fever of which he died. I attended his funeral, and found that the grave had been opened to receive his corpse on exactly the patch of sward to which the beam had turned.

The third and last year of my apprenticeship expired on the first of November this year; but as the work for which my master had contracted was not completed so early I wrought with him until Martimas [sic], and then quitted his service.[34] Both he and my uncle James praised me for the manner in which I had acquitted myself during the term; but the particular circumstances of my conduct which they approved were different. What my master expatiated upon was my docility. Though not secured to me, he has said, by any written agreement, I have found him beyond comparison more tractable and obedient than any indentured apprentice I ever had. My uncle James on the other hand praised me for having so faithfully fulfilled an engagement to which I was bound by only a sense of honour, I deserved, however, little of the approbation of either. I acted in the way I had done merely because it would have been less pleasant to me to have acted differently. Had I been indentured I would probably have been much less patient and docile; as the pride which enabled me to bear what I could easily have resisted, merely because I was conscious that I could have resisted it, would have been then employed on the side of the opposition; and so far was I from entertaining any inclination for breaking my engagement that at its close I felt much in the same way I had done when entering on it. The exemption from care which it secured to me had made me regard it as a kind of second boyhood; and when on its extreme verge I looked into the future, in which I would have to bustle and toil on my own account, with a feeling of dread and anxiety.

I was still attached to my friend of the cave, but I found reason to suspect that the attachment was not mutual. Two of our common acquaintance, who were sailors, had told me that they frequently saw and spoke to him; but I was mortified to learn that he had not so much as mentioned my name to either of them. He was only a Grocers apprentice and consequently of a rank not much removed from my own. There is a pride however, which while it affects to spurn at the distinctions of fortune, and to regard the people who set a value on these as contemptible, – that yet in reality magnifies their importance. Mine was of this kind. I was proudly jealous of my poverty, and weighed with extreme minuteness the condition of life in every one who approached me, with my own. By this balance I was shewn that my early friend was what the world would deem my superior. He has formed, I have said to myself, friendships among the spruce clerks and shop-keepers of London, and looks upon his old acquaintance, the poor mechanic, as beneath his notice. Well I shall scarcely affront him by reminding him of the past. The man who does not recognize me as his equal I shall never own for my friend. I still, however, occasionally repeated my enquiries at the sailors, and early in this winter was told by one of them that my friend when he saw him last looked miserably pale and consumptive. The intelligence alarmed me and broke through my high resolutions. A few days after I saw the other sailor, and put to him the accustomed query, whether he had of late seen my friend? He replied that he had. 'Well,' I rejoined, 'when you see him again, tell him it would give me pleasure to learn that he has not quite forgotten me.' 'And why not tell him so yourself?' said the sailor, 'he is now in town here, and has been so for several days past: – It is scarcely half an hour since I saw him on the quay.' This was a piece of astounding intelligence, and spoke very audibly of coldness and indifference. I set out for the quay, however, scarcely knowing what I intended, – my heart full of an undefinable solicitous feeling which was neither pride, affection, displeasure, nor regret, but a something composed of them all. I was not so hurried, however, as entirely to neglect making preparations for the interview. As I had been unemployed for some time before my apron had been thrown aside; I now proudly resumed it and my worst bonnet to boot, that I might have as much the appearance of the poor operative mechanic as possible. 'If my early friend has determined,' thought I, 'on being acquainted with only the genteel, he shall have a very excellent apology for not renewing his intimacy with me.' I saw him leaning over the gunwale of the vessel in which he had come from London, and, though he was considerably altered from what he had been three years before I knew him at the first glance. As I passed by he raised his head, regarded me with a slight indifferent look, and then walked to the opposite side of the vessel. I could have seen him shot; – nay, I could have drawn the trigger myself. The evening had set in before I left the house, and it was now approaching to dark; the dress I wore was different from any in which my friend had ever seen me; I had besides grown nearly six inches taller since he had left the country; but of those circumstances I never once thought; – my conclusion was that he knowingly slighted me. He has since told me that he has not the slightest recollection of the rencounter. Next day I was engaged with a companion in playing at bowls. My friend was on the bowling ground at the time; he recognized me, and stood as if waiting my approach; but without seeming to take any notice of him I shot off my bowl and stalked after it. He afterwards opened a shop in town; and during the two succeeding years when we chanced to meet he spoke to me in the manner of a common acquaintance; but as a common acquaintance I could not regard him, and so the tone in which I replied was invariably more dry and cold than his own.

This winter and spring were not entirely occupied by my accustomed amusements. I was employed in building a house for one of my mother's sisters Janet Wright, a woman to whom I have cause to be attached. When I was a child every time I met aunt Jenny, and that was not seldom, she had something nice for me, a piece of cake or gingerbread, or a few caraways; and on the eve of every holiday I could calculate more surely on her halfpenny than on that of any of my other friends. During my father's life time she lived with my mother, assisting her in the affairs of the household; – after his death she served as housemaid with an old lady who resided in our neighbour-hood. Who is it that does not entertain some favourite wish, or cherish some darling hope. The hope and wish of my relative was that a time should come when she could live independent of strangers, – supporting herself by spinning and knitting. Her wishes, however, were continually baulked by the considera-tion how difficult it would be for her to pay out of her scanty earnings a house rent. The bad temper of her mistress had for years before given her much uneasiness, and as she herself was now becoming old she could not bear so well with it as formerly. Of all this my mother informed me on my return to Cromarty; and it gave me pleasure to think that I was a mason and could build my aunt a house. I accordingly pitched on a spot in the corner of a little garden that had been left me by my father, as a proper site; and I built on it a snug cottage in which aunt Jenny now resides, and will I trust when she lives.

Before I had completed the building of the cottage the spring season was well nigh over, and as there was no appearance of employment for me, I was a good deal depressed. I was somewhat diffident of my skill as a workman; and I felt too very strongly the force of that sentiment of Burns to which we are indebted for his exquisite elegiac poem 'Man is made to mourn.'[35] 'There is nothing,' said the poet, 'that gives me a more mortifying picture of human life than a man seeking work.' Late in April, however, I received a letter from my Master's former employer stating that he had contracted to build a Gothic gateway of polished stone, near Conan-Side, and that he wished me to work at it. In a few days I had removed to that place, where I found three other workmen with whom I had previously been acquainted.

In a few weeks we had nearly completed the gateway; but we had no fear of wanting employment, as our master had contracted for building a large addition to the manse of Gairloch (a parish of the Western Highlands) which he said would keep us busy until the middle of Autumn. It was necessary that one of us should go to Gairloch before the others, to engage labourers, and prepare materials for the building. I was the person pitched upon, and as I was unacquainted with Gaelic, the only language in which business can be transacted in the remote Highlands, one of the apprentices, a Highlander, was appointed to accompany me. I was to have the pleasure too of riding in a cart it being necesary for us to bring such a vehicle along with us, as there were no wheeled carriages used in Gairloch. Our carter was a singular, half witted fellow, named Mackay, to whom the master had lent a considerable sum of money and finding payment in any other way hopeless, he had contrived to furnish him with a seasons employment.

Assisted by the apprentice John McLeod, a shrewd, intelligent lad, I was loading the horse with our tools and baggage, preparatory to our setting out for the Highlands, when a female, whom I had observed for about half an hour before sauntering along the road, came up to us, and stood for a few seconds looking at us from under the hood of a dark coloured cloak, which concealed her features. It was my poor old friend Mrs Mackenzie, the madwoman. She had wandered, she said, about eighteen months before, into the Western Highlands, where she was received into the house of a gentlewoman, who showed her much kindness, until the unhappy spirit of wandering had come upon her, and hurried her away. At parting she told me that, though people could not understand us, there was meaning both in my thoughts and in hers.

We had not driven more than two miles when we found that a small lever used in settling large stones had inadvertently been left behind; and I returned for it, bidding my companion wait for me at Contin, – the village at which we expected to meet Mackay the carter. I ought to have mentioned that Mackay had gone to a neighbouring town of the previous night, after assuring his employer that before twelve o'clock next day he would be waiting us at the village. After finding the lever I was shewn a foot path which afforded a much nearer route to Contin than the main road; – the latter winding for nearly two miles in a direction contrary to that of our journey, to accomodate itself to the bridge on the Conan. I took the path as directed, and had of course to wade across the river, – a feat, as I was unacquainted with the fords, of some risk and difficulty. I felt the gravel hollowing beneath my feet by the sweep of the current, and without quite losing my footing, I was hurried down in a slanting direction for several yards. A dark deep pool, that boiled like a caldron, was just at hand. I was preparing to fling away my trowsers [sic] and shoes, – they hung over shoulders on the lever, and betake myself to swimming; when making a violent effort, I gained a few paces on the stream and reached the bank. In similar cases of danger, and when my mind was in a state of excitement, I have much oftener found my imagination employed in portraying the ludic-rous circumstance which might be possibly arise out of my silvation than in anticipating, as might be expected, the more disastrous. At this time when on the eve of being carried away by the stream, instead of being impressed with the danger of having to struggle with an impetuous torrent in which my skill in swimming might little avail me my mind was filled with thoughts of the singular figure I would make when return-ing home without shoes or trowsers [sic]. My experience of so strange a feeling enables me to conceive how Sir Walter Raleigh could jest on the scaffold. Soon after reaching the bank I arrived at Contin, where I found my companion.

Mackay had not yet come up, and from Macleods description of his habits, added to what I had learned of him from my employer I deemed it exceedingly doubtful whether we should see him before we arrived at Gairloch. He was one of that unfortunate class of persons whose lives are divided into two distinct existences with a distinct set of resolutions and opin-ions peculiar to each. In the morning he was sober, and though and determined after one fashion; in the evening he was drunk, and though and determined after another. We waited for him more than two hours after the time fixed upon, and then set off without him. There are features in the landscape with which I became acquainted during my stay at this place, that are still prominent in my recollection, and a group of figures which passed me in the way, that were I a painter I could even now transfer from my memory to canvass [sic]. I still see in a picture, the huge, snow-streaked Ben-Wevis towering over the lesser hills, like the elephant among the animals that crowded round Adam to receive their names, and the tall, grey, time-shattered tower of Fairburn below its own dark hill, like a giant eremite musing in solitude; while a company of sun-burned Highlanders stalk along a dry dusty road, – bare legged and bare footed with their breeches slung across their shoulders.

We arrived at the solitary inn of Achnicion about ten o'clock, barely in time to escape a storm which we had seen gathering for hours before. The hills were covered with huge turbans of mist which on our arrival began to unroll their folds into the vallies; and we were seated only a few minutes by the fire when the rain began to patter on the windows and the blast to howl wildly over the roof. About eleven o'clock a Highlander entered the inn dropping like a mill-wheel. He was charged, he said with a message to two mason lads, and the landlord of Achnicion, from one Mackay, a carter. Of the landlord the carter requested that his horse might be detained until he came up in the morning. His particular charge to us the Highlander had forgot; but he ingeniously remarked that were we to string together all the oaths and imprecations peculiar to both the Gaelic and English we might acquire a pretty correct notion of what it conveyed. The carter had travelled with him from Contin, but fatigued by a large bundle, and galled by a pair of large shoes, he was knocked up by the way and compelled to take up his lodgings for the night in a house seven miles east of Achnicion. 'He never ceased swearing and vowing vengeance,' said the Highlander, 'from the time we left Contin until we parted.'

Next morning Macleod and I were awakened by a loud noise in the adjoining apartment. 'It is the carter['] whispered my comrade. We immediately started up, flung on our clothes and set ourselves seriously to reconnoitre the strength and appearance of the enemy through the crannies of the partition. Standing in the middle of the floor of the adjoining room I saw the formidable Mackay in the form of a tall raw-boned man, apparently turned of forty. A tattered great-coat of coarse brown stuff descended from his neck to his heels, and opening in front, shewed a pair of trowsers [sic] and waistcoat, still more tattered. He spoke, partly in soliloquy, partly to our landlord, – a kind obliging old man who stood by him, – with a volubility altogether extraordinary, and in his haste contrived to mingle the languages of the Celt and the Saxon so strangely together, that neither Macleod nor I, though the one pretended to an acquaintance with Gaelic, and the other to a knowledge of English, understood the meaning of half what he uttered. The more our kind apologist, who spoke as the opportunity

offered, strove to pacify him, the more boisterous he became.
'Macleod,' said I, 'you speak both languages fluently; – away
and attack him. Be sure you call him rascal every time he
opens his mouth; threaten him with prosecution, and every
thing else you can think of; and if he attempts striking you I
will step in and take up the quarrel.' Our stratagem had the
desired effect. My comrade acted his part to admiration, and
perseveringly retorted on the carter, whose voice and courage
gradually lowered in the contest, the more significant expressions of his own abuse. At length I joined them, and going up
to my comrade, who seemed ferociously angry, I began to
apologize to him for poor Mackay. I then despatched our landlord for some whisky and peace was immediately restored.
Late on the evening of this day we arrived at the manse of
Gairloch.

Our first care on the following morning was to procure a
lodging. The ministers hay barn was the place pitched upon
for our accomodation, and the minister himself, a stout, portly,
good looking man, shewed us the way to this cell of hardship.
It reminded me of the stables which Hercules could not clean
until he had turned a river through them. The floor where not
covered by a pool of green stagnant water, which had flowed
from the adjoining dung-hill, was littered over with rotten
hay. Two small windows admitted light in abundance, but as
they were unfurnished with either glass or frames, the sea
breezes, which at even at this season (midsummer) was keen
and piercing, found access as freely. The roof leaked in several
places. To transform this cell into a comfortable barrack was
a work of some labour. McLeod and I began to clear it out;
and Mackay who had at first looked the very picture of blank
dismay, took heart as the work proceeded, and seizing a shovel
began to lay about him in the very superior style of one well
acquainted with the labours of the stable. In a few hours the
litter was carried away, and the water drained. Mackay I
despatched to the shore for a load of sand with which to form
a floor; Macleod I sent out to procure fuel and fire; – I found
employment for myself in filling up one of the windows with
turf, and in fitting into the other an old unglazed frame, which

though it added little to the warmth of the apartment, much improved its appearance. A pair of the minister's harrows, over which I laid an old door, and a bundle of dried grass formed an excellent bed; and three smooth blocks of granite which I carried from the neighbouring moor supplied the places of chairs. Every thing succeeded with us to our best wishes. Mackay discovered a hill of fine dry sand which made an excellent floor; and McLeod returned laden not with fire and fuel only; but also with a bag of oat meal, a pot and a large wooden bowl. He had borrowed the pot and the meal from the inmates of the manse, and the bowl and the fuel he had been ingenious enough to steal. In short we found ourselves in a condition to subsist, and when after finishing our labours we sat by the fire which now roared in the chimney, it was with no common feeling of complacency that we congratulated ourselves on the comforts of our situation.

In a few days we were joined by the other workmen from Conan-side. A sloop which our employer had freighted from Inverness, with wood and sandstone for the building brought us plenty of oat-meal, our staple food, and from the Dairy of the manse we were supplied with skimmed milk at nearly the common price. The last however was a luxury which we did not long enjoy; for one of our party, a sarcastic old man, who had wrought as a mason for more than forty years, and who was strongly marked by those traits which I have described as characteristic of the profession, asked the dairy maid one day whether she thought that milk like wine, became better as it grew old, and the consequence of the joke was that we had to diet for the rest of the time on the meal alone. This we considered a hardship. We were besides annoyed by a number of other petty vexations. When the hay season came on we were ejected from our barrack to make way for the ministers hay, and as the cowhouse, our second lodging, had no chimney we narrowly escaped being suffocated in it with smoke. As the weather during the summer and autumn of this year was rainy and tempestuous we were frequently drenched to the skin; and the turf our only article of fuel, was so saturated with water that we were fain at times to eat our victuals half raw

from the impossibility of getting them properly cooked. The
rats cut up our meal bag into shreds, and when we had trans-
fered the meal to a large cask, we discovered that our redoubted
carter had as knavish designs on it as the rats themselves. The
sarcastic old mason whose unlucky humour had deprived us
of the milk, but who was a great favourite with us notwithstanding, would frequently smooth the surface of the meal
before going out to work, and engrave upon it with the point
of his finger the eighth commandment, but the writing we
found almost always effaced by Mackay. He was well known
in Gairloch, where the Highlanders considered him as a species
of vampire, a report having reached them that in the Lowlands
he had been employed as a resurrexionist; and as if to be
avenged on them for the feeling of abhorrence with which
they regarded him, he contrived to fare sumptously when the
nights began to lengthen, on their fish and potatoes. On leaving
us, which he did when he had collected the materials for the
building, I gave him a shilling and a dram that he might
convey my blanket in his cart to Conan-side. He carried it as
far as the next inn, – a distance of twelve miles, and pledging
it for a second shilling and second dram he there left it. I may
remark in parting with Mackay that he was one of the class of
persons who are termed the half witted; and that though I
have known idiocy in its more unmixed state united to honesty,
I never knew one of this cast of intellect who was not a rogue.

The manse of Gairloch is not more than two hundred yards
from the sea shore, which in this place is rocky and abrupt. In
the evenings I frequently amused myself with my old favourite
pastime swimming. At the place where I commonly bathed
there is a steep wall of rock whose base barely dries during the
ebb of stream tides, and whose top is nearly covered at the
height of flood. From this wall I have practised the Indian
method of diving, – that in which the diver carries a weight
with him to facilitate his sinking, and to keep him steadily at
the bottom. I became in this way as well acquainted with
submarine scenery in its natural appearance, as I had been
with it formerly in the descriptions of the poets. From its great
beauty the real scenery might very properly take place of the

fictitious. I shall attempt a description. Behind me was the rock, – a dark, undefined, cloud-like mass, irregularly speckled over with little, circular, greyish-coloured figures, which resembled the brighter stars when seen through a thin cloud of mist. Beneath my feet was a carpet of a singular, but not very irregular pattern. It appeared as if laid out into perfectly formed circles of various colours and sizes, – every peeble [sic], rock, and bunch of weed taking this form. The light coloured circles on the wall of rock behind were shell-fish. Over this carpet and wall there stretched a beautiful firmament of vivid green, which, unlike the real one, was dark in its horizen [sic], and pale in its centre, where there shone a flickering dancing light, unlike any thing I have seen through the thinner medium of air, and which was occasioned by the beams of the sun striking on the undulations of the surface.

About the middle of September this year I had a singular dream, the particulars of which retain even to this day, as firm a hold of my memory as if they had been those of a real incident. I dreamed that my friend William Ross had died, and that I was watching the corpse in a large darkened apartment. I felt sad and unhappy. Suddenly there appeared near the couch where the body lay an upright wreath of thin vapour, which gradually assumed the figure of my deceased friend. The face of the spectre was turned towards the body, and the robes of white in which it was dressed, appeared, compared with the winding sheet beside it, as a piece of combric exposed to the rays of the sun would to another piece hung up in the shade. The figure turned round and I spoke to it, but though from the splendour of the dress it wore and the placid expression of the face, which was of feminine beauty, I inferred it to be a spirit of Heaven, by one of those inconsistencies common in dreams, my question to it regarded the state of the damned. 'I know nothing,' it said, 'of the damned.' 'Then describe to me,' I rejoined, 'the happiness of the blest.' The reply was strong and pointed. 'Live a good life, and in seven days, seven weeks, and seven years you shall know.' I must add that I have since thought much oftener of the prediction than of the advice.

When we had completed our work at the manse two of the

workmen returned home, and I and the other two removed to
a little village south of the parish church where we built a
house for an innkeeper, a native of the Lowlands. We were
not less unfortunate in our lodgings at this place than we had
been at the one we had left. One half of a large salt cellar, of
which the other half had been pulled down to furnish materials
for our building, served us as a barrack. It was cold and comfortless, and though we hung a screen of mats across the open end
to serve as a gable, so inefficient was this barrier that when,
in the night time the wind accompanied by showers blew
against it, we have been awakened by the rain pattering in
our faces, as we lay abed. Our employer, however, who was a
rare mixture of kindness and ostentation did all in his power
to render us comfortable. He supplied us with excellent milk,
and every sabbath we were invited to dine with him. He was
a loquacious little man, full of himself, and desirous of being
reckoned a wit, – though, like almost all people of a similar
character, a smart unexpected repartee completely upset him.
As I was more taciturn than either of my companions he
regarded me as a safe butt for his little pleasantries; and as I
deemed him in turn, a kind weak man I bore for some time his
ridicule with great good humour. One day, however, I wantonly
replied to his ironies in a strain that completely silenced him;
and the consequence was that next sunday, when my two
companions were called to take dinner with him as usual, I
was left behind to do penance on the not very luxurious viands
of the barrack. But before leaving the place I found an opportunity of being avenged. He was of a mechanical turn, and had
bargained for a hammer and trowel with one of my companions,
who preferred parting with the weightiest of his tools at even
an under value, to carrying them in his bundle to the low-
country; but on the day we finished our work an unexpected
opportunity presented of having them conveyed; and the mason
embraced it, regardless of his engagement. I was informed of
the circumstance when on the eve of setting out for the low
country; and taking my hammer and trowel from my bundle,
I presented them to the inkeeper's wife; – alleging when she
urged me to set a price on them that they were a very inadequate

return for her husbands kindness to me during the first two weeks of our acquaintance.

My master taught me an excellent practical lesson this year, on the impropriety of confiding too implicitly on the honesty of that class which we designate mere men of the world. He appeared to me to be an open hearted obliging man; and I deemed it unnecessary to fix the rate of my wages when engaging with him, in the early part of the season. At its close he contrived to pay me with somewhat less than half a guinea per week, though the amount of wages this year averaged sixteen shillings. Though much vexed at the time by treatment so unexpected and ungenerous, I soon recovered my spirits, and consoled myself with the best sentiment of my favourite philosopher 'It is better to suffer wrong than to do it.'

I have said that the history of my education is also that of my life. There is, however, one branch of the former which is but imperfectly described, if at all, in my detail of the incident of the latter; – the knowledge I have acquired of the peculiarities of the Celtic character. I must not forget for whom I write; – a gentleman whose exertions towards civilizing the Highlands have extended his fame not only among the people by whom a proper estimate can be formed of the dignity of superior talent, and the excellence of an almost unlimited benevolence, but also among those who better able to appreciate virtue than ability have no high respect for learning, and but little admiration of genius. I shall therefore lay down such random recollections of the Highlands as are still retained in my memory, and such of my thoughts as were first suggested by the peculiarities of the inhabitants.

States like individuals decay as they advance in years, and they at length expire. Their progress from youth to age includes two extremes and a medium. But in one respect bodies politic differ from bodies natural; for in the several members of the former there may be different degrees of age. In this country there are districts peopled by men who have not yet reached the medium line, and there are others whose inhabitants have gone beyond it. Of the former kind are the Highland districts; of the latter are the greater number of those of the Lowlands,

– especially such of these as contain large towns. But it is only
among the lower classes that the differences of the several
stages are discernable; for the people in the upper walks of
society bear almost the same character all over the kingdom.
And it is perhaps only by an observer who is placed on the
same level with the former, and who from this circumstance
becomes intimately acquainted with their manners, habits,
and modes of thought, that, at least the minuter differences
can be discerned[.] By such a person however, if the theory be
a just one, a tour through Scotland may be regarded, not
merely as a journey through various places but also as an
extended existence through different ages.

When I first arrived at Gairloch I could almost have imagined
that I had taken a journey not from one part of the kingdom
to another, but from the present times to those of my early
ancestors, who having wearied themselves in the first stage of
society by living as hunters and fishers, had newly entered
into the second, and were making their first rude essays in the
art of tillage. My opportunities of minute observation in this
district, were restricted mostly to a small straggling village,
which lies about three hundred yards north and west of the
manse. The appearance of the piece of cultivated land attached
to the village, when I first saw it, and from a distance not a
little surprized to me; – like the campaign country of Lilliput,
as described by Gulliver, it is divided into patches of about
sixty feet square, – some of which are surrounded by fences of
stone. A nearer view convinced me that the enclosures are
not the fruits of a useless and uncharacteristic industry. The
ground had originally been full of stones; and instead of remov-
ing these to the moor above or the shore below (either only
distant about two hundred yards from the centre of the land
cultivated) the clearers had piled them up in the manner
described. In some of the upper patches I saw numbers of little
pyramids of loose stones rising above the sward like tents in
an encampment. When looking at them I could almost have
fancied that some malignant magician had passed the way in
the time of harvest, and by a stroke of his wand had converted
the shocks of corn into heaps of stone. The pyramids had been

constructed by the builders of the surrounding enclosures, and with the same intention, – that of clearing the land. There is neither plough nor horse in the village. In the spring season the manure is removed, mostly by women, in large creels, from the dunghill to the field. The creels open at bottom, and are locked and hinged with wattles of birch. At the proper place the lock is slipped; the contents fall behind the bearer; and when the patch intended to be cultivated is manured in this way, the man commences his task of digging it up; which he performs with a long crook handled spade, termed a *casschrom*. Nor it is merely as husbandmen that the inhabitants of this part of Gairloch prosecute their labours in as simple a manner and with the assistance of implements which were they to be dug out of the masses or sandhills of the eastern coast of Scotland would be pronounced by the antiquary the relics of some very remote era. I have seen primitive anchors constructed of wood and stone; primitive tackle spun out of the fibres of mire-fir; boats caulked with moss; and in some instances furnished with sails of woolen; and bags made, like the bottles of the antients, of the untanned skins of animals, with the hairy side turned outwards.

Late on the evening of the second day after my arrival at the manse, I went, accompanied by my companion Macleod to the adjoining village; my business there being to procure a labourer. We passed several miserable looking cottages, until we came in front of one which though formed in a similar style with the others was more nearly built; and concluding that the inhabitant was less indolent, or more ingenious than his neighbours, we agreed to enter and try whether he would not engage with us. My companion who from his acquaintance with the Gaelic, was best fitted to take the lead, stepped up to the door; and bending his head to accomodate himself to a lintel raised nearly four feet above the soil, he plunged into a gulph which, unseen in the darkness, yawned behind the threshold, and immediately disappeared. He had fallen into the dunghill, which, according to the laudable custom of this part of the country, lay entrenched behind the door. We spent about half a minute in this singular antichamber, groping for the inner opening, which we at length discovered by the bursts of smoke which issued from it. The threshold was raised to the level of that of the outer door. We climbed up, stooped, and entered. In the centre of the floor there smouldered a large peat fire, from whence eddied huge volumes of smoke, that at the height of about four feet spread over the whole apartment, – forming a ceiling as smooth, and apparently as tangible as one of plaster. On one side the fire and dimly discovered by its light there sat a strong looking, red headed, red bearded man, and opposite to him his wife, the mistress of the mansion, – a woman of a dark, pale complexion, but a rather agreeable expression of countenance, who was busied in spinning on that primitive implement, the distaff and spindle. My companion stepped forward and introduced himself to the Highlander; who received him with a courtesy peculiar to his country, and then turned to me; but as we spoke no common language our conference was summed up in a nod and a smile. In half a minute we were seated by the fire on a large settle, and when my companion was employed in opening to our host the cause of our visit I was occupied in transferring to my memory by minute observation, a picture of the apartment. It was about ten feet square. The walls as shewn by the light of the fire, which was now brightened up by a few pieces of splintered fir, were rudely constructed of large undressed masses of red granite. The crevices were caulked with moss. There were no openings of any kind left in the walls for windows, but in the day time two holes in the roof, neither of them directly over the fire served the double purpose of letting the smoke out and the light in. The Highlander's furniture was in character with the shell of the mansion. Two settles (seats of plank) supplied the places of chairs, and a third, rather higher and broader, served as a table. A few wooden vessels occupied a recess of the wall, and in a corner of the apartment there was a bed of rough deal. The other utensils were the pot which hung over the fire, the primitive implements used in spinning, a sphere-like basket which contained wool, and a wreath of herring nets which hung half hid, half revealed, in the cloud above. When I had finished my survey I turned to the speakers, and observed that the tone of their conversation had considerably changed. It was no longer that of business, but deep and sympathetic, and it struck me that I myself was the subject of discourse. The woman, who had hitherto been silent, now joined in the dialogue with exclamations of the tenderest pity. 'O,' said my companion, addressing me, 'if you only knew how much you are obliged to these kind people.' 'For what?' 'For their sincerest pity.' 'And what makes me its object?' 'Why, what but your being a Lowlander, and your ignorance of the Gaelic: – are there other circumstances think you that could give you an equal claim!'

This incident, little as it may appear, first furnished me with a key for laying open a principle in the Celtic character which I have since viewed in a variety of lights, and which I am confident has stamped it with many of its more excellent traits. The Highlander, living in such a cottage, and possessed of such a knowledge of agriculture as I have described, could yet regard with sincere pity one who was so unfortunate as not to resemble himself, a Lowlander of the same class would have felt very differently. He would have recognized me, or any other common mechanic as at least his equal, and would consequently have deemed me no legitimate object of pity. And lest the Lowlander's apparently juster estimate appear merely the result of superior knowledge I venture to affirm that were he as ignorant of the real circumstances of the person thus brought within his observation as the Highlander was of mine he would rather deem me happier than himself, than the contrary. I assert this, having before me, with other proof, a pretty extensive experience of the fact that common journeymen mechanics who are men of principle, and attached to their children, seldom bring up these to what they term their own miserable profession, but indenture them to trades which they suppose can be prosecuted to greater advantage. I have seen shoemakers apprenticing their children to blacksmiths, and blacksmiths to shoemakers, masons to joiners, and joiners to masons; – each acting on the supposition that the profession prosecuted by himself was less advantageous than that pursued by his neighbour. The genuine Highlander forms a very different estimate of his circumstances and situation. He has pity to bestow upon those whom he considers

less happy or fortunate than himself; and so contented is he
with his condition, that it is not among the unequivocally
wretched alone he looks for such. Nor with all his apparent
poverty does he deem himself too poor to bestow. It was not
for his pity only I was indebted to my host of Gairloch. I was
invited to share in his supper, and he afterwards frequently
supplied my companion and me with fish and potatoes, for
which he would accept of no return. When we were joined by
the workmen from Conan-side there were at least once a week
presents of a similar kind sent to our barrack, and this frequently
by individuals with whom we had not the slightest acquaintance. Indeed all the Highlanders of the district seemed to
regard us as having claims on their compassion and hospitality;
and the claim of the poor Saxon lad they deemed doubly
strong from the circumstances of his being unacquainted with
their language.

Though the hospitality of the Scottish Highlander is a virtue
certainly not of late discovery, it has, I suspect, seldom been
seen from the proper point of view, and has not often been
traced to its legitimate principle. Indeed it is seldom at all
observed by one qualified to judge of it. The intelligent men
who travel through the Highlands, with the intention of becoming acquainted with the condition of the inhabitants, are in
general raised too high above them for ascertaining whether
the virtue be real or merely apparent; and even the men of
similar powers of discernment who reside among them are
placed in nearly as unfavourable a point of observation as the
mere traveller, – and from the same cause. The latter are the
Highlanders great men, the former he regards as the great men
of another country. His attachments to the latter may appear
to be merely a consequence of that species of Toryism which
is so frequently to be found in people of a mean and sordid
cast of mind; his respect for the former may seem the same
Toryism differently directed. The poor-spirited pauper who is
not even in imagination either charitable or generous, – the
mean selfish man who without one particle of pity in himself,
solicits the pity of others are full of this Toryism; for the only
pleasure of such lies in acquirement; and they worship Wealth

and Influence as the deities from whom they hope to receive. Now this principle is exactly the converse of that which in the Celtic character, so far as a respect for rank and influence is concerned, produces almost the same effects. The rude Celt, amid all his privations, is contented with his condition, and in consequence his chief pleasure does not consist in acquirement. He is respectful, because he feels none of that jealousy of wealth and power (a consequence of discontent) which constitutes the Whiggism of the lower classes in great towns; and he is hospitable because, according to the remarkable language of Revelation, he deems it more blessed to give than to receive. This I consider the main principle of his character. I have deemed it alike apparent in the pity with which the red-bearded Highlander regarded his guest, and in the disinterested respect which I have seen his countrymen pay to persons who approached them in the garb of gentlemen. And I am much mistaken if the point of observation which I occupied when at Gairloch was not the best possible for ascertaining this. I was in reality, and according to my own estimate, on the same level with the people whose character I studied; and what was not less in my favour as an observer, and was besides confirmatory of my theory, I was according to their estimate so far below this level as to be an object of their pity. – To my own evidence on this point I can add testimony of a somewhat singular cast.

I have perused a curious pamphlet 'The life of John Magee, written by himself,' and have seen the author from whom alone the work can be procured.[36] He is a rare personage, – old and crazed, – a Deist one week, a Methodist the next, combining in himself the occupations of flying-stationer, author, and beggar, – and in his discontent with existing establishments, and his pretensions to visions and prophecy the very counterpart of Martin the incendiary. It is sufficiently obvious that a man of so singular a character and profession should have a sad tale to tell of the disrespect and inhospitality with which he has been treated; – of the uncharitableness of even the charitable, and the hard heartedness of even the humane. His pamphlet is a grievous satire on human nature and manners as he found these in the Lowlands of Scotland; and yet even this man has praise to bestow on the humanity and hospitality of the Highlanders. I have recognized in his description of them the principle described. 'When towards evening,' say he, (I quote from memory) 'I enter one of the Highland cottages, instead of meeting with that repulsive surliness, or that marked impatience of my presence, which in similar circumstances I always experience in the Lowlands, – I am received with a kindness not more apparent than real; and instead of having my solicitation to partake for the night of the shelter of their roof met by an abrupt and contemptous [sic] refusal, I am commonly invited to stay with them even before I have time to urge my request. They share their food with me, with the sincerest good will; deeming themselves more than compensated by the information I give them concerning the state of the country.' – The conversation between this poor man and the inmates of a Highland cottage would form no bad subject for the skilful dramatist. There would be interest at least in contemplating in the latter the workings of that principle which enabled them to derive satisfaction from doing acts of kindness to so disreputable a guest.

Were what I have here advanced regarding this principle submitted to the public, it is probable that some people of a philosophical turn, would be inclined to consider me as one of those speculative persons who build systems sweepingly general on the scanty data afforded by a few particular instances; – and hence they would remain sceptical with regard to my statement. It is probable too that another, and very different class, those whose feelings of nationality it seems to flatter, might be elated by finding it adjudged to their countrymen the palm of superiority over the Lowlanders in one of the most important fundamentals of moral character. But perhaps by tracing the principle to that rude stage of society in which it is first apparent the scepticism of the one class might to a certain extent be removed, and the exultations of the other a little lowered. It is indisputable that the inhabitants of the Highlands have not yet reached the proper medium of civilization; and it is obvious that they must in consequence be marked by some of the peculiarities characteristic of the rude and early extreme of Society. Among these, as inimitably marked out by Robertson in his estimate of the character of the Americans, is that decided partiality which savage tribes always manifest towards their own rude manners; and that lofty idea which they always entertain of their own preeminence over the rest of mankind. Till of late the same traits prominently marked the Scottish Highlanders. Never did an Iroques [sic] or Cherokee savage regard with more perfect contempt the white men, whom he believed to be a species of creatures produced by the froth of the sea without father or mother, – than did the Celt of a century ago the inhabitants of the Lowlands. Hospitality was a virtue for which even then the Highlanders had become famous; – it marked too, as pleasingly described by Franklin the north American Indians of the last age; – a proof that both were at least one degree removed from the extreme of barbarism.[37] The proud consciousness of superiority still remained with them; but the hardness & insensibility of heart, – the sullen reserve of manners so remarkable in all savage nations were gone. – That hospitality should be a consequence partly from the one trait being lost; partly that the other remained, is obvious. It is according to experience that men who are contented with themselves, and respect themselves, should live in a state of at least passive happiness; – it is agreeable to reason that to passive happiness they should desire to add positive enjoyment; it is in consonance with both reason and experience that such an enjoyment should be derived by such men not from acquiring but from conferring, – not from becoming the receivers but the bestowers of benefits. And surely the most sceptical may deem it rational to believe that Scottish Highlanders are characterized by a tone of feeling natural to their stage of advancement in civilization. On the other hand the Celt who plumes himself on the merits of his countrymen may not feel much disposed to boast of that virtue and happiness which they possess and enjoy in common with almost all semi-barbarous tribes.

But by the philosopher virtue whereever found, & happiness whereever enjoyed is not deemed other than virtue and happiness. – Perhaps the proper medium of civilization cannot be

better defined than as that middle state in which the virtues &
pleasures natural to the ruder stages of society are mingled with
those peculiar to the stages of refinement. – And the exertions
which are directed to hasten the advances of a people towards
this state are truly philanthropic. Two different methods have
been pointed out as proper to be pursued for civilizing the poor
Highlanders. Perhaps the gentlemen I address will forgive me
should I state freely my sentiments concerning these, by
pointing out what I regard (with reference to my theory of the
medium) as the errors of the one method, and the advantages of
the other. – One of them has fortunately been acted upon to a
considerable extent, – the other, I believe, continues merely a
thing of theory.

According to the first method education is regarded as a
proper means for bringing the Highlander to the knowledge of
God; and this knowledge is reckoned of paramount importance
towards ameliorating his condition and raising his character.
According to the second it is considered as one of the means
(for there are several others, – such as the introducing of
manufactures, the encouraging of fisheries, and the building
of towns) of making him such a one as his neighbour the
Lowlander. The first I deem to be founded on truly religious,
and consequently on truly philosophical principles, – the principles of the second I consider as equally apparent, – and they
may, I am of opinion, be thus explained.

No one who has visited the Highlands, not even the most
superficial, can fail of becoming acquainted with what may
be termed the physical privations of the inhabitants. A system
of agriculture such as I have described must appear to every
one who has ability enough to observe & compare, artless and
unprofitable; and a cottage such as that in which I first experienced Celtic hospitality cannot fail of seeming rude and incon-
venient. It is obvious to every one that a plough is a better
implement for breaking up the land than a *cass chrom*; that
the carriage of manure is an employemnt better suited to the
capacities of a horse than of a woman; that windows and
chimnies ought to be seperate [sic] apertures; and that it is
much better to have the dunghill outside the door than within.

Now to a certain class of observers, that which may be termed the physical condition of man is every thing; for of their moral character they can form no proper estimate. They look upon the tribes and classes of human society as a person destitute of taste and discernment would upon a collection of pictures; and they judge of them by nearly similar rules. Show and glitter, riches of drapery and splendour of colouring, are the sole merits of painting according to the judgement of the one; skill in the arts, and refined ideas of what is necessary to comfort made evident in neat houses and fine clothes constitute the grand virtues of society in the estimate of the others. Opinions of this kind seem to direct the philanthropy of that class of men who aim at converting the Celt into such a one as the Saxon. And certainly were this philanthropy more active (for as yet it has slept and the theories of the class are merely its dreams) it would to a certain extent confer a benefit on both the Highlander and the State. The former would be taught how to build a comfortable cottage, and to transfer more than half his labour of tillage from himself to his horse; – The latter could reckon the value of the change in the increase of the Revenue.

But if we do not err in considering man as a creature of both time and eternity, nor in believing that the men who live best are those who enjoy happiness in this world, and secure through the practice of virtue the felicities of the world which is to come; them must it necessarly follow that the condition of any class of human beings can only be improved by rendering them happier and better. And this principle, simple as it is, may be advantageously applied in this case. Were a certain class of men to quit their place in society, for that of another class, who equalled them in happiness and virtue, but who differed from them in their manners and habits, we would justly infer from it that the transaction was merely a change not an improvement. Nor would it produce the slightest altera-tion in the case though the one class should be termed semi barbarous and the other civilized. If we imagine further that this profitless transition from semi-barbarism to refinement is brought about by a certain body of men, we must deem the labour by which they effect it to be idle and useless; but if we suppose the rude primitive tribe superior in virtue and happiness to the civilized, it is evident that the former are injured by being made to approximate to the state of the latter; and that the efforts by which the approximation is produced are not simply idle, – they are mischievous. Now I have no hesitation in affirming from what I have seen of each, that the people of the Highlands are in general happier and more virtuous than those of the Lowlands. And I venture to add that even were the balance in these respects equal between them, the state of the former would notwithstanding when considered in its connexion with the future, be by much the better state. Old age and infancy have their respective evils, but even supposing these evils equal, it is evident that the state which must terminate in manhood is superior to that which must end in death. In like manner the people who are advancing towards the proper medium of happiness and virtue are in a better condition than those who are retrograding from it; – even supposing that the distance which the one has to advance and which the other has retrograded is exactly the same.

It is to be remarked too, that the Highlander would in the supposed transition remove from his place in the extreme he now occupies to a low stage in the opposite one without passing through the intervening medium. I have observed that the least interesting, – least virtuous people of the Highlands are those who inhabit the districts that border on the Lowlands. They are in many respects unlike the men who people the fastnesses of the country. They are less simple, less hospitable, less honest. There is a variety of character singularly *outre* in some of its features which I deem peculiar to these border districts, and of which several examples have come within my notice. I have studied it in Highlanders who had either spent some years in the southern parts of the kingdom, or had been employed at that great national undertaking, the Caledonian-Canal. The more prominent features are curious from their contrariety. There is the credulousness of the vulgar Tory blended with the obtrusive, impudent confidence of the vulgar Whig; – there is the smartness of the south country mechanic combined with a non-descript something which was once the simplicity of the north country Celt; – there is the quiet, negative ignorance natural to the cottage wrought up with the positive obtrusive ignorance peculiar to the town.

There is a steep hill rather more than a mile from the manse of Gairloch to the summit of which I frequently extended my walks. The view which the eye commands from thence is of a character wilder and more sublime than can be either rightly imagined or described. Towards the east and south there spreads a wide savage prospect of rugged mountains, towering the one over the other from the foreground to the horizen [sic], and varying in colour, in proportion to the distance, from the darkest russet to the faintest purple. They are divided by deep gloomy ravines that seem the clefts and fissures of a shattered and ruined planet; and their summits are either indented into rough naked crags, or whitened over with unwasting snows; – forming fit thrones upon which the spirits of winter might repose, each in a seperate [sic] insulated territory, and from whence they might defy the milder seasons as they passed below. To the north and west the scene is of a different description, – it presents a rocky, indented shore, and a wide sea speckled over with islands. On both sides, however, though the features are dissimilar, the expression is the same. Scarcely more of the works of man appear visible in the whole wide circumference than appeared to the gaze of Noah when he first stood on the summit of Mount Araret [sic], and contemplated the wreck of the Deluge.

It was on a beautiful evening in the month of June that I first climbed the steep side of this hill and rested on its summit. I was much impressed by the wide extent and sublime grandeur of the scene. Part of the eastern skirt of the Atlantic was spread out beneath me, mottled with the Hebrides. In one glance I had a view of Longa, Skye, Lewis, Harris, Rona, Raza, and several other islands with whose names I was unacquainted. The sky and sea were both coloured with the same warm hue of sunset, and appeared as if blended together; while the islands which lay on the verge of the horizen [sic] seemed dense purple clouds, which though motionless in the calm,

the first sea breeze might sweep away. Towards the south my
eye was caught by two gigantic mountains, which, as if emulous
of each other, towered above the rest, like the contending
chiefs of a divided people; while towards the east I beheld a
scene of terrible ruin, and sublime disorder, – mountain pilled
upon mountain, and ravine intersecting ravine. All my faculties
of reason and imagination seemed at first as if prostrated and
held down by some superior power; – the magnitude of the
scene oppressed me; – I felt as if in the presence of the spirit of
the Universe; – and the apology of the Jewish spies recurred to
me 'We were as grasshoopers [sic] before them.' In a short
time, however, I felt relieved of the burden; my thoughts began
to flow freely; and the object to which they were directed was
connected with the scene. I considered the peculiarities which
constituted the character of the people of so singular a country;
and I enquired of myself to what extent that character could
be meliorated and improved.

There seemed to me something plausible and ingenious in
the scheme that would convert the rude, simple inhabitants
of so sterile a district into artists and manufacturers. I saw
that were the energies of the people roused, there was no
internal object to which they could be directed. I saw that no
human industry could give fertility to the naked cliffs, and
brown swelling hills which rose before me; and when I turned
to the other hand, I was pleased to see, as in a picture, an
active & ingenious people ministering on the bleak shore which
stretched beneath me to the wants and luxuries of distant
nations, and receiving the recompense of their services in the
abundance which poured in upon them, adding to their comforts, and supplying their privations. The intellectual scene
varied as I gazed on it. I saw the inhabitants increasing on the
shores, – the bays filled with trading vessels, and the many-
windowed manufactories springing up in almost every valley.
But the next change presented a less pleasing aspect. I saw a
whole people converted from the inhabitants of a province
into the prisoners of a desert; – their very existence depending
less on their own industry than on the fluctuations of distant
markets and the decrees of foreign governors. I saw that they

were poor in their most prosperous seasons; for they had become luxurious in the midst of a sterile country that had no internal resources; – I saw that from the same cause failure in trade was followed by famine. I examined narrowly into the character of the poeple and found they were no longer Scottish High-landers. I saw among them ingenious mechanics who were adepts in the philosophy of Paine and Williams, and whose beau ideal of character seemed embodied in the Macheath of the Beggar's Opera.[38] I found that the upper classes among them were composed of men who had worn out on the whet-stone of refinement all love of country and of their species, – and with whom a knowledge of bills and of bonds was reckoned of much greater importance than a belief in the Bible. On awakening from this reverie I was glad to perceive that the shores were still solitary; that in the wide expanse of ocean below the eye could not discern a single vessel; and that for the crowded manufactories, I could find only a few scattered cottages, – each half enveloped in its blue cloud of smoke. I was glad too to turn from the character of the depraved mech-anic to that of the poor simple Highlander. He is poor, thought I, but his desires are moderate; he is ignorant, but he believes in the Bible; he is unacquainted with the arts of civilization, but then he abhors its vices; he is a stranger to the polish of refinement, but he possesses that warmth of heart which mere politeness fails to imitate with success; he is the quietest of subjects in the time of peace, and his country's best defence in the season of war.

The plan of civilizing the Highlands which does not refer to the manners of any particular people as a standard, but derives its standard from the perfect rule of Scripture, cannot, I am of opionion, be too highly praised. I have perused a sketch of the use and progress of the 'General Assembly's scheme for promot-ing education and religious instruction throughout the High-lands and Islands,' and have identified it with the better plan. It gratified me to find that it unsealed the writings of Inspiration to the people in general, and those of Virgil and Horace to the few on whom Nature has bestowed minds of a superior capacity. The certain consequences of the one provision will be the

moral improvement of the people; – they will march onwards
to the proper medium; and, inhabiting as they do the sterile
fastnesses of Nature, they will rest longer in it than the people
of richer and more accessible countries. And what the probable
effects of the other provision! These schools may yet give to
the world some second Macintosh [sic] to raise mens conceptions of the strength and dignity of the human understanding,
or some second Macpherson to new model the literature of
Europe.[39]

But I must exemplify a little further my theory of the medium:
– The people of a state constitute when depraved of either
barbarism or luxury a huge machine of mere physical force,
whose powers may be directed with equal facility by their
rulers to the accomplishment of either good or evil. The population of France formed such a machine during the atrociously
splendid reign of Louis 14. and the equally splendid and atro-
cious reign of the Emperor. The inhabitants of the Highlands
formed such a machine in that age when the fertile genius of
a wicked Prelate could devise no fitter instrument of persecution
than a Highland army. It may be inferred from such instances
that both the people who linger in the extreme of barbarism,
and those who have passed through the medium into the contrary extreme are alike passive instruments which may be
wielded for any purpose.

Almost every nation of which history has preserved the records has been more marked by public spirit and virtue at one
certain era than at any other. Greece and Rome had their
respective periods of liberty and patriotism. The citizens of
Lacedemon and Athens did not constitute mere machines in
the age of Leonidas and Aristides, nor those of Rome in the
times of the Fabii. But though by the inhabitants of countries
not favoured by Revelation the proper medium may in a certain
degree be attained, it can only be rightly and fully attained
through the inclucence of Christianity. The Christian, so far as
the imperfection of a fallen nature permits, is perfect in his
morals. He is the subject of God; and he renders obedience to
the powers that be because such is the command of his king; –
remembering, however, that the command must have its limits;

as no single law of any code can demand an obedience subversive of the other laws. – He obeys his ruler when obedience is a
duty and compatible with the laws of heaven. But he is a
moral intelligent agent, and no machine. – and it is evident
that such being the character of the individual that age of a
nation or state in which the number of such individuals bears
the greatest proportion to the number of its whole people
must be its best and most virtuous age. It must be remarked
however, that religion can not only raise men out of the extreme
of barbarism to the proper medium, but can also bring them
back to it out of the opposite extreme. Thus, there may be
many excellent men in a country where there is a general
decline in morals. But then among a people that have nearly
arrived at the proper medium Religion gives a tone to society
in general; – there is an amalgamation, if I may so speak,
between the two grand classes of which they consist, – those
who are truly religious, and those who merely respect religion:
In the other case the reverse of this is the fact. – Between the
religious class in a country that has passed the medium, and
the class that is not religious there is a broad line of demarcation
across which there extend no ties of sympathy, no bonds of
union.

In this medium state it is perhaps not positively essential
that the people have that slight acquaintance with the sciences,
– that smothering of general knowledge, which in an advanced
state of society consititute their learning, – the learning of the
multitude. They need not believe with Copernicus that the
sun stands always still, if they but believe that it stood still at
the command of Joshua; – a belief which from its connection
with the morals of the Bible is by much the more important of
the two. But though this smothering of learning be not positively essential, the general attainment of it is desirable. –
Nay, when I consider that there are certain sentiments imparted
by philosophy which are proper to be entertained, but which
are not always held by the religious, I feel inclined still more
to modify the assertion. The southern districts of Scotland
which made so glorious a stand against the encroachments of
Charles 2. seem to have attained in that reign the medium

described; but who does not regret that so virtuous and magnan-
imous a people had not been better taught in that branch of
Ethics which inculcates toleration.

With reference to my theory I have stated that in different
districts of the country there are different degrees of age. The
meridian period seems to have been attained by some of the
southern countries of the kingdom in the reign of Charles 2: –
the Cromarty district did not reach it until about eighty years
later. My townsmen of the reign of Charles parted quietly
with their clergyman, who was one of the number outed in
1662; they received as quietly the curate appointed to occupy
his place, and as the latter was a kind obliging man, they
became much attached to him; and he officiated among them
until his death, which did not happen till several years after
the Revolution. Not until they had lost the curate did the
outed Presbyterian minister return to them. There is now in
my possession a manuscript collection of original hymns written by a Presbyterian native of the parish who was much
famed in his day for his poetry and his piety. It bears date
1743. The whole of it is full of the leven of Episcopacy. Almost
every red-letter day of the Calendar has its hymn. Cromarty,
however, had the outrage of 1662 been repeated in it seventy
years ago, would have presented a scene of as determined
resistance, or of as stubborn endurance as any of the southern
counties did ninety years before. It was then inhabited by a
numerous class of religious and much respected people, – genuine transcripts of the old Covenantors.

I spent when a boy several weeks in the central Highlands
of Sutherland. I was not at the time, as may be thought,
much addicted to the study of character, but there are recollections of what I then observed of the people which confirm
what I have since heard of them from others. They have
advanced nearer the proper medium of civilization than the
Highlanders of almost any of the other counties. I still remember
the pleasant sounds of singing which I used to hear rising from
every cottage at a certain hour night and morning. There is a
river that divides this county from Ross concerning which I
have heard one of those curious prophecies that are still so

rife in the Highlands. It pleased me exceedingly. It fortells a bloody persecution to be raised against those who adhere to the truth. The Seer beheld the river choked up in its course by the bodies of the good men who had suffered for their Religion; and he was much struck to find that every one of them was dressed out in the bonnet and plaid. In the event of such a persecution such I daresay would be the dress of many of the victims of it. It would be no Highland Host that a second Sharpe would turn loose upon them; – it would probably be an army of radicals from the districts of the old Covenantors.

Burns was an admirer of the spirit of young Elihu the Buzite 'I will show my opinion.'[40] From what I have written on the Highlands my practical admiration of the same spirit must appear pretty evident. On one of the two great means of civilizing them, – the school and the pulpit, I have yet a few remarks to make: – of the latter I have not yet said any thing.

The Highlanders like all ignorant people are fond of novelty. They listen with much greater attention to the occasional sermons of the Clergyman of a distant parish than to the stated discourses of the minister of their own. The travelling Missionary has, of course, an equal command over them. To the eloquent speaker and just reasoner a power over the attention of his auditors must often prove a power over their passions and opinions. To the pious and zealous Missionary, though perhaps not distinguished for either argumentative skill or eloquence this power must prove in many instances an instrument of good; and of this power he is possessed from the mere circumstance of his being a Missionary. Resoning [sic] from these facts I infer that were the number of the settled clergy of the Highlands to be even trebled, the travelling clergyman who went from parish to parish, like a comet from system to system, would be of use. I would prefer, however, missionaries who are members of the Church of Scotland to those of any other persuasion, and lest the preference appear illiberal, I add that I would think after the same manner even were I myself not a member of this church. It is the belief of certain philosophers that the religion which is sanctioned by the laws of any country, is best for that country's inhabitants; – the sentiment is evidently founded in infidelity, and places every religion true and false on the same level; yet I dare imitate it so far as to say that it is best for a protestant country that its missionaries be of that church within whose nominal pale the great bulk of the inhabitants are included. Religion as it exists in the mind of a pious clergymen of a protestant establishment is a complete, well proportioned image. There is indeed an obscurity in the shaded parts of the picture and there the outlines may be incorrectly drawn, but the inaccuracies do not court observation, – all that is prominent is strongly lighted and well defined. But religion seldom presents this aspect in the mind of a Sectary, however pious. The general interests of Christianity are too much identified by him with those of his own particular sect; and he deems the peculiar tenets of the latter of paramount importance, not because they are really so, but because they are disputed. The impression of religion on his mind resembles that image of oneself which one sees in a convex mirror, where the advanced finger vies in bulk with the more distant head.

A fervant [sic] enthusiasm is one of the most striking characteristics of Scottish Highlanders. Hence the more popular preachers among them are those who appeal to the passions. But it is as necessary to teach an audience how to think as to make them feel; and there is another method of preaching, less common in the Highlands by which good might be done and popularity attained. Mr Lauchlin Mackenzie of Loch-Carron excelled in this less common way. His sermons were formed neither on the Aristotlian method like those of the old school of Divinity, nor yet on the Demosthenian, like those of the new. He was a preacher after the manner of our Saviour. He knew that an ignorant audience are not to be instructed by the subtleties of argument, but that they delight in comparison, allegory, and narrative; and as he was possessed of genius his discourses were happy mixtures of all these. He is said to have begun one of his sermons with 'There was once an Inn-keeper who lived in Perth.' Fragments of this mans discourses are still scattered over the Highlands of Ross-shire, though he has been dead thirteen years; – a circumstance from which something ought to be learned. I am aware it is not everyone who is qualified to instruct by parable and similitude, but with Highlanders for an audience, the ability could be turned to singular account.

A description of all the scenes and circumstances which engaged my attention during my stay at Gairloch, and my acquaintance with which I reckon a species of learning, would fill a volume. There is a beautiful uninhabited island in the south side of the loch in which I wrought for several days, quarrying stone. My recollection of it is that I never laboured in any place where I could so completly forget that labour is a curse. There is a wild solitary ravine too whose peculiar features of scenery are strongly impressed on my memory. My imagination is quite filled with images which I owe to the studies of this year. There are low rocky hills from whose hanging cliffs the hazel and mountain ash shoot out their gnarled and twisted branches almost horizentally [sic] over the darkened recesses below; clear springs gushing from these recesses and splashing on rounded pebbles of granite; bleak extended moors, through which a few mossy streams rather ooze than flow; trees whose upper branches are decayed and bleached white by the storms of winter; extensive lakes speckled with islands and winding beneath dark precipices and blue hills; solitary tarns edged with reeds and morass; bold naked promontories stretching far into the ocean; and deep narrow arms of the sea skirted with rock and moor, and mottled here and there with the dingy little cottage of the crofter and the fisherman. Some of the circumstances too which attracted my notice are sufficiently curious. In Gairloch it is quite common that two members of the same family bear the same name. I was acquainted with two brothers each of whom was named James, and two sisters each of whom was named Christian. I chanced to meet in the district with two instances of peculiar genius; – one of these in a boatbuilder, a native of the place, who had brought his art, through a natural ingenuity, to a point much nearer perfection than that which it has attained on the eastern coast of Scotland. His superior skill acquired in a country so deficient in mechanical ability in general, reminded me of the skill

possessed by the members of my own profession, in the dark
ages of castles and cathederals [sic]. The other instance was in
an elderly Highlander, also a native of the place, who had
attained by dint of study a complete command of such English
as is to be found in the narrative parts of the Bible. His mind
was not of a high order; and yet when I thought of the difficulties which he must have had to overcome in forming his
peculiar style, and heard him applying with propriety (with
what was at least propriety when I debarred improper association) the phrases of Scripture in his commonest relations and
details, I could scarcely avoid recognizing in him a genius
similar to that which rendered the European Literati of the
sixteenth century eloquent in the language of Virgil.

The winter of 1823 was little marked by either incident or
attainment. I felt in it my usual want, – that of a friend. There
was a little mischievous boy of about ten years of age whom I
chose as a companion for lack of a better. He was spirited and
sensible for his years, and deemed me a very superior kind of
playfellow. I taught him how to climb and leap and wrestle,
how to build bridges and rig ships, and how to make baskets
and rush caps. I told him stories, and lent him books, and
shewed him how to act plays, and lighted fires with him in the
caves of the hill of Cromarty and, – in short went on in such a
manner that my acquaintances began to shake thier own heads
and to question the soundness of mine. My uncle James who
used sturdily to assert in the face of all opposing evidence, that
my powers of mind averaged rather above than below the common standard seriously told me about this time that if I would
not act more in the manner of other people, he would defend
me no longer. His case was becoming desperate.

My father a few weeks before setting out on his last voyage
had fallen heir by the death of a relative to the ground floor of
a house in Leith; – a legacy by which my poor mother was well
nigh ruined. It was valued at about four hundred pounds, but
there were debts on it which amounted to more than half that
sum; and to clear off these my mother had to part with almost
all the money paid her by the Insurance Office, my fathers vessel
having been partially insured. The property had long been occu-

pied as a Spirit-Shop and Tavern, and brought in a high rent; but shortly after my father's death, from some alteration in the harbour, business forsook the part of the town in which it was situated, and the rent in consequence, in the course of a single twelvemonth suffered a reduction of fifty per cent. It was peculiarly unfortunate too in its tenants. I remember that when a boy I used to listen with great interest to pieces of their history which in the form of letters my mother received from her agent. Two of them made moonlight flittings, each on the eve of the term; and the little furniture which they left behind them was converted into a sum of money which it would seem, as none of it reached Cromarty barely covered the expence [sic] of the transmutation. The house was next taken by a woman who turned out to be one of that class who keep a certain description of lodgers; and we not only lost the rent as usual, but the poor house lost also it character. It then lay for nearly five years unoccupied, except by a mischievous, noisy ghost, which vexed and disturbed the whole neighbourhood, and was supposed to be the spirit of some person who had been murdered by the former inmates. A police officer at length dispossessed it of its mysterious inhabitant, an unfortunate female, by exorcising her not into the Red-Sea, but into Bridewell. The next tenant was a person of character; but the first years rent was expended in repairs, and that of the second went to the building of a church in South Leith. It then lay unoccupied as before.

I had now attained my twenty first year; and towards the close of May 1824, I took my passage to Leith with the double intention of getting rid, if possible, of this unfortunate property, and of procuring employment. On the fourth day after leaving Cromarty the smack in which I was a passenger was lying too in Leith Roads, waiting till the Pilots signal should invite her into the harbour. I had previously become acquainted with Edinburgh by the vivid descriptions of it in Marmion and the Abbot, but the appearance it this day presented was of a character different from what I had anticipated.[41]

It has been remarked by a philosophical critic that an unfinished sketch is often more pleasing than a complete picture, and this from the scope it gives the imagination to conceive of its latent excellences. A scene of Nature when half enveloped in mist, presents on a large scale a sketch of this description. On the morning after my arrival in Gairloch a dull fog partially obscured the distant country, and I found employment until it dispersed in drawing on its blank surface a chain of huge overhanging mountains, broken into precipices and streaked with snows. Edinburgh this day afforded my imaginative powers a similar exercise. The morning had been thick and foggy, but before noon the mist, assailed by a light sea breeze, was sweeping towards the west in huge dense masses, reminding me of the retreating battalions of a discomfitted army; – or rather of that hour of judgement when the fountains of the great deep were broken up, and the huge billows of the Deluge rolled over the cities of Cain, and the mountains which had sheltered them. The features of the whole country partially enveloped in shrouds of vapour, wore a spectral and terrible appearance. Imagination ran riot in gazing on them. At one time I likened the spires, and monuments rising above the cloud, to spears and banners on a field of battle; at another when the wreath swept still lower I compared the myriads of chimnies which peeped through it to shocks of corn on a field newly reaped. The blue Pentlands, ragged on their edges and obscured by the haze, seemed portions of a firmament, dark and threatening; and the summit of Aurther-Seat towering over the grey volume that obscured its base, appeared to me the fragment of a broken planet hovering above the earth. There was another, not less poetical idea which the scene suggested. The town of Leith in the foreground, though it appeared blue through the haze seemed entire, and stood out from the blank behind as the figures of a good picture do from the surrounding landscape. I likened it to the little city of Zoar; while the scene of apparent ruin and conflagration beyond, reminded me of those cities which Heaven visited in judgement when the sun had risen on that morning on which Lot took his departure from them.

I had several relatives in Leith the children of a paternal uncle; but as my mother had held scarcely any intercourse with them since my fathers death, and I had not acquaintance with them myself, I calculated but little on their friendship. I waited, however, on landing, on one of my cousins, a Mrs Marshall, whom I found to be an excellent woman, of superior sense and information. She received me with much kindness. My next business was to visit the unfortunate property that had given my mother so much vexation. I saw it and became heartily ashamed of it. It presented me with a scene of ruin and desolation of a character entirely new. I had no sooner thrown open the door than I was struck by a damp unwholsome [sic] scent, which issued from it as if it were a charnel house. The windows had been shut up for nearly two years, and the atmosphere had become so foul and stagnant that the flame of the candle with which I explored the apartments, burned dull and yellow, and assumed a nearly circular form, like the light of a miner. The floors were littered with rotten straw, and broken up in a hundred different places. The walls were blackened with smoke, huge patches of plaster had fallen from the ceilings, the partitions were crazed and tottering, and the bars of the grates were rusted to the colour and roughness of foxes tails. 'Few people,' thought I, as I explored the miserable apartments, 'have had a more extensive experience of all the varieties of bad and uncomfortable habitations than I myself, and yet there are appearances of squalidness and ruin in this unfortunate domicile, which all I have hitherto seen or imagined could not have led me to anticipate. I wonder whether any person will think it worthwhile to ask it of me; for as a gift I shall be ashamed to offer it to any one.' Half melancholy, half inclined to joke on the subject, but there was no one to listen to me, I locked the door pocketed the key, and set out for Edinburgh in quest of my friend William Ross. I luckily met with him at the head of Leith Walk, and spent the evening with him at his lodgings; where without the assistance of the bottle, for neither of us were drinkers, I quite forgot the house, and every thing else that was unpleasant or disagreeable.

I waited next day on Mr Veitch the Town Clerk. My father shortly before his death, had deposited his will with this gentleman; and I now wished to see the clause of it which related to my unfortunate house. I was besides desirous to consult with him on the means by which it might be most advantageously disposed of. I found him civil and friendly, and on my stating to him that I was a mason, and that my intention partly in coming to Leith was to procure employment, he obligingly introduced me to a Mr James Russel, a Builder, who engaged me to work for him at Niddry, a gentleman's seat about four miles south of Edinburgh. To this place I immediately went; Mr Veitch having kindly assured me that he would endeavour to procure either a tenant or purchaser for my house.

There was a party of sixteen masons employed at Niddry, besides apprentices and labourers. As the hewing shed was fully occupied at the time I arrived, I was set to hew in front of it exposed to the sun and wind, and what annoyed me more, for I had long been accustomed to every vicissitude of weather, to the contemptuous observations of the workmen it sheltered. With a few exceptions they all appeared decidedly hostile to me, and seemed to consider me as a legitimate butt for their ridicule. They had learned that I was a native of the North of Scotland, and inferred that as the place of my birth was nearly two hundred miles from the Metropolis, I could not possibly be a person of sense or spirit. This species of Cockneyism seems an ingredient in the character of that not very amicable class, the knowing vulgar of all great towns. They identify themselves with all that is beautiful and excellent around them, and value themselves accordingly; while the opinion they form of a poor provincial is derived, not from his individual character or attainments, but from the ideas they entertain regarding the place of his nativity.

I lodged for the ten months I wrought at this place in a snug little cottage pleasantly situated at the side of the Dalkeith road. It consisted of only one apartment which I shared with my landlord and landlady, and latterly with another lodger; but as I had been accustomed to the privations of a crowded barrack this single apartment afforded me both comfort and convenience. The cottage was sheltered on the north and east by the Niddry woods, which when the wind was high regaled me with a pleasant music, that when I wakened in the night time never failed to remind me of the sea breaking on the shores of Cromarty. Through these woods the road forms a beautiful vista, arched above, like the roof of a Gothic Cathed-eral [sic]; and through this vista gleamed every evening the Inchkeith light. My fellow lodger was a John Wilson, one of the labourers engaged at Niddry-House. Though I wrought there for more than a month before he quitted the cottage in which he had previously resided for my landlady's I knew scarcely any thing of his character except that he was nearly as unpopular among most of the other workmen as myself. A man, whatever be his powers of discernment, lies always under a great disadvantage when introduced into a company the members of which are all strangers to him, but acquainted with one another. He finds there maybe as formidable odds in the forming of opinion as in fighting. Each of the party have but one object on which to direct their attention, – their united powers of discernment seem to pass through a kind of convex lens of which the stranger is the focus; – he on the other hand is perplexed by a multiplicity of objects, – his discriminative faculties are dissipated and weakened as if thrown off from the surface of a convex reflector.

I had been frozen by the contemptuous treatment which I received at the hands of my brother workmen into my old habits of solitude; and my new companion, for the first few days seemed as distant and reserved as myself. I soon, however, began to perceive from the tenor of his conduct that he was a man of more than common worth, and from the few remarks he occasionally dropped (for he was exceedingly taciturn) that he possessed a more than ordinary understanding. Every evening and morning he was regularly absent from his lodgings for about half an hour, and the rest of his leisure time was mostly occupied in reading the Bible and books of devotion. In short it required little discernment to discover that he was the diciple [sic] of a Philosophy more admirable than that of Socrates. I have since wished that some of our modern sceptics had occupied my place of observation with regard to this man, and become acquainted with the effects as exemplified in his conduct of what they regard, with the Roman Historian as a gross and contemptible superstition. What I have to add con-cerning him must appear strange to every one acquainted with the weakness and frailty of human nature, and yet it is not a whit more strange than true. During the nine months of my acquaintance with him, though for the last eight of these we lived on terms of the closest intimacy, he never once either said or did any thing I could deem in the slightest degree improper or immoral. I state with a feeling of pride that this poor labourer was my friend and that I possessed his esteem.

One evening, a few weeks from the time we had first lodged together I could perceive there was some matter that pressed on his spirits. He was more absent than usual, and sat less quietly in his chair; and though a volume of Dodridges [sic] sermons lay open before him, it was evident his favourite author failed that evening to engage his attention.[42] I noticed him several times looking at the landlord and myself, and my curiosity was considerably excited. As it drew near bedtime he became more perplexed and restless. At length he mustered resolution enough to ask whether we did not think it proper, and according to Scripture, that evening worship should be kept in the family. The landlord hesitated, but I immediately replied in the affirmative. And we had prayers regularly every evening all the time we afterwards lodged together. This little incident added to the good opinion I had previously entertained of my pious and excellent friend. I still reflect with pleasure on the conflict in which I saw him this evening engaged; – pressed by a sense of duty on the one hand, and on the other by a fear of giving offence, mingled with the dread of being deemed obtrusive.

Our next door neighbour at this place was an ill tempered, foolish old woman who seemed desirous of acquiring the reputation of a witch. The children of the village used to tease her by calling her names, and throwing stones at her favourite cat; and she frequently mingled the imprecations they thus drew from her with obscure threats of taking vengeance on them through the power of the Devil. It was observed, however, that her threatenings invariably fell to the ground; and so she was famed, not for being a witch, but for her desire of becoming one. This is not the only instance that has come within my notice of a class of persons who from fixing their standard of character too low, cannot sink to it and are consequently compelled to remain less mischievous than they are desirous of becoming. – We had another neighbour of a very different, though scarcely less curious cast of character, in one of Mr Russel's apprentices. He was so desperately affected by a dramatic mania that the world and the stage seemed to have changed places in his imagination, – this appearing to him in the light of a reality, – that in the colours of fiction. He was an adept in the natural language of action, and when he spoke it was in that kind of verse which Dr Young believed to be the language of Angels.[43] I soon became a prodigious favourite with him on account both of what I knew and what I did not know. He found that my reading in the dramatic department of literature, was at least as extensive as his own, but that I had never seen plays acted except by strollers; and so there was much that was common ground for us to expatiate upon, and much in which he was my superior, and could instruct me. He was by no means destitute of judgement on subjects legitimately connected with the Drama, or on such as were entirely seperated [sic] from it; but every matter which the associative faculty could bring within the verge of the theatre he treated in the wildest and most fantastical manner imaginable. Unfortunately too nine tenths of all human knowledge proved to him of the latter description.

My wages at this place amounted to twenty two shillings per week; and as I had been accustomed to simple fare, and had no taste for dress, I found I could subsist on somewhat less than seven. This left me a balance of fifteen shillings per week; but as I had not of the practical economist in my disposition, I scarcely thought of the matter until I found that the money in the corner of my chest had accumulated to six pounds. I then called to remembrance what I had read of Franklin, and determined to become economical on system. Cheaply as I had lived hitherto, I resolved on living at a still less expence; and making allowance for the fall of wages and the frosts of winter I calculated on saving about thirty pounds annually. Thirty pounds, thought I, may appear no great sum to the persons who regard the king's coin as a species of draughts or

pawns with which they play at the great game of Loss and
Gain, nor yet to those to whom money is the staple barter for
luxury; but to one who has been accustomed to consider it as
the price of independence, leisure, and amusement, and who
in Cromarty could enjoy all these at the rate of six shillings
per week it is by no means an inconsiderable one. Four years
of labour will purchase for me six years of leisure and enjoyment. All these fine calculations, however, came to nothing.
They were beginning to haunt me every time I sat down to
eat, and to associate rather unpleasantly with every glance I
gave the threadbare parts of my dress; and I had just determined
on discarding them altogether, – deeming such slavery of mind
a woful [sic] earnest of independence, when a train of untoward
circumstances discarded them for me. I was presented with a
piece of paper by a decent, officer looking man from which I
learned that I was one of the Heritors of a Church in South
Leith, and that I was indebted for the building of it a sum of
nearly three pounds. There, thought I, as I paid the money, is
a dead loss of eight weeks of independence. A few days after I
was waited upon by a woman, who brought me a letter she
had recently received from my step-father, – one of her tenants.
The part of it intended for my perusal was an order on me for
his house rent, amounting to three pounds. This I also paid;
and then calling to mind that the money which I had short
before deemed myself possessed of had not been wholly my
own, as my mother had advanced me two pounds on my setting
out on my voyage, I took double that sum out of my chest to
send her; and perceiving that only a single pound was now
left behind, and recollecting too that I had promised a frock
to each of my little sisters, I sent it also. Thus terminated my
scheme of economy. Shortly after I fell into two unfortunate
habits; – one of buying books, – the other of never reckoning
my money. I was lucky, however, in their going together; for
though the one tended to poverty the other kept me from the
knowledge of it.

My economical scheme had not the effect of rendering me
less unpopular among my brother workmen. They found me
perfectly incorrigible. I would neither join in their drinking

parties nor accompany them to town, though some of them kindly offered to initiate me into all the mysteries of the tavern and bagnio. I was evidently a fellow of no spirit; and, what was worse, I seemed to understand ridicule so imperfectly as not to be at all affected by it. When they described Cromarty as a semi-barbarous little town, I was merely sorry that it should be so; and when they boasted of Edinburgh I only regretted that there was so little chance of that city returning the compliment by boasting of them. I shifted my working place from the front to the end of the shed where there was a fine spreading elm that screened me from the sun; and when hewing under it I amused myself in composing the 'The Boatmans Tale'. But neither philosophy nor poetry rendered me quite easy under the contemptuous treatment which I received from my companions. I felt at times their ridicule so keenly as to learn to appreciate better than I had ever done before the scope of that petition of the Psalmist in which he prays to be delivered from the scorn of the fool; and I entertained in my less patient moments a too bitter contempt for the men who could take such advantage of odds against an inoffensive stranger; and in whose hands a dull and clumsy raillery was converted into an instrument of persecution. This warfare terminated several months before I left the place; for after having been regarded in succession as a silly ignorant provincial, a money gatherer, and a shred ill natured satirist, I was at length considered as rather a fine fellow.

There were among the workmen two brothers, natives of Perth. The elder was a remarkably fine looking young man, – tall and slender; – and though disipated [sic] in his habits and of a fiery temperament, in the main good natured and sensible. The younger was of a somewhat unprepossessing appearance, taller than his brother, strong and broad shouldered, and possessed of an excellent temper, and a superior understanding. The former sometimes joined in the laugh raised against me by some of his companions, – the latter never; and yet he was beyond comparison richer in humour than any other person in the squad. I became acquainted with both; and a revolution in the opinions of all the other workmen regarding me was a consequence of the intimacy. The character of the younger brother was an interesting object of study. He was in every respect such a one as Farquhar or Wycherly would have made choice of for the hero of some of their comedies, – a wit, a humourist, a man of sense & courage, generous, high spirited, dissipated, and a rake.[44] Though scarcely older than myself, his adventures would have filled a volume, which, had he the art of writing a story as agreeably as of telling one, would be a work of some value. His experience of life was as extensive as my own, though perhaps somewhat less diversified; but there was this difference between us that from the first year of my apprenticeship I had lived in the world rather as a spectator than an actor, whereas he, on the contrary, though in his twenty second year, was as active and as much the leader of a party as I had been when a schoolboy. All the other workmen looked up to him as their head. Four years before, when residing in the vicinity of Perth, he had got embroiled in a quarrel, and had treated his antagonist so roughly, that to escape the cognizance of the law it behoved him to quit that part of the country. He accordingly came to Edinburgh where he procured employment; but one evening when returning to his lodgings, he was laid hold of by two officers and lodged in prison. He was afterwards sent in irons to Perth, tried at the Assizes, and sentenced to three months imprisonment. His narrative of the circumstances of this affair would have done honour to Crabbe himself.[45] He was particularly happy in his descriptions of the prison; and in drawing the characters of its several inmates, from the simple Highland smuggler to the pickpocket. He dwelt with great complacency on the circumstance of his having passed when on his way to Perth through a party of masons, among whom he had wrought about four weeks before, and on the rich variety of expression their countenances exhibited as they thronged round him and saw his handcuffs. I have heard him relate fifty other adventures and have been much amused by his pictures of character. The adventures, however, were invariably of the tavern, bagnio, or ring; – the characters were generally of the worst and meanest cast. From the narratives of this poor fellow, for whom wild as he was, I entertained a very sincere regard, – I acquired my imperfect acquaintance with that lowest class of society which infests large towns, and in which human nature is to be seen in its worst and most repulsive phases. The contemplation of his own character was a sufficiently sad one to a person of sense and principle. It was naturally excellent, but every trait and impression which it owed to habit was vicious. It reminded me in its more prominent features of the Smugglers in Red Gauntlet. There was in both the same scorn of every thing that was mean, and the same recklessness in achieving any thing that was simply bad; but what chiefly led me to institute the comparison was the feeling of blended remorse and regret with which my poor friend cherished the memory of his father, who had been a man of superior virtue and understanding I have seen him affected almost to tears by the recollection of his death-bed remonstrances and advice.

I did not experience in my evening walks of Niddry a pleasure equal to what I had been accustomed to derive from my evening walks at Gairloch and Conan-side. The country to the south of Edinburgh with the exception of the exquisite piece of mountain scenery in its immediate vicinity I regarded as too tame and Lowland. Art had been by far too busy in it. I could not look with complacency on a dull campaign country, which from the number of its fields reminded me of an immense draught board. Even Edinburgh itself disappointed me. I had read of its streets of palaces, but I had acquired my ideas of palaces from the descriptions of those of fairies and genii. I had heard too of the great height of its houses, and my ideas of them associated with those of mountains and rocks, and now when I found myself among them I felt much in the manner that Gulliver did on his arrival in England from the kingdom of Brobingnag [sic]. I had built a much finer Edinburgh of my own. I am not certain, however, that my disappointment was solely owing to the grandeur and beauty of the pictures which had been presented to me by my imagination; for I am by no means sure that a stone-mason is susceptible in the common degree of that feeling of admiration which a fine building or a great city is calculated to produce. The more

conversant a person is with the tricks of a juggler the less will
he admire his skill. 'Sublimity' says a celebrated author, 'is
produced by aggregation, littleness by dispersion.'[46] Perhaps
both these principles had their share in rendering Edinburgh
less an object of interest to me than it would have been otherwise; – for I was acquainted with the art which had reared its
finest buildings; and I considered both them and it as things
consisting of parts; – it as an assemblage of houses the building
of any one of which I could have superintended; – each of
them as a combination of little pieces any one of which I
could have executed. 'Give me matter and motion,' said Descartes, 'and I will create a world.' – Give me matter and
motion, said I, and I will build an Edinburgh.[47]

I several times attended the theatre but I did not derive
from theatrical representation half the pleasure I had anticipated. I had read a great many plays of the different English
authors from the days of Shakespeare down to those of Cumberland and Sheridan.[48] I had perused too translations of Terence
and Moliere.[49] My acquaintance with this department of literature was perhaps somewhat premature; for I perused most of
these works at too early an age to appreciate their merits as
compositions, or to draw comparisons between their *Dramats*
[sic] – *personae* and the people of the world. The impressions,
however, which the more striking scenes and characters had
left on my imagination were uneffaciably vivid. Most of the
scenes were identified in my mind with the beautiful scenes of
the hill of Cromarty. The cliff of Dover, even in Shakespear,
could not surpass in grandeur of feature the rock of the *apple-
yardie*, a rugged, hoary, perpendicular precipice, nearly three
hundred feet in height, – created by a dark wood, – skirted by
a foaming sea, – partially mantled with ivy, – caverned at its
base, – and continually lifting up its voice in hollow echoes as
if holding converse with the waves that toil beneath it, or the
innumerable flocks of sea birds that scream around it. The
Jaques of my imagination moralized in a solitary opening in
the thicket above, from which a long vista that penetrates
into the recesses of the wood, and becomes narrower and darker
in the distance is seen to terminate in a small circular opening

which when the evening sun rests on the hill behind, may remind one of the beacon of a lighthouse. I found it the easiest thing imaginable to convert the cavern in which I had been once imprisoned, into the cave of Belarius; and an old vault in a ruinous chapel dedicated to St Regulus; and nearly buried among the wooods of the hill, furnished me with a proper tomb for the Capulets. The other scenes were of as suitable a character; and the figures with which I peopled them were as strongly, though in some instances more whimsically defined. I conceived of Calaban as a monster that scarcely less resembled a huge beetle than a human creature, and that walked erect and on all fours by turns. The witches of Macbeth appeared to me in the forms of some of the most disagreeable looking old women in the country, – not, however, in their living aspects but in those which I fancied their corpses would have assumed should they, after being committed to the grave, be possessed by evil spirits. The ideas of female grace and elegance which I connected with the heroines of Shakespear, and the Lady of the Mask of Comus were mostly derived from a beautiful painting in Cromarty House, – a copy of Guidos famous Aurora, which when a boy I have contemplated for hours together. [50] – It was a consequence of my having acquired such ideas as these of the characters and scenes of Dramatic poetry, that I was now displeased with both actors and the Stage. The stage I regarded as merely a little area floored with fir deal, and surrounded by painted sheets; – the actors as a company of indifferent looking people who could bear no comparison with either the ideal *Dramatis personae* of my imagination, or the real characters whom I had seen acting their parts in the great drama of life. On the evening I first sat in the Theatre-Royal of Edinburgh I felt as if after having admired an exquisite portrait which the art of the painter had almost awakened into life, I should be asked whether I could not recognize the original of it in an inanimate effigy of wax.

But though almost every object from which I had anticipated pleasure in some degree disappointed me, I derived much satisfaction from the contemplation of some others of which previously I had possessed no idea. I was more pleased with the

Panarama [sic] then exhibiting on the Mound, – it represented
the battle of Trafalgar, and a series of scenes connected with
the fortunes of Napoleon, than with the Theatre; and I felt
more of interest when contemplating the little mutilated bust
of John Knox, at the foot of the High street, than I did when
standing before the horse and man of Parliment Square [sic]. I
found Edinburgh a fertile field of scenes and incidents. After
nightfall I have frequently sauntered amid the intricacies of
the old town, deeming it a school in which much was to be
learned; and in which I discovered with regret rather than
surprize, that the lesson which taught of human wretchedness
and depravity, was oftener repeated than all the others. I was
a spectator of the great fires which broke out this year in the
High street; and I was one of eight hundred workmen who
assembled on Bruntsfield links at the close of the season to
deliberate how a proposed encroachment on wages might be
best resisted. When I got access to any of the Churchyards I
derived much pleasure from sauntering among the tombs, and
reading on them the names of men by whose writings I had
been instructed and amused. I have visited the burying places
of Blair, Robertson, Ramsay, Ferguson, and Hume.[51] But there
was one pleasure on which I had calculated on coming to
Edinburgh that I had no opportunity of enjoying. From a rather
whimsical bent of mind my curiosity is never more active
than when it has the person of a great man for its object; and
I have never felt more delighted than in associating in my
mind, when that curiosity was gratified, my newly acquired
idea of the personal appearance of such a man with the ideas
I had previously entertained of his character and genius. On
my arrival in Edinburgh I had hoped to become acquainted
with the personal appearance of its more eminent citizens; –
Such as Scott, Jeffrey, Wilson, Stewart, McCrie, McKenzie,
and the gentleman whom I have now the honour of addressing,
and whom I then knew as the successor of Roberton [sic], the
frend [sic] and correspondent of Burns, and the Editor of the
poems of Michael Bruce.[52] My companions, however, who had
merely heard of these men, could neither point them out to
me, nor give me any new information concerning them and so

unlucky was I that on quitting Edinburgh I had only seen of
the whole constellation the Historian of Knox and Melvile
[sic].[53]

I had a maternal cousin in Edinburgh who was at this time
clerk and sub-manager of the Theatre Royal. I was entrusted
by his father on my leaving Cromarty with a letter for him; I
knew the letter, however, to be altogether recommendatory of
myself; I knew besides that I was merely a journeyman mason,
and that my cousin derived from his office a salary of nearly
two hundred pounds per annum; and so I suffered the letter to
lie by me in a corner of my chest; in obedience to the dictates
of a pride, which, as I was even then aware has often led me
to act very imprudently; but which I flattered myself would
prove a protection to me from every species of meanness. I
have since found, however, that it furnishes no consistent
principle of conduct. In this instance by rendering me unwilling
to claim kindred to one whom I could not meet as an equal, it
led me from a dread of one kind of meanness into the commital
of another; – I acted ungratefully. My cousin, a kind warm
hearted man, having heard when I was a boy of my taste for
reading and making pictures, sent me a great many amusing
little works and a fine box of colours; and he promised too to
make me a present of some valuable works of science and
literature whenever I should have *gained my first prize at
College*. A few weeks after my arrival his friends wrote him of
my being in Edinburgh, and he made repeated enquiries regarding me; but found no one who could tell him where I was
employed. About a month before I left the place, I waited on
him, and gave him the letter I had received for him nine
months before. He was very angry with me, attributing, very
naturally my conduct to sheer indifference; but he was so
kind notwithstanding that I found reason to regret my not
having waited on him earlier. For the four following weeks I
regarded his house as my own. His manners were those of the
finished gentleman, and he seemed to take a pleasure in the
forming of mine; – but though I proved an apt pupil I relapsed,
on my quitting Edinburgh, into my old habits of solitude &
taciturnity, and quite forgot all his lessons. I was introduced

by him to several young gentlemen; students of Divinity and Physic; and was gratified to discover by coming in contact with them that I was not quite so devoid of conversational powers as I had previously imagined; and that from my very irregular course of education I had acquired nearly as much real learning as is derived by the common scholar from the Academy and the College.

Mr Veitch informed me about this time that he had at length found a purchaser for my property, and I employed him to dispose of it in the manner he might deem most advantageous. After the expence of transferring it to the buyer had been deducted I pocketed a balance of fifty pounds. An equal sum, the remainder of the Insurance Money of my fathers vessel had been deposited on my account, by my mother, in the hands of a commercial gentleman of Leith; and she now wrote to me that I ought to raise it. I did so, and then set out for Cromarty a richer man than I had ever been before. My little fortune, however, was soon dissipated. Two thirds of it I lost by an unfortunate friend, and with the remainder I paid for the printing of my poems. I am quite as happy now, however, as when I was richer.

What I saw of the mechanics of Edinburgh during the ten months I resided among them was ill calculated to leave on my mind a favourable impression of their general character. And with this character I had peculiar opportunities of becoming closely acquainted. The summer and autumn of 1824 were seasons of super abundant employment, and high wages, and the worse traits peculiar to it were, in consequence, fully developed. – Besides my point of observation was so uncomfortably near the object of view that I could more than see it.

Between opposite extremes there is in many instances so striking a resemblance that Philosophy has traced out a kind of moral circle, one side of the circumference of which is occupied by the medium, – the other by the two contraries. The extremes meet. From my acquaintance with this principle I was led to institute a comparison between the lower stages of the states of natural and artificial society, – between the character of savage tribes and that of the profligate mechanics of a large town. And from the similarity of some of the more marked traits I was convinvced as far at least as one cause could authenticate it, of the truth of the principle. Imagination had perhaps some influence in conforming to resemblance the less prominent features of the two classes, but the identity of the more striking ones was I believe established without her interference.

To the people of both extremes an overweening conceit of themselves and a contempt of others are alike common. Nor are the conceit and contempt of the one class effects of a cause different from that of the conceit and contempt of the other. Both entertain false standards of excellence in character on which their own characters are moulded; and from ignorance they deem all who differ from these standards to differ from them for the worse. The savage holds the stranger in contempt whom he finds unskilled in the stratagems of war and the chase; – the depraved mechanic deems the person whom he discovers to be ignorant of the cant terms and low tricks of the tavern and brothel, a fit object for ridicule.

An almost total want of foresight is another characteristic common to the extremes of both savage and civilized life. The Caffer or Hottentot feasts in the evening on the game which he has entrapped or run down during the day, and the spareness of his meal, or the depth of his debauch is in proportion to the scantiness or abundance of his prey.[54] There is no thought with him of the morrow, and his life is accordingly spent in the extremes of gluttony and starvation. – The town mechanic receives his wages at the close of the week, carries them to the tavern or bagnio, and seldom returns to his employment until the whole is squandered. When residing in the vicinity of Edinburgh almost every week brought instances of this kind under my notice. On a Saturday evening three of the Niddry workmen after having received a fortnights wages, which in all amounted to more than six pounds, went to Edinburgh, and there spent the night in a house of bad fame. Next morning they hired a coach, and accompanied by three women of the town set out for Roslin on a jaunt of pleasure. They came back to Edinburgh in the evening, passed the night, as they had done the preceeding one, and returned to Niddry on Monday without a single shilling. This piece of madness was much applauded as a frolic that shewed no ordinary spirit. It brought to the remembrance of the other workmen exploits of a similar character with the details of which they regaled one another for several days after. I was told of an Edinburgh mechanic, a mason, who on the death of a relative received a legacy of about eighty pounds. He was no sooner paid the money than he carried home his tool chest, and shoved it under his bed. He then commenced a new course of life. He bought an elegant suit of clothes; hired a hackney coach by the week; attended all the fashionable amusements of the place; and regularly once every day called in his carriage on his brother workmen. In six weeks the whole of his money was expended. He then took out his tool chest from under his bed and returned to his former employment.

A surly unsocial independence is almost always a character-istic of savage life. Despotic power in the few and implicit subjection in the many, is first seen by the minute observer, in the stage of society next the primitive; – and that interchange of good offices which creates bonds of mutual obligation to unite man to man does not form a prominent feature in the character of a people until a stage still more advanced. The savage has neither the power of controlling the wills of his brother savages, nor the desire of awakening their gratitude by acts of kindness. He depends on himself alone; and whether he purposes or achieves it is with an exclusive eye to himself. A similar selfishness, acted upon by circumstances not quite dissimilar, marks the lower classes of mechanics in a great town with a resembling ferocity of independence. In the coun-try, or in small villages, – where trade is little apt to fluctuate, – where the rate of wages is in consequence almost fixed, – and where a single mechanic with one or two apprentices supplies with the staple articles of his profession, a certain number of individuals, with whom he is personally intimate, – there is commonly a feeling of kindness kept up between the employers and the person employed. There is usually a sense of obligation on the one side, & the remembrance of a series of kind offices on the other. Even in professions (such as that of the mason) in which one master employs a number of journeymen, a similar feeling is kept up. Year after year the same contractor furnishes employment to the same workmen; and the latter are bound by the ties of obligation not to the former alone, but also through him to the people of the higher classes, his employers. But in a large town the case is entirely different. The upper classes are there furnished with the articles of home manufacture which they may require through the medium of persons who employ great numbers of operatives, – and between whom and these operatives there subsists no intercourse of kindness. The rate of wages fluctuates according to the rise or fall of the demand for labour. When the demand is urgent the operative exacts more than the average hire from the master who he knows cannot dispense with his services; when the contrary is the case, the master lowers as far below average the wages of the operative who, he is aware, cannot subsist unless he employ him. Hence the deliberations of employers to diminish the rate of hire, and the combinations of operatives to increase it. And thus the two classes instead of entertaining a mutual sense of favours received and benefits conferred, as in the country, are actuated by a spirit of hostility; – which, added to that recklessness of character which is invariably a consequence of dissipation, has the effect of rendering the members of the operative class savagly [sic] independent.

The town mechanic is the rudest and most uncomplying of all Whigs: – Whiggism with him is not a matter of opinion but of feeling. It is not some particular system of Govenment that he deprecates, – it is Government itself. As he is wild and reckless he would fain set himself above the law which controls him; as his improvidence, while it keeps him poor gives him a taste for expensive pleasures, his imagination if flattered by every anticipation of Revolution:– It would afford him an opportuntiy of ransacking the hoards of the wealthy. The doctrine of Liberty and Equality, among a certain class, was, from its being met with by this principle, the most popular ever broached in this country. It was an immense favourite with the Radicals of 1819. – The ostensible objects of some of their leaders were almost those of the proper Whigs; – the real ones of the great bulk of the party were of a kind more congenial to men of the character I describe; – the destruction of every Establishment and the passing of an Agrarian law.

The parallel between the classes of the two extremes could easily be followed out still farther. A want of tenderness of heart, – of sympathy with pain or sorrow, is scarcely more characteristic of savages than of the depraved mechanics of large towns. There is also in their social relations the same want of affection common to each. I have seen im many instances the relation of father and son rendered apparent by only the continual bickerings which took place between the parties it connected. – A debasing, credulous superstition is another characteristic of the savage state, and the parallel holds in this respect also; but the superstition of the people of the opposite extreme is not that of credulity, but of that kind which Bacon describes as the superstition of scepticism; – they believe nothing.

But there are some points of character peculiar to the extreme of artificial society which are rather to be contrasted than compared with the traits of the opposite extreme. 'The savage,' says Robertson, 'is a serious melancholy animal;' – the genuine vulgar of a large town are on the contrary wildly frolicsome, and adepts in the whole art of merriment. Power in ridicule, command of repartee, and skill in every species of practical joking, are accomplishments essential to their beau ideal of character. From the consideration of this bent to the ludicrous, and what I have seen of its effects, I have been enabled to conceive why it was that Socrates, when he bestowed praise on the serious dramas of Euripides, reprobated the comic ones of Aristophanes. I have known an indifferent jest reckoned a suitable apology for a mean and indecent action; and have regarded the laugh raised by the representation of some immoral frolic in only its ludicrous point of view, as the knell of that Monitor which is stationed in the soul of every man to prevent him from being at once vicious and happy. The excursion to Roslin was esteemed an excellent practical joke, which, unlike most other jokes, would lose nothing by being repeated; the affair of the legacy was deemed a still better one; – but they were both eclipsed by a third. An Edinburgh mechanic had been employed in England; work failed him, and he set out on his journey homewards; but meeting with an acquaintance somewhere about Berrick, he squandered with him all the money which should have supported him by the way. He was a choice spirit, however, and fertile in stratagem, and he soon found means of procuring a fresh supply. He had been trained in a debating society to a considerable readiness in extempore discourse, tolerably well acquainted with the doctrines of Religion, and the suit of clothes which he wore was luckily a black one. At the first stage he reached after parting from his companion, he assumed the character of a Methodist preacher, and preaching a sermon which he had composed by the way, he was so successful at its close in raising a collection that he was enabled to prosecute his journey to Edinburgh; where by a certain class his stratagem was deemed a consummate effort of spirit and ingenuity. – This unfortunate disposition of viewing every object in a ludicrous point of view is subversive of all steadiness of resolution. I have said I was one of eight hundred workmen who assembled on Bruntsfield links to deliberate how a proposed reduction of wages, which we deemed an undue encroachment, might be best resisted. When we had all assembled, and formed into a ring, a thin, dark-complexioned, little man stepped into the centre of the opening, and addressed us in a long and by no means contemptible speech. He had a considerable command of language, and the power of stating clearly and correctly arguments of that common place kind which from their simplicity, are better suited for moving popular assemblies than more original or more powerful ones. Unfortunately, however, the orator was also a wit; and no sooner had he succeeded in setting his auditors a thinking than he undid all he had done by setting them to laugh. His witticisms proved productive of many others, but the meeting in consequence produced nothing; – the threatened reduction met with no effectual resistance.

The class I describe is composed of two different castes; – those who have mind enough to conceive pretty justly of the character they deem proper to assume, and those who having no just conception of this character are mere imitators of the others. Ridicule, which is the favourite weapon of both, might be happily enough employed against either; but the poor fellows of the latter caste are peculiarly open to it. The men of the first can confer on their immoralities a something like grace; and there are apparent in even their worst frolics redeeming touches of wit and humour. But what the people of the second intend for imitations of these frolics are hideous caricatures, faithful in only the worse traits. With the members of the first class the practical joke must not degenerate into an act of downright felony; – there is a line beyond which they would cease to consider boldness or merriment as indications of spirit or humour. They will allow that a visit to the bagnio may properly enough be made a subject of boast; not so, however, the contraction of disease, a common enough result. But these distinctions are ill understood by the members of the second caste. One of my brother workmen, a young man of genteel appearance, but imbecile of intellect, was one of its least knowing members. He had not energy enough to take an active part in anything, nor ingenuity enough to appropriate to himself the adventures of others; but he was full of anecdote, and the stories he related of his spirited companions were of a character somewhat worse than singular. Most of them would be deemed serious informations in a court of Justice. His prime hero was a reckless profligate apprentice whose spirit made use of his talents in stealing out of warehouses, when he resided in town and in robbing orchards when he lived in the country. I had an acquaintance in Edinburgh, who like my comrade at Niddry ranked very low among the members of the imitative class. He was a native of the North of Scotland and had like myself come to Edinburgh for employemnt. Nature seemed to have purposed that he should be one of those simple people who pass through life without attracting notice in even the slightest degree; and without doing any thing worthy of either praise or censure. The fortune, however, which sent him to Edinburgh determined differently. When first exposed to the gibes of his new companions, he winced under them with that morbid impatience of ridicule which seems peculiar to the dull; and to escape what he found so harassing he set himself to conform his character to theirs. By mere dint of exertion he became in a few months as vicious as his natural powers permitted. I spent the evening of the Bruntsfield-meeting-day in his company. He began to boast to me of his newly acquired attainments, and to ridicule his former ignorance and want of spirit; and as he had a kind of regard for me he set himself to instruct me in the usages of the place. 'In the north country,' said he, 'it is customary for persons who drink together to strive among themselves about settling the reckoning, – each being desirous of paying for himself and the others. The case is very different here; – no one pays except for what he drinks, – not even for that if he can avoid it. Were a person to make the north country offer there would be little risk of its not being accepted, but he would lose his money by it, and be heartily laughed at to boot. In the north country one feels ashamed to confess he has no money, and if urged to any thing that cant be done without it makes a hundred excuses to conceal the want of it. Here, however, poverty is one of the commonest, and readiest, and best pleas possible.' He then began to initiate me into the mysteries of the bagnio, but I sturdily refused to believe that he himself had any practical knowledge of them. He vowed and protested, but all to no purpose. I told him I was certain that all which he termed his experience in this province was picked up at second hand. To convince me that the contrary was the fact he produced a pair of ear-rings of which, he affirmed, he had robbed a girl of the town; but as he could produce no direct proof of the robbery, I pretended still to remain incredulous. He next assured me that at that very time he was infected by a certain disease. Still, however, I professed not to credit him and he appeared vexed to the heart by the pertinacity of my unbelief. He deliberated; – he went to his chest which lay in a corner of the room, and after arranging its contents he called on me to examine them. One of the corners was filled with packages phials and pill boxes without number, over which was strewed surgeons prescriptions and little printed bills. 'Look there,' he exclaimed with

an air of triumph, 'examine that.' I did so, and saw it would
be doing the poor fellow injustice to remain sceptical any
longer.

I have frequently had to regret in young people, natives of
the country a perversion of character similar to that exhibited
in my acquaintance. In most men the formation of moral
character depends less on principle than accident. Chameleon-
like they take their colour from the surrounding objects. Remove the simple, inoffensive, country apprentice, who may
be regarded as a personification of the harmless quiet of his
native village to the purlieus of a populous town, – introduce
him to its depraved society, and the chance is ten to one that
in the course of a few months he has become as reckless and
profligate as any of his new associates. His awkwardness and
innocence are alike assailed by the gibes of his companions;
he is distressed at being regarded as their butt; and to escape
their ridicule he strives to conform his character to theirs. But
personal manners are less easily improved than moral ones
deteriorated; and he retains his awkardness long after he has
ceased to be innocent. Several curious instances have been
brought within my notice of the profligacy of town manners
blended with the rusticities of those of the country. On a
Sabbath morning in autumn (a time when employment was
general, and wages at the highest) I was passing along the
High street, between the hours of six and seven. The lanes
and pavement were crowded with tradesmen and labourers,
whose appearance was indicative of last nights debauch. Some
of them had not yet cast aside their aprons; and the countenances of almost all of them wore the blank ghostly aspect of
dissipation in its last and most wretched stage. Nearly one
third of the number were natives of the country. One of these,
a poor Highlander, would have formed a good subject for the
pencil of Wilkie.[55] His apron still hung before him, his bonnet
was plumed with cobwebs which it had raked from some recess,
his tartan coat was rent open from the nape to the skirts, and
a considerable quantity of blood which had issued from his
nose, was clotted in a broad, ragged strip, from his chin to the
bottom of his apron. He was accompanied by a mechanic of

the town, and described to him as he went, in broken English ludicrously mingled with the smart cant phrases of the place, the misadventure of the previous evening.

Addison has said that all mankind may be divided into two classes, the volatile and the serious, and Burns in one of his early prose writings has repeated the remark.[56] I remember have classed all my acquaintances into into [sic] one or other of these divisions long ere I had perused the writings of either. I found it difficult, however, when in the country, to trace the line of demarcation between the classes. There were individuals so faintly marked that they appeared to belong to a neutral party, – or rather to constitute a medium which softened the extremes into each other. I found when in Edinburgh, that among the lower classes of a large town this kind of twilight party is entirely a wanting. The line of demarcation between the classes does not resemble that indefinite strip of mingled light and shade which seperates [sic] the dark from the sunshinny side of a circular column, but rather that hard sharp edge which breaks them apart in a pilaster. There are striking differences too in the class which we may term the volatile from the corresponding class of the country. In town, in proportion to the general population, it is beyond comparison more numerous. It consists not only of all those who are naturally gay, but also of a whole horde who are wits and humourists despite of nature. In the country this class, like the other, bears the traits of nationality, – the members of it are Scotchmen. In town, on the contrary, they are mere citizens of the world, and only resemble the corresponding classes of other large towns. With individuals of the serious cast I found the case different. Though inhabitants of the Metropollis they are also people of Scotland.

I was accompanied to the vessel in which I took my passage for Cromarty, by my Cousin, and my friend William Ross. With the latter I parted never to see him again. On the day previous I took leave of my fellow lodger, John Wilson. Never shall I forget the prayer with which he concluded the last religious service in which I saw him engaged. It was fraught with a lofty and powerful eloquence; and there was something irresistably affecting in the manner in which he recommended his friend to his God. He was a native of Long-Niddry, a small village in the vicinity of Tranent.

The voyage through calms and contrary winds was slow and tardy; but as it afforded me an opportunity of perusing a new page of character, I did not deem it tedious. I passed the greater part of the time in the forecastle with the sailors, in hearing and relating wild superstitious stories of ghosts and witches, and the blue lights that appear in the night time on the rigging of vessels to fortell [sic] shipwreck. One of the stories I heard at this time seemed to have furnished the basis of that interesting tale 'The doomed man,' which appeared a few months before in one of the London Magazines. After passing seven days on sea I arrived at Cromarty. My mother, my uncles, my cousins, were waiting for me on the beach; and I felt when among them how good a thing it is to have friends.

The first news of interest I heard in Cromarty was that my old friend of the cave had given up Shopkeeping, and had gone to College to prepare for the Church. I had been told on my return from Gairloch eighteen months before that his mind had taken a serious bent; that his customers frequently found him engaged in reading the Scriptures and books of devotion; and that, what with books, what with writings, he had converted his shop into a kind of *study*. I had long regarded him with a fond romantic attachment; and even when most offended with him my imagination delighted in dreaming of our reconcilment. But I was proud and displeased, and the circumstances of these dreams were characterized by feelings of pride and displeasure. I longed for some opportunity of risking my life in the defence of his that he might be made to feel how much he had injured me by his neglect. Ere now, however, I had almost ceased to think of him at all. In proportion as my judgement strengthened my imagination became less active in portraying adventures and exploits of which I myself was the hero; much too of the romance of my character had been worn away in the workshed and the barrack.

One day about the middle of May this year (1825) one of

my cousins (the person whom I introduced to your notice, and whose recollections of your kindness will not readily be effaced)[57] told me he had just been in company with my old friend and his mother; and that the latter wished me to drink tea with her that evening. On first thoughts I determined not to accept the invitation. 'Why should I who am but a journeyman mason, seek the acquaintance of one who has already slighted me; and who as he is now pursuing one of the liberal professions, will look for his companions among gentlemen.' My second thoughts were different. 'Why should I fear to come in contact with him, or any one else! I will go and meet him as a man of independence ought. If he values himself on being a scholar, he shall find that I am not very ignorant; – If he only remembers me as a wild dreaming schoolboy, he shall find that I can now mantain [sic] the character of a man of sense.[']

I accordingly went, accompanied by my cousin, and was soon engaged in conversation with my friend. Nearly six years had elapsed since we had met before on similar terms; and that space of time had changed us in all the old traits of mind and person by which we remembered each other. My friend had been one of the handsomest and best looking boys I ever saw. In all games that required strength and activity no one of his years and inches could excell him. He was equal too to any exploit that required only conduct and courage; – the achievement of what was desperate he always left to me. The character of his mind was not of a decidedly original cast considered as that of a man, though somewhat singular regarded as that of a boy. His judgement seemed almost fully developed at an age when his imagination, the faculty whose growth in most cases keeps pace with that of the memory, was comparatively weak. The complexion of the workings of such a mind is easy of conception. In whatever he said or did there was scarcely any thing puerile; and though his powers of invention were weak, few grown people could decide more justly on any matter brought under his consideration. The worse points in his character were a predilection for scarcasm [sic] and irony and an apparent coldness which seemed the effect of an obtuseness of feeling. Such were the traits by which I remembered him; Me he could only have recollected as a wild reckless young fellow with whom to resolve and to act was nearly the same thing; and if he knew any thing else of me from hearsay it could only have been that I had become so singularly reserved that no one knew me, and that I had attained the not very uncommon knack of escaping observation by doing nothing.

He was now though still interesting in his appearance pale and thin and of a slim delicate figure. I soon discovered that he had lost the dry sarcastic humour which I had formerly disliked in him; that his heart was of more than common warmth; that he was somewhat keen of temper; and that his judgement had attained a strength and niceness of edge which I had not before found equalled. We were delighted with each other; and in the course of a few hours were better friends than we had been in all our lives before. After parting with him for the evening my spirits were so exhilarated that I felt as if intoxicated.

Next day we had a long walk together through the scenes of our early rambles. I found my friend to be one of the few persons who become wise in proportion as they grow learned. – My acquaintance with men of education though not very extensive is yet sufficiently so to convince me that the people whose capacities average between mediocrity and the lower extreme of intellect are rather injured than benefited by being made scholars. Men of this kind when bred up to a common mechanical profession, are generally quiet and unpretending, useful to society and possessed of an almost instinctive knowledge of those rules of conduct and attention to which makes easy the passage through life. As scholars, however, they frequently bear a character much the reverse of this. I have met with such newly set loose from College, and have taken an inventory of their intellectual stock[.] A smattering of Greek and Latin; an affected admiration of writings whose merits they have neither taste nor judgement enough to appreciate; a few confused philosophical notions; a few broken ideas, the imperfect transcripts, not of things, but of other ideas; an ability of conveying trite thoughts in common language; a pride that gloats enraptured over these attainments; and a sincere contempt for the class of people whom they deem the ignorant. Parnell's beautiful descriptions of a lake when perfectly calm and when ruffled by a peeble [sic] illustrates happily the minds of men of true and of fictitious learning.[58] The sensoriums of the former are mirrors of the Universe, – those of the latter present only scenes of broken fragments.

The attainments of my friend at this time were of a kind suitable to the character of his genius. He had not a close acquaintance with history or general literature; but he was an acute metaphysician, and skilled in the Mathematics. The writers he was most conversant with were Locke, Hume, Berkly [sic], and Reid.[59] Our intimacy was the means of undeceiving each of us with respect to two particular departments of literature. My friend had been accustomed to consider every species of lighter writing as unworthy the serious attention of a man of vigorous understanding, and I on the other hand to regard the metaphysics as a dry unpleasing study. In a few months, however, he had become an admirer of the elegances of composition, and I of metaphysical accuteness [sic]. He perused the Paradise Lost of Milton with astonishment; I the Essays of Hume with admiration.[60]

But there was one subject of much greater importance than either Philosophy or the Belles Lettres on which my friend was particularly desirous to fix my attention. A few years before the renewal of our intimacy he had been led seriously to consider the end for which he had been sent into the world; and believing that the Bible and he himself were productions of the same author, he had taken it for the rule of his conduct and his belief. He was in short, a philosopher of the same school with my friend at Niddry. I could have conversed with him on any other topic with more readiness and pleasure than on Religion; for when I had confessed that I had a general belief in the doctrines of the Church, but that these doctrines had scarce any influence on my conduct, I had said all I deemed proper to say. He persisted nevertheless, in making it the grand theme of his discourse. I had repeatedly seen instances of a kind of disease of mind, which originates in a bending of the attention too exclusively to some certain object, and which seems to consist in a preternatural growth and almost continual recurrence of some certain train of ideas; but I was convinced the mind of my friend had no taint of this disease; for reason told me that Religion ought to be the main business of life, – that it ought to govern every thought, and furnish the motive of almost every action. The history of the different opinions which I have at different times entertained regarding it, is, I believe more than commonly curious.

*   *   *

I have written what I may term the second chapter of my life. A third part is still a wanting, which will perhaps be of a character somewhat different from that of the other two; and to which I will devote some of my leisure hours in the approaching summer, should it be the will of Providence to grant me life and health, and that opportunity of amusement which he has hitherto vouchsafed me. You see Honoured Sir that my course of education has had its advantages and its disadvantages. It has been favourable to the formation of originality of thought but it has been confined to a very few of the departments of knowledge. My peculiar cast of mind, too, resembles in this respect the school in which I have studied. It has its good and evil properties. There is nothing I so suspiciously examine as an argument which comes backed by an ipse dixit; and the consequence is that I am seldom much deceived by the errors of others; on the other hand there is nothing from which I derive more pleasure than from the building up of a system, and the effect is that I am not infrequently involved in mistakes of my own. From the disadvantages of the school in which I have studied, I have yet much to learn; – from the manner in which my studies have been conducted, I have perhaps a good deal to forget. Socrates spoke very pointedly of the common error of mens thinking they know what they do not know. When I consider that the greater part of my knowledge has been acquired I know not how, I find reason to suspect that I must be in this predicament though perhaps Socrates himself would have permitted me to consider such knowledge as the half remembered learning of a state of prior existence.

NOTES ON THE TEXT

1. Miller's *Poems, Written in the Leisure Hours of a Journeyman Mason* was published anonymously in 1829.
2. Hugh Miller (1758–1807).
3. Jean Miller (1805–16) and Catherine Miller (1807–16).
4. Harriet Wright (1784–c. 1867).
5. James Wright (1765–1828), Alexander ('Sandy') Wright (1768–1841).
6. Blind Harry (c. 1470–92) celebrated in a poem the deeds of the thirteenth-century Scottish patriot Sir William Wallace, chief champion of Scotland's independence. The poem appeared in new edition in 1820, but the book Miller refers to was one of the many popular versions in prose available at the time.
7. Sir John Graham (d. 1298), a Scottish warrior, friend of Wallace and character in Blind Harry's poem; his sword was apparently inscribed with the words, 'Sir John the Grame, verry vicht and wyse . . .'.
8. James Cook (1728–79), navigator and author of several voyages; George Anson (1696–1762), admiral of the fleet, author of *Voyage Round the World* (1748).
9. Presumably, the hero of *The English Hermit; or the Adventures of Philip Quarll* (1816).
10. John Swanson; see Introduction, pp. 26–7.
11. In *My Schools and Schoolmasters*, Miller recalls how his adventures elicited such interest that 'some enormously bad verses, in which the writer described the incident a few days after, became popular enough to be handed about in manuscript, and read at tea-parties by the *elite* of the town' (p. 83). The verses appear in his note-book, 'Juvenile Poems', as 'The Cave: A Poem', National Library of Scotland MS 7520, pp. 3–4. There are several later accounts which reveal different emphases: 'The Ducat Cave' was written in 1821 and appears in two poetry notebooks: National Library of Scotland MS 7521, pp. 5–7 and MS 7522, pp. 1–2; a much extended and amended version was published as 'A Tale of Youth' in *Poems*, pp. 171–96.
12. Sebastian Le Prestre de Vauban (1637–1707) wrote several works

on fortification; his *New Method of Fortification* appeared in English in 1693.

13. Pierre Bayle (1647–1706), *Dictionnaire historique et critique*, 2 vols (1695–7).

14. James Macpherson (1736–96) published *Fingal, an Ancient Epic Poem, in Six Books* (1762), which purported to be a faithful translation of an epic written by Ossian, son of Fingal, which dated from some vague but remote period of Scottish history.

15. Zimri is a character in John Dryden's (1631–1700) allegorical poem *Absalom and Achitophel* (1681).

16. William Guthrie (1708–70), *Geographical, Historical, and Commercial Grammnar* (1770), which went through many editions.

17. Robert Hamilton (1743–1829), *Heads of a Course in Mathematics* (1800).

18. 'The Boatman's Tale' is perhaps the most successful poem in Miller's *Poems* (pp. 105–41), and received praise from, amongst others, the editor of the *Inverness Courier*, Robert Carruthers, who published the *Poems*.

19. [Hugh Miller], *Letters on the Herring Fishing in the Moray Frith* (1829) was published by Robert Carruthers in Inverness.

20. John Gordon subsequently commissioned Miller to write the entry on Cromarty for *The New Statistical Account of Scotland*; the article was written in 1835–6 and appeared in volume 14, pp. 1–18, published in 1845.

21. Miller may, perhaps, have confused the criticism of the *Inverness Courier*, which was positive, with that of the *Caledonain Mercury*, which was not. In acknowledging receipt of the first part of Miller's Memoir, Principal Baird wrote: 'I had no hand whatever, directly or indirectly, in the criticism of the *Caledonian Mercury*: – one of the Periodicals desirous of gaining notoriety by attacks on generally acknowledged merit, and provoking if they can to literary contests those with whom a contest might give eclat, spoke rather unfavourably of the Stone Mason's Poems' (Baird to Miller, 4 November 1829, *LB*, 2). The first part of Miller's Memoir ends here.

22. To Andrew Williamson, on 5 June 1819.

23. This is 'old David Williamson' not 'old David Wright', as Bayne has it, *Hugh Miller*, I, p. 59. 'Wright' was David's wife's maiden name.

24. Andrew Marvell (1621–78).

25. William Wordsworth (1770–1850), 'A Poet's Epitaph' (1800).

26. Wordsworth's 'The Ruined Cottage' or 'The Story of Margaret' was written in 1797 and was subsequently embodied in Book I of *The Excursion* (1814).

27. The reference is clearly to Sir Walter Scott's (1771–1832) *Minstrelsy of the Scottish Border*, 3 vols (1802–3), and *The Lay of the Last Minstrel* (1805). Edwin, the sensitive son of a shepherd who finds education in nature, appears in James Beattie's (1735–1803) poem *The Minstrel* (1771–4).

28. Ulrica in Scott's novel *Ivanhoe* (1819) is the old sibyl who sets fire to the castle of Torquilstone and perishes in the flames. Ivanhoe is a pure-bred Saxon. Meg Merrilies is the fearsome

prophetess in Scott's *Guy Mannering, or the Astrologer* (1815), described by one of the characters as a 'harlot, thief, witch, and gypsy'.

29. Brochan was a kind of boiled oatmeal.
30. Sir Thomas Urquhart (1611–60) translated the first three books of Rabelais's *Gargantua and Pantagruel* in 1653 and 1693–4; he also wrote *Ekskubalauron* (1651), known as 'The Jewel'.
31. Oliver Goldsmith (?1730–74); the reference has not been traced.
32. Duc de la Rochefoucauld (1613–80), author of *Maximes* (1665).
33. Gavin (or Gawin) Douglas (?1475–1522), Scottish poet and bishop of Dunkeld, wrote in the vernacular and translated the *Aeneid* into English, or rather 'Scottis'. Wiliam Dunbar (?1456–1513), Scottish poet.
34. Martinmas, the feast of St Martin, 11 November.
35. Robert Burns (1759–96), 'Man Made to Mourn' (1786).
36. *Some Account of the Travels of John Magee, Pedlar and Flying Stationer, in North and South Britain . . . 1806 and 1808* (1826).
37. Perhaps a reference to the writings of the explorer Sir John Franklin (1786–1847), who wrote on the Arctic region as well as on the inhabitants of the northern American coast.
38. Thomas Paine (1737–1809), radical author of *The Rights of Man* (1791–2). The *Dictionary of National Biography* reveals several radicals by the name of Williams; Miller's reference is possibly to Thomas Williams, a bookseller convicted in 1797 for the publication of Paine's *Age of Reason*. Macheath is Captain Macheath, a highwayman who ends up in prison in John Gay's musical play *The Beggar's Opera* (1728).
39. Sir James Mackintosh (1765–1832), Scottish historian, philosopher and barrister. James Macpherson (1736–96), Scottish 'translator' of the ossianic poems, *Fingal, an Epic Poem, in Six Books* (1762). Much admired for their romantic spirit but whose authenticity as Gaelic or Erse language verses was challenged.
40. Elihu 'the son of Barachel the Buzite' appears in the Book of Job, chapters 32 to 37.
41. Walter Scott, *Marmion* (1808) and *The Abbot* (1820).
42. Philip Doddridge (1702–51), celebrated non-conformist divine, author of *The Rise and Progress of Religion in the Soul* (1745) and *Sermons on Various Subjects*, 4 vols (1826).
43. Presumably Dr Thomas Young (1773–1829), physician, natural philosopher and linguist, who made pioneering contributions to the deciphering of Egyptian hieroglyphs.
44. George Farquhar (1678–1707), best known for *The Recruiting Officer* (1706) and *The Beaux' Strategem* (1707). William Wycherley (1641–1715), author of *The Plain-dealer* (1676). Each playwright was sometimes criticised for licentiousness and indecency.
45. George Crabbe (1754–1832), wrote poems which offered closely observed and realistic portraits of rural life and landscape.
46. Edmund Burke (1729–97), *A Philosophical Enquiry into the Sublime and the Beautiful* (1757).
47. René Descartes (1596–1650), French philosopher.
48. Richard Cumberland (1732–1811), tragedian and comedian; Richard Brinsley Sheridan (1751–1816), playwright.

49. Molière (1622–73), French comic playwright; Terence (c. 190 or c. 180–159 BC), Roman comic poet.
50. [John Milton] (1608–74), *Comus, a Maske* (1637). Guido Reni (1575–1642), Bolognese painter of the vast fresco 'Phoebus and the Hours preceded by Aurora'.
51. Hugh Blair (1718–1800), divine and essayist; William Robertson (1721–93), historian; Allan Ramsay (1686–1758), poet; Adam Ferguson (1723–1816), philosopher; David Hume (1711–76), philosopher and historian.
52. Francis Jeffrey (1773–1850), critic and journal editor; John Wilson (1785–1854), writer and critic; Dugald Stewart (1753–1828), philosopher; Thomas McCrie (1772–1835), ecclesiastical historian; Henry Mackenzie (1745–1831), novelist. Robertson was appointed Principal of the University of Edinburgh in 1762.
53. That is, McCrie, whose *Life of John Knox* appeared in 1812 and *Life of Andrew Melville* appeared in 1819.
54. Caffer = Caffre or Kaffer or Kaffir, a Southern African Bantu.
55. Sir David Wilkie (1785–1841), Scottish painter.
56. Joseph Addison (1672–1719), poet, playwright, essayist.
57. George Munro bore a letter of introduction written by Miller, who sought to help him gain a position as a school teacher. See Miller to Baird, 29 December 1829, *LB*, 7. Baird was unable to help.
58. Thomas Parnell (1679–1718), poet.
59. John Locke (1632–1704), George Berkeley (1685–1753), Thomas Reid (1710–96), all philosophers.
60. *Paradise Lost* (1667); *Esays Moral and Political* (1741–2).

APPENDIX I

Hugh Miller's 1830 Letter to Isaac Forsyth*

Your kind letter and its elegant accompanyment found me engaged in writing my long auto-biographical narrative for Principal Baird; a work which has occupied my leisure hours for the last two months, and which is not yet wholly completed. I do not proceed with it on the supposition that my personal adventures are either very striking in themselves, or that they can be rendered interesting by my manner of narrating them; but as for the last ten years the study of character, as exhibited in different parts of the country, and in the lower classes of society has been one of my favourite amusements, and as I occupy in my memoir the place rather of a spectator than of an actor, I trust my sketches and remark may prove not quite unacceptable to the venerable Principal. The theory of the moral character of the people of Scotland which my narrative is in part intended to illustrate is, I believe, new; and as it is founded on observation is I hope also just . . .

Each situation in life regarded as a point of observation has advantages peculiar to itself, by commanding a view of certain objects which cannot be so happily studied from any other point; but the situations of the middle and higher classes of society have been so repeatedly occupied by skilful observers that their fields of view present not a single object which has not already been examined and described. This is not yet the case with the lower points of observation. The gentleman philosopher who writes upon character will, if he desires to attain originality, have perhaps to become either a mere theorist or to set himself to unfold hidden principles and motives; but how different would the case be with a philosophical Gipsy, could we imagine such a person. His range of observation, however contracted, would be perfectly new; and to attain originality he would have only

* Miller to Isaac Forsyth, 12 February 1830, *LB*, 15.

to describe. I reckon it one of the advantages of my place in society (it would require to have some, for the disadvantages incident to it are somewhat numerous) that it commands a wide and diversified prospect of the latter description. I have wandered as a stone mason over a considerable part of the country, and have seen and I trust also studied what may be regarded as the extremes of Scottish character; – the one extreme in a remote district of the western Highlands, the other in the vicinity of Edinburgh. Holding such opinions I proceed with my letter to the Principal in confidence, that whatever my deficiencies as a writer, the facts I adduce, and perhaps some of the remarks with which I accompany them, shall have at least the recommendation of novelty. I shall have the merit of saying something that has not been said before. But with regard to that species of writing in which you have so obligingly furnished me with an opportunity of exercising my pen I feel somewhat differently. It is a department in which I must either stand or fall from the strength or weakness of my native powers, or from my skill or want of skill in the art of writing. If I fail in it, however, it shall not, I trust, be through any lack of exertion.

This part of the country contains a rich, and as yet unexplored mine of tradition; but some of the stories are of too wild and fantastic a character for furnishing a suitable basis for a prose tale; and the great bulk of them, though they might prove interesting when wrought up together, are too simple and too naked of both detail and description to stand alone. They resemble some of the minuter flowers that scarcely appear beautiful until bound up in a nosegay. Last Autumn, when I had finished my series of letters on the Herring Fishery, I set myself to gather such a nosegay; and the two sketches which appeared in the *Inverness Courier* 'Halloween' and 'St. Rules,' were the flowers first cropped for it. The ribbons by which I intended they should be bound together were two of the associative principles, similarity, and contiguity of time and place. I had only commenced the work, however, when I was introduced to the notice of Principal Baird, and experienced at his hand such kindness as I shall not readily forget. I was much flattered by his expressing it as his opinion that my writings betrayed few of the faults incident to an imperfect education; and by his requesting me that I should state to him by letter the manner in which I attained my skill in the art of composition. I soon found that the history of my education was also that of my life; and that in consequence his request had furnished me with sufficient employment for the greater part of the coming winter. The traditional scheme was therefore laid aside but at some future period I intend resuming it.

Conversation to me proves generally an imperfect medium for the conveyance of thought; and I expressed myself rather loosely in what I said when in your company in Cromarty, regarding the assistance which in detailing these traditions my memory derives from my ima-

gination. Imagination frequently assists me in giving a something
like life to narratives which were before dead. It draws landscapes
too around the figures to which tradition has introduced me, and
sometimes furnishes these figures with the language of dialogue. This,
however, was not at all what I at that time had meant to state; but I
may perhaps be more happy in conveying my meaning by the pen.
The faculty of my mind which was first developed was imagination,
and the development was neither partial nor gradual. Before I had
attained my fifth year I had become the inhabitant of two distinct
worlds, the true and the ideal; and the images of the latter appeared
to me scarcely less tangible or less clearly defined than those of the
former. My mind presented me with a vivid picture of every incident
of which I was told. This faculty was productive in some instances,
of consequences of a rather ludicrous cast. As early as the period
referred to I was one day sitting beside my mother, listening with
great attention to a recital with which she was entertaining a neighbour, of some of the circumstances connected with my birth, – such
as a singular dream my father had concerning me, an unusual conformation of head which the midwife observed in me, and which she
deemed indicative of idiotism, and the details of the christening.
According to custom my imagination presented me at the time with
pictures of all I heard described. Well, – about eighteen years after,
by one of those sudden freaks of memory which are not very easily
explained even on the associative principle these pictures were again
brought before me; and as I did not at first remember any thing of
the narrative which had produced them sadly was I puzzled to account
for the recollection. And after thinking on the subject for a few days
I had a narrow escape from becoming one of the most singular of
metaphysicians by being enabled to unravel the whole circumstances
of the matter as related. – I have also two several recollections of
spectres which would render me a firm believer in apparitions, could
I not account for them in this way as the creatures of an imagination
which had attained an unusual and even morbid strength at a time
when the other mental faculties were scarcely at all unfolded. But I
must to the point. From the early development described my traditional stories are remembered, not faintly and confusedly as narratives
which I have heard but vividly and distinctly as scenes and incidents
which I have witnessed.

Such of my books as are returned by the book sellers may be sent to
Cromarty; – I think it will be best to let them lie by me, as something,
it is possible, may yet be done to buoy them up. Byrons Hours of
Idleness [sic] would never have become a popular volume had it been
his only production. Perhaps my hope of yet possessing a complete
command of the pen is unfounded; but when I measure the degree of
strength which my mind has attained in the best of its faculties
within the last four years; when I compare it with what it was
before; and consider that all my little skill in the art of writing was

acquired during that period, it is a hope in which I deem it rational to indulge. The publication of the volume of poems was on the whole an unadvisable and imprudent step, and yet the result has not been altogether disastrous. It has been the means of introducing me to Principal Baird one of the best and most benevolent men in the kingdom, and of affording me the present opportunity of subscribing myself.

APPENDIX II

Hugh Miller's 1836 Letter to Alexander Finlay*

Yes the wise old king was quite in the right 'As cold waters to the thirsty soul so is good news from a far country.' My very hopes regarding the boy-friend whom I loved so much and regretted so long have been dead for the last twelve years. I could think of you as a *present existence* only in relation to the other world; – in your relation to this one merely as a recollection of the past. And yet here is a kind affectionate letter so full of heart that it has opened all the sluices of mine, – that assures me your pulses are still beating, and shews me they deserve to beat for ever. I cannot tell you how much and often I have thought of you, or how sincerely the *man* has longed after and regretted the friend of the *boy*; – you were lost to me ere I knew how much I valued and loved you. – I daresay you don't remember that shortly before you left Cromarty you scrawled your name with a piece of burnt stick on the eastern side of *Marcus-cave* a little within the opening. I have renewed these characters twenty and twenty times; and it was not until a few years ago when a party of gipsies took possession of the cave and smoked it all as black as a chimney that they finally disappeared . . .

What, dear Finlay, have the seventeen intervening years been doing with your face and figure! – the heart is, I know unchanged, but what like are you? Are you still a handsome, slender, high featured boy, dressed in green? John Swanson is a little black *mannie* with a wig; and I have been growing older, but you won't believe it, for the last eighteen years. Great reason to be thankful, I am still ugly as ever, – five feet eleven when I straighten myself, with hair which my friends call brown and my not friends red, features irregular but not at all ill natured in the expression, an immense head, and a forehead three quarters of a yard across. Is'nt the last a good thing in these

* Miller to Alexander Finlay, 15 October 1836, LB, 174.

days of Phrenology! And is'nt it a still better thing that a bonny
sweet lassie with a great deal of fine sense and a highly cultivated
mind does'nt think me too ugly to be liked very much and promises
to marry me sometime in Spring! – Do give me a portrait of yourself
first time you write, and dearest Finlay, don't let other seventeen
years pass ere then. Ross, Andrew Forbes, Adam McGlashan, Walter
Williamson are all dead; – of all our cave companions only John
Swanson survives. John is a capital fine fellow. He was quite as wild
a boy you know as either of ourselves and perhaps a little worse
tempered but growing *good* about twelve years ago he put himself to
College about twelve years ago with an eye to the Church and is
now a Missionary at Fort William. Dearest Finlay, have you grown
good too! I was in danger of becoming a wild infidel; – argued with
uncle Sandy about cause and effect and the categories, – read Hume
and Voltaire and Volney, and all the other witty fellows who had
too much sense to go to Heavan and was getting nearly as much
sense in that way as themselves; but John cured me, and you may
now say of me what Gray says of himself 'No very great wit, he
believes in God.' The Bible is a much more cheerful book than I once
used to think it, and has a world of sound philosophy in it besides . . .

You give me the outlines of your history, and I must give you those
of mine in turn. But they are sadly unlike. You have been going on
through life, like a horseman on a journey, and are now far in advance
of the starting point; – I on the contrary have been mounted whip
and spur on a hobby, and after seventeen years hard driving here I
am on exactly the spot I set out from. But I have had rare sport in
the fine ups and downs, and have kept saddle the whole time. You
remember I was on the eve of becoming a mason apprentice when
you left me. The four following years were passed in wandering over
the northern and western Highlands, amid hills and lochs and rivers,
one of the happiest and most contented, though apparently most
forlorn of stone masons. I lived in these days in kilns and barns, on
something less than half a crown per week, and have been located
for months together in wild savage districts where I could scarce find
in a weeks time a person with English enough to speak to me; but I
was dreaming behind my apron of poets and poetry, and of making
myself a name; and so the tasks and hardships of the present were
lost in the uncertain good of the future. Would we not be poor
unhappy creatures, dear Finlay, were there more of sober sense in
our composition and less of foolish hope! In 1824 I went to Edinburgh
where I wrought for part of two years. I was sanguine in my expectations of meeting with you. I have looked a thousand times after the
College students and smart lawyer clerks whom I have seen thronging
the pavement, in the hope of identifying some one of them with my
early fiend. On one occasion I even supposed I had found him, and
then blessed God I had not. I was sauntering on the Calton on a
sunny Sabbath morning of an autumn when I met with a poor maniac

who seemed to recognize me, and whose features bore certainly a marked resemblance to yours. I cannot give expression to what I felt; and yet the sickening unhappy feeling of that moment is still as fresh in my recollection as if I had experienced it but yesterday. Strange as it may seem I gave up from this time all hope of ever seeing you, and felt that even were you dead; and I had some such presentiment, – there are much worse ways of losing a friend than by death.

After returning from Edinburgh I plied the mallet for a season or two in the neighbourhood, – working mostly in Churchyards, – a second edition of *Old Mortality*, – and then did a very foolish thing. I published a volume of poems. They were mostly juvenile; and I was beguiled into the belief that they had some little merit by the pleasing images and recollections of early life and lost friends which they awakened in my own mind through the influence of the associative faculty. But this sort of merit lay all outside of them, if I may so speak, and existed in relation to the writer alone; just as some little trinket may awaken in one mind the memory of a dear friend, and be a mere toy of no value to every body else. – My poems like the vicar of Wakefields tracts on the great *Monogamical* question are in the hands of only the happy few; they made me some friends however among the class of men whose friendship is disposed to boast of; and at least one of them *Stanzas on a Sun Dial* promises to live. Chambers alludes to it in the notice to which I owe the restoration of a long lost friend. The volume which maugre its indifferent prose broken into still more indifferent rhime, and all its other imperfections I yet venture to send you is dedicated to our common friend Swanson, but being as tender of his name as of my own the whole is anonymous. In the latter part of the year in which it appeared I sent a few letters on a rather unpromising subject, the Herring Fishery, to one of the Inverness Newspapers. They were more fortunate however than the poems, and attracted so much notice that the proprietors of the paper published them in a pamphlet which has had an extensive circulation. I send it to you with the volume. Every mind large or small, is you know, fitted for its predestined work; – some to make Epic poems, and other to write Letters on the Herring Fishery.

I continued to divide my time between the mallet and the pen till about two years ago, when I was nominated Accountant to a Branch of the Commercial Bank recently established in Cromarty. I owe the appointment to the kindness of the Banker Mr. Robert Ross, whom I daresay you will remember as an old neighbour, and who when you left Cromarty was extensively engaged as a provision merchant and ship owner. I published my last, and I believe best work *Scenes and Legends of the North of Scotland* shortly after. Some minds, like winter pears, ripen late, and some minds like exotics in a northern climate, dont ripen at all; – and mine seems to belong to an intermediate class. Sure I am it is still wofully green, somewhat like our present late crop, but it is now twenty per cent more mature than when I published my former volume, and I flatter myself with the hope that if winter does'nt come on too rapidly it may get better still. Read, dear Finlay, my *Scenes and Legends* first; you may afterwards, if you feel inclined, peep into the other two as curiosities, and for the sake of lang syne; but I wish to be introduced to you as I am at present not as I was ten years ago. The critics have been all exceedingly good natured and I would fain send you some of the reviews with which they have favoured me (these taken together would form as bulky a volume as the one on which they are written but I have only beside me at present the opinion expressed by Leigh Hunt (the friend and coajutor of Byron you know) and the notice of a literary paper, *The Spectator*. These I make up in the parcel. I am still more wishful to send you an account of the town and parish of Cromarty which I drew up some time ago for the Statistical work now publishing, and in which you could renew your acquaintance with the *Coalheugh* and *McFarquhars Bed*; but though the Editor has promised me a few copies they have not yet come to hand. – My story is told, dear Finlay, and is no story at all.

Where think you am I now! On the grassy summit of McFarquhars Bed. It is evening and the precipices throw their cold dark shadows athwart the beach. But the red light of the sun is still resting on the higher foliage of the hill above, and the opposite land so blue and dim, stretches along the horizon, with all its speck-like dwellings shimmering to the light like pearls. Not a feature of the scene has changed since we last gazed on it together. What seem the same waves are still fretting against the same peebles; and yonder spring at which we have so often filled our pitcher, comes gushing down from the same little jet of sand that it did eighteen years ago. But where are all our old companions Finlay? Lying widely scattered in solitary graves! David Ross lies in the sea. John Mann died in a foreign hospital, Logfield in Berlice, McGlashan in England, Walter Williamson in North America. And here am I though still in the vigour of early manhood the oldest of all the groupe. Who could have told these poor fellows when they last met in the cave yonder that 'Eternity should have so soon enquired of them what Time had been doing.'

Our old schoolfellow Daniel Ross is a fine decent fellow, a shop-keeper; – W. Watson, scarcely ditto and much a Radical, is a shop-keeper too. J. Forsyth also keeps a shop. Alex, his brother, the fine looking lad who seemed as if born to live for ever, is gone. Three fingered Andrew McLeod, 'The artist' as we now call him, has broken down in his course through life and become disreputable; – his brother, the promising painter, has turned out a poor mediocretist. I am still happy in my mother, but one of my uncles, not your acquaintance, however, has been dead for the last eight years. Your old landlord, D. Fraser, resides at Invergordon – his mother who was employed in tending a flock of sheep on the day of Culloden and heard the thunderings of the cannon, is still alive, but I cannot ennumerate every change nor yet the fewer cases in which there has been none; – half a generation has passed from off the stage and another half entered on it since you left us. Regard, my dear Finlay my *Scenes and Legends* as a long letter from Cromarty. I send the parcel by the Duchess of Sutherland Steamer to your London Merchants. You will find in it a *proof*, miserably dirty of Wilsons *Tales of the Borders*, containing two stories and will perhaps recognize the writer of the first, but remember I am not the blockhead who wrote the second.

There is a neighbour of my mothers, a Mr. Forbes who has a son in Jamaica from whom he has not heard for the last three years. Should he chance to be in your neighbourhood or known to you a single line regarding him would set the old man at rest. The name of the son is Gustavus. – Do write me a little newspaper. Tell me something of your mode of life. Give me some idea of a Jamaica landscape. What are your politics? what your creed? What have you been doing, and thinking, and saying since I last saw you? Tell me all. Your letter is the greatest luxury I have enjoyed for I know not how long. Believe, dearest Finlay, that I am your attached and faithful friend.

APPENDIX III

John Strahan's 1830 Letter
*to Hugh Miller**

In sitting down in pursuance of your request to tell you the story of my early days, and to trace with the pencil of truth the dawn and development of the taste and turn for poetry, of which you are pleased to express your appreciation in terms so highly gratifying, I feel a considerable diffidence; arising from the knowledge that a narrative so divested of incidents as mine, can only be rendered interesting by the skill and talent of the narrator; which skill and talent I am too well aware I do not possess. Yet on the other hand I feel encouraged to proceed from the conviction that you will listen with a partial ear, and that as I address myself to you alone my story will not lose its interest although my manner of telling it may come far short of perfection.

My father (who too was a weaver to trade) died in 1807 (the ninth year of my age, being born on the 14 Nov 1798) leaving behind him a widow and four children of whom I was the eldest. He left at his death (the fruits of his industry and economy) a property of about sixty pounds value, which was sold to a relative, and the purchase money assisted my mother (who is still alive) to rear her helpless family. I had been sent to school nearby as soon as I could speak, but up to the death of my father I made but little progress in learning, and still less during the remainder of the time I remained in school. I had all along been averse to study, and finding myself relieved by the death of my father from the awe which his presence alone could impress me with, I gave way to the bent of my inclination; which was at the head of my companions to stroll through the fields, to wander the woods, and seek for adventures among rocks and rivers, as the whim of birds nesting or searching for wild fruits might prevail. And many a hair breadth escape have I made in these excursions; for

* See John Strahan to Miller, 6 April 1830, *LB*, 22.

as I was the leader of my brother adventurers, it became me to be the first at a venture; and there are many who have followed the fortunes of the Duke of Wellington from the time he entered the army until his last and greatest of fields, Waterloo, that cannot boast of half the scars and remembrances of perils by flood and field that I can. My mother and some of my other relatives seeing that humming over a lesson, forming letters, and making figures had no charms for me (although it was allowed by all that I would have been a scholar had I been attentive) resolved to send me to Perth, and bind me apprentice to my mothers brother, who followed the trade of a weaver there. In pursuance of this plan I was marched off from Forres to Perth on the 13th March 1809.

When I remained at school my reading so far as I can remember was wholly confined to my school books which consisted in the first place of my Catechism, on which I learned to read, then the Bible, and last of all the Collection. I do not remember of being particularly fond of any thing which I then read, save in one solitary instance, – I read Cowpers ludicrous description of John Gilpin's ride so often, that I retain the greater part of it on my memory till this day. But there were few boys of my years, and certainly none of my acquaintance that had such an extensive stock of stories both of the wonderful and the terrific, as I had been able to collect. There was a man, a native of Paisley, who wrought in my fathers shop, whose mind was a perfect repository of ballads, riddles and tales suited to the capacity of children; and often to induce me to assist him in taking in his webs, a process which I hated for its tediousness, he would draw o his inexhaustible fund of fairy lore, and thereby beguile the time I employed in assisting him; – by this means he obtained my willing service, which neither threats nor rewards could induce me to give to another. I remember till this hour the impression which his tale of Jack and the Bear made on my young mind; but when he came to dwell on the exploits of Jack the giant-killer, when he went forth with his invisible coat, his cap of knowledge, his shoes of swiftness, and his sword of sharpness, overthrowing giants, breaking enchantments, and relieving captives, who waited to be swallowed up alive by the monsters who held them in thrall, my imagination was wrought up to a pitch of enthusiasm and thrilling delight, seldom equalled since, even in my happiest moments on Parnassus. Many and various were the tales which I picked up from this man's mouth; and I took great delight in telling them again to a staring and wondering audience of youngsters circled 'round the winter-evening's fire. And I was early instructed in the superstitions of the olden time by an aged grandmother, who was so deeply versed in the mystic lore of witches, fairies, and spirits, good and evil, that she could have laid open the whole science of supernatural agency, and might have been the compiler of 'Satan's Invisible World.'

Thus with a spirit deeply imbued with the superstition of the last century, a head full of the wild and romantic tales of my Paisley friend, as much knowledge of letters as enabled me to read an English lesson with tolerable correctness, and as much practice in penmanship as I had gained from writing copies for two or three years, and setting down my Arithmetical labours, which went no farther than the Rule of Three, I arrived at my eleventh year, at which time I was set to the loom.

I would willingly pass by the four years of my apprenticeship; – the remembrance of these years of sorrow and suffering awaken feelings of a very painful and distressing nature. The recollection of a continuation of injurious treatment and accumulated wrongs must in all cases excite unpleasant sensations; but it is doubly distressing when those who occasioned our suffering were trusted to be, and should have been the guardians of our comfort and improvement. My uncle at Perth had no children of his own, and my mother and other relatives in the north imagined from this circumstance that when placed under his care I should share the more of his kindness and affection. As well as to give me my business, they believed that he would not neglect my education, but would watch over my improvement, and treat me in every respect as if I were his own. When left in his power I soon felt that a wrong estimate had been formed of his character. The flow of affection in his bosom was frozen at its source; – it is true he paid strict attention to the outward forms of Religion, and thereby carried himself fair before the world; but at the same time he was an entire stranger to the practice of all christian and moral virtues. In dealing with his dependents the love of worldly self surmounted every other consideration; and being constitutionally of a savage disposition, those who were under his control were compelled in ministering to his avarice to submit to almost every species of harsh and cruel treatment. He had several other apprentices; but none of them were allowed to remain longer with him than till his cruelty became known; save two boys, nephews of his wife's who like me were delivered over to him early and came from a distance; – their parents like my mother being deceived by the sanctity of his character, until it was too late; for one of them was ruined for life by being rendered unable to work for his maintenance in consequence of a hurt on the arm, and by the perseverance of his own aunt and my uncle in a line of treatment towards him of such refined cruelty that you would scarcely credit me were I to inform you of it.

I remember that on one or two occasions I contemplated a run away; but as I was never allowed any other covering for my head than that which nature gave me, and as the greater part of my dress was generally in rags, and never having the command of a single penny, I could not bear the idea of begging my way, and arriving at my home half naked. The neighbours who were aware of the treatment which I received, often spoke of applying to the civil magistrate on my behalf, and demanding from him the protection which the law allowed; but my oppressor was my uncle, and they did not like to interfere; nor had I the boldness to take this step myself, although I was often advised to it; for I could not forget that the man against whom I needed protection was my mothers brother. You can easily imagine that this was no place for the improvement of the mind. My uncle had a few religious books in his keeping, but like all his other good things they were carefully locked up. I do not remember of being allowed to read a single page of them. The Bible was the only book to which I had access. I was charged not to lift a pen at my highest peril; because it was dreaded that I might whisper something of my condition to my relatives. And it was a crime sure to be severely punished, to enter a neighbours house, lest I should disclose secrets regarding my situation which my uncle thought it would be better to conceal. Thus did four weary years pass over me, secluded from all society, and kept a stranger to men and manners, save the austere and unlovely manners of my prison house. At length the reign of oppression was o'er; – a few days before the expiration of my fourth year my mother arrived to take me away. I wept for joy when I saw her, and she wept for sorrow to learn the cruel treatment which I had received. From being overlaboured to an incredible degree I had not grown an inch from the time I entered in bondage; whilst my eye sight was considerably impaired by confinement. There is no doubt but that had I been subjected to undergo for other four years the like treatment, my constitution, which as yet continued un-impaired, must have given way; and by all likelihood long ere now I should have been in my grave. This picture, gloomy as it may appear, is not so darkly drawn as truth would sanction; – but let the memory of it depart; – I have long since forgiven my uncle who is still alive, and I pray God to do the same. On returning to Forres, at the sight of my friends with whom and the scenes with which every idea of earthly happiness was associated, my spirit, although long depressed and broken, resumed by degrees its wonted vigour, and rejoiced in its new and happy existence.

In the spring of 1813 I commenced working journeymen with a young man named Robert Sandison. It is to this individual I owe the formation of my literary taste. He was fond of reading, had a lively fancy and a kind heart. I had access to the few books that passed through his hands, – most of which I read with considerable interest. It was one summer evening, after we had dropped work, that he took up the first copy of Burns Poems I had ever seen, – and probably this was the first time I heard of the authors name. He read the 'Cottars Saturday Night,' and a few other favourite pieces; – I was struck with the force and beauty of the Ploughmans 'manners painting strains,' – a chord was awakened in my bosom that vibrated a sweeter tone than I had hitherto known. I felt that a new source of enjoyment was opened to me; and from that moment I became enamoured of the Scottish Muse. I dwelt with rapture on the glowing pages of the bard of Kyle, and he with Ramsay and Ferguson, became my favourite authors. Such was the veneration in which I held those mighty masters of the Lyre, and such the divinity with which my imagination clothed them, that had I been then told that at some future time I myself should have followed so far in their tract as to become an author not despised by the learned, nor disapproved of by the good, I believe I would have died for joy. My taste for reading now became a passion. All the stray and odd volumes which I could find (and they were all stray and odd volumes that I did find) were kept piled around my loom; and a stranger entering the shop was much more likely to find me with a book than with my shuttle in my hand.

I must not forget another circumstance which tended greatly to extend my views of men and men's matters. There is a Tinsmith in Forres of the name of Petrie, who was long looked upon as the oracle of the district; – and never was the Delphian Oracle itself consulted on matters of importance with more profound respect, if not veneration than was this son of wisdom and logic. In his youth, for he is now getting into years, he had been a great reader and a pretty deep thinker; and from his having early imbibed the principles of Republicanism he made himself particularly well acquainted with the histories of all Republics, both antient and modern. The constitution of America was, and still is his idol; – he had great hopes on the outbreaking of the French Revolution, and was no doubt greatly disappointed in that country relapsing into Monarchy; but he still continued till the end of the war to support with great warmth the motives and proceedings of the French Government in opposition to those of our own. He was in his element when engaged in disputation; and he had such a particular knack in wrangling that it was not easy to overcome him in an argument, 'For even though vanquished he could argue still.'

Round this veteran Politician, like the Satellites of Saturn round their centre, would the mechanical politicians of the good town circle. Every evening for a series of years his shop was crammed; and passing events were there noticed, and their merits discussed. It was here, for I was a very punctual attender, I first heard, and came to understand the meaning of the terms Republic, Monarchy, Democracy, Aristocracy, and all the other names and the natures of the different governments on and off the earth. The whole science of Civil Government was here delineated, as if on a map, and the properties and bearings of its respective branches as clearly pointed out as if each of the speakers had been a Solon or a Solomon. I ventured occasionally to take a part in the high debates of this manufactory of politicians and tinwork, and even dared at times to grapple with the giant himself; but my Lilliputian powers were but ill matched against his Herculean strength.

From this sketch hastily as it has been drawn up I trust you will be able to form an idea of my training up to the summer of 1816, at which time I became one of the

> Poor simple race who waste their toil
> For the vain tribute of a smile.

But I must here pause. Should you, however, think it worth while to revert to the subject I shall resume it at my earliest convenience.

Gropings of a Working Man in Geology

BY HUGH MILLER
AUTHOR OF 'THE TRADITIONARY HISTORY OF CROMARTY'*

It was eighteen years last February since I set out from my mother's cottage a little before sunrise, to make my first acquaintance with a life of labour and restraint; and I have rarely had a heavier heart than on that morning. I was a slim loose-jointed boy at the time, fond of the pretty intangibilities of romance, and of dreaming when broad awake; and I was now going to work as a mason's apprentice in one of the Cromarty quarries. Bating the passing uneasinesses occasioned by a few gloomy anticipations, the portion of my life which had already gone by had been happy beyond the common lot. I had been a wanderer among rocks and woods, a reader of curious little books, a gleaner of old traditionary stories. I had written bad verses too, without knowing they were bad, and indulged in unrealisable hopes, without being in the least aware that they were unrealisable; and I was now going to exchange all my day-dreams and all my amusements for the kind of life in which men toil every day, that they may be enabled to eat, and eat every day, that they may be enabled to toil. The time I had so long dreaded had at length arrived, and I felt that I was going down into a wilderness more desolate than that of Sinai, with little prospect of ever getting beyond it, and no hope of return.

The quarry in which my master wrought, lies on the southern side of the bay of my native town, and an hundred yards from the shore, with a little clear stream on the one side, and a thick fir wood on the other. It has been opened in the old red sandstone of the district, and

---

* *Chambers's Edinburgh Journal*, 28 April 1838, pp. 109–10, and 26 May 1838, pp. 137–9.

is overtopped by a huge bank of diluvial clay, which rises over it in some places to the height of nearly thirty feet, and which was at this time rent and shivered, wherever it presented an open front to the weather, by a recent frost. A heap of loose fragments which had fallen from above, blocked up the face of the quarry, and the first employment assigned me by my master was to clear them away. The friction of the shovel soon blistered my hands, but the pain was by no means very severe; and I wrought hard and willingly, that I might see how the huge strata below, which presented us with so unbroken a frontage, were to be torn up and removed. Picks and wedges and levers were applied by my brother workmen; and simple and rude as I had been accustomed to regard these implements, I found I had much to learn in the way of using them. They all proved insufficient, however, and we had to bore into one of the inferior strata, and employ gunpowder. The process was new to me, and I deemed it a highly amusing one – it had the merit too of being attended by some such degree of danger as a boating excursion, and thus an interest independent of its novelty. We had a few capital shots – the fragments flew in every direction, and an immense mass of the diluvium came toppling down, bearing with it two dead birds that in a recent storm had crept into one of the deeper fissures to die in the shelter. I felt a new interest in examining them. The one was a pretty cock-goldfinch, with its hood of vermillion, and its wings inlaid with the gold to which it owes its name, as unsoiled and smooth as if it had been preserved for a museum; the other, a somewhat rarer bird of the woodpecker tribe, was variegated with light blue and greyish yellow. I was engaged in admiring the poor little things, more disposed to be sentimental than if I had been ten years older, and thinking of the contrast between the warmth of and jollity of their green summer haunts, and the cold and darkness of their last retreat, when I heard my master bidding the workmen lay by their tools. I looked up, and saw the sun sinking behind the thick fur wood beside us, and the long dark shadows of the trees stretching downwards towards the shore.

This was no very formidable beginning of the course of life I had so much dreaded. To be sure, my hands were a little sore, and I felt nearly as much fatigued as if I had been climbing among the rocks; but I had wrought and been useful, and had yet enjoyed the day fully as much as usual. It was no small matter, too, that the evening, converted by a rare transmutation into the delicious 'blink of rest' which Burns so truthfully describes, was all my own. I was as light of heart next morning as any of my brother workmen. There had been a smart frost during the night, and the grass was white and crisp as we passed onward through the fields; but the sun rose in a clear atmosphere, and the day mellowed as it advanced into one of those delightful days of early spring which give so pleasing an earnest of whatever is mild and genial in the better half of the year. We all rested at mid-day, and I went to enjoy my half hour alone on a mossy knoll in the neighbouring wood, which commands through the trees a wide prospect of the bay and the opposite shore. There was not a wrinkle on the water nor a cloud in the sky, and the branches were as moveless in the calm as if they had been traced on canvass. From a wooded promontory that stretches half way across the firth, there ascended a thin column of smoke. It rose as straight as the line of a plummet for more than a thousand yards, and then, on reaching a thinner stratum of air, spread out equally on every side like the foliage of a stately tree. Ben-Weavis rose to the west, white with the yet unwasted snows of winter, and as sharply defined in the clear atmosphere, as if all its sunny slopes and blue retiring hollows had been chiselled in marble. A line of snow ran along the opposite hills; all above was white, and all below was purple. They reminded me of the pretty French story, in which an old artist is described as tasking the ingenuity of his future son-in-law, by giving him, as a subject for his pencil, a flower piece composed of only white flowers, the one-half of them in their proper colour, the other half of a deep purple, and yet all perfectly natural; and how the young man resolved the riddle and gained his mistress by introducing a transparent purple vase into the picture, and making the light pass through it on the flowers that were drooping over the edge. I returned to the quarry, convinced that a very exquisite pleasure may be a very cheap one, and that the busiest employments may afford leisure enough to enjoy it.

The gunpowder had loosened a large mass in one of the inferior strata, and our first employment on resuming our labours was to raise it from its bed. I assisted in placing it on edge, and was much struck by the appearance of the platform on which it had rested. The entire surface was ridged and furrowed like a bank of sand that had been left by the tide not half an hour before; I could trace every bend and curvature, every cross hollow and counter ridge of the corresponding phenomena, for the resemblance was no half resemblance, it was the thing itself; and I had observed it an hundred and an hundred times when sailing my little schooner on the shallows left by the ebb. But what had become of the waves that had thus fretted the solid rock, or of what element had they been composed? I felt as completely at fault as Robinson Crusoe did on his discovering the print of the man's foot in the sand. The evening furnished me with still further cause of wonder. We raised another block in a different part of the quarry, and found that the area of a circular depression in the stratum below was broken and flawed in every direction, as if it had been the bottom of a pool recently dried up, which had shrunk and split in the hardening. Several large stones came rolling down from the diluvium in the course of the afternoon. They were of different qualities from the sandstone below, and from one another; and what was more wonderful still, they were all rounded and water-worn, as if they had been tossed about in the sea or the bed of a river for hundreds of years. There could not surely be a more conclusive proof that the bank which had enclosed them so long, could not have been created on the rock on which it rested; no workman every manufactures a half-worn article, and the stones were all half-worn; and if not the bank, why then the sandstone underneath? I was lost in conjecture, and found I had food enough for thought that evening, without once thinking of the unhappiness of a life of labour.

The immense masses of diluvium which we had to clear away, rendered the working of the quarry laborious and expensive, and we all quitted it in a few days to make trial of another that seemed to promise better. The one we left is situated, as I have said, on the southern shore of the bay of Cromarty; the one to which we removed has been opened in a lofty wall of cliffs that overhangs the northern shore of the Moray Firth. I soon found I was to be no loser by the change. Not the united labours of a thousand men for more than a thousand years, could have furnished a better section of the geology of the district that this range of cliffs. It may be regarded as a sort of chance dissection on the earth's crust. We see in one place the primary rock, with its veins of granite and quartz, its dizzy precipices of gneiss, and its huge masses of hornblend. In another we find the secondary rock, with its beds of sandstone and shale, its spars, its clays, and its nodular limestones. We discover the obscure but highly interesting fossils of the old red sandstone in one deposition; we find the more perfectly preserved shells and lignites of the lias in another. There are the remains of two several creations at once before us. The shore, too, is heaped with rolled fragments of almost every variety of rock – basalts, ironstones, hyperstones, porphyries, bituminous shales, and micacious schists. In short, the young geologist, had he all Europe before him, could hardly choose for himself a better field. I had, however, no one to tell me so at the time, for geology had not yet travelled so far north; and so, without guide or vocabulary, I had to grope my way as I best might, and find out all its wonders for myself. But so slow was the process, and so much was I a seeker in the dark, that the facts contained in the few foregoing sentences are the patient gatherings of years.

In the course of the first day's employment I picked up a nodular mass of blue limestone, and laid it open by a stroke of the hammer. Wonderful to relate, it contained inside a beautifully finished piece of sculpture – one of the volutes apparently of an Ionic capital; and not the farfamed walnut of the fairy tale, had I broken the shell and found the little dog lying within, could have surprised me more. Was there another such curiosity in the whole world? I broke open a few other nodules of similar appearance, for they lay pretty thickly on the shore, and found that there might. In one of these there were what seemed to be scales of fish, and the impressions of a few minute bivalves, prettily striated; in the centre of another there was actually a piece of decayed wood. Of all nature's riddles, these seemed to me to be at once the most interesting and the most difficult to expound. I treasured them carefully up, and was told by one of the workmen to whom I showed them, that there was a part of the shore about two miles farther to the west, where curiously shaped stones, somewhat like the heads of boarding-pikes, were occasionally picked up; and that in his father's days the country people called them thunderbolts, and deemed them of sovereign efficacy in curing bewitched cattle. My master, on quitting the quarry for the building of which we were to be engaged, gave us all a half holiday. I employed it in visiting the place where the thunderbolts had fallen so thickly, and found it a richer scene of wonder than I could have fancied even in my dreams.

What first attracted my notice was a detached group of low-lying skerries, wholly different in form and colour from the sandstone cliffs above, or the primary rocks a little farther to the west. I found they were composed of thin strata of limestone, alternating with thicker beds of a black slaty substance, which, as I ascertained in the course of the evening, burns with a powerful flame, and emits a strong bituminous odour. The layers into which the latter readily separates are hardly an eighth part of an inch in thickness, and yet on every layer there are the impressions of thousands and tens of thousands of the various fossils peculiar to the lias. We may turn over these wonderful leaves, one after one, like the leaves of a herbarium, and find the pictorial records of a former creation in every page. Scallops, and gryphites, and ammonites, of almost every variety, and at least two varieties of belemite; twigs of wood, leaves of plants, cones of the pine, bits of charcoal, and the scales of fish; and, as if to render their pictorial appearance more striking, though the leaves of this interesting volume are of a deep black, most of the impressions are of a chalky whiteness. I was lost in admiration and astonishment, and found my very imagination paralysed by an assemblage of wonders that seemed to outrival, in the fantastic and the extravagant, even its wildest conceptions. I passed on from ledge to ledge, like the traveller of the tale through the city of statues, and at length found one of the supposed aërolites I had come in quest of, firmly embedded in a mass of shale. But I had skill enough to determine that it was other than what it had been deemed. My father, who had perished at sea when I was almost an infant, and who had been a sailor in his time on almost every ocean, and had visited almost every quarter of the globe, had brought home one of these stones with him from the coast of Java. It was of a cylindrical shape and vitreous texture, and it seemed to have parted in the middle when in a half molten state, and to have united again somewhat awry, ere it had cooled enough to have lost the adhesive quality. But there was nothing organic in its structure, whereas the stone I had now found was organised very curiously indeed. It was of a conical form and filamentary texture – the filaments radiating in straight lines from the centre to the circumference. Finely marked veins, like white threads, ran transversely through these, in its upper half, to the point, while the space below was occupied by an internal cone, formed of plates that lay parallel to the base, and which, like watchglasses, were concave on the under side and convex on the upper. I learned in time to call this stone a belemite, and became acquainted with enough of its history to know that it once formed part of a variety of cuttle-fish long since extinct.

But enough of geology for the time. There may be some interest in showing with how few opportunities of instruction the alphabet of the science may be acquired; but this is for some future number. My object at present is to show how possible it is to pursue very mean and very laborious employments, and yet enjoy much happiness. There are few professions, however humble, that do not present their peculiar advantages of observation; there are none in which the exercise of the faculties does not lead to enjoyment. The first year of my apprenticeship came to a close, and I found that the amount of my happiness had not been less than in the last of my boyhood. My knowledge, too, had certainly increased in more than the ratio of former seasons; and as I had acquired the skill of at least the common mechanic, I had fitted myself for independence. The additional experience of seventeen years has not shown me that there is any necessary connection between a life of toil and a life of wretchedness; and when I have found good men anticipating a better and a happier time than either the present or the past, the conviction that in every period of the world's history the great bulk of mankind must pass their days in labour, has not in the least inclined me to scepticism.[1]

I need not retrace the history of my first acquaintance with the glorious truths of geology, already detailed in a previous paper. My curiosity had been fully awakened. I had taken my first geological lessons amid the old red sandstones of the Cromarty quarries and the lias of Eathie, and had formed a small collection of rocks and fossils from the strata and the shore. My profession was a wandering one. I had been employed, for two seasons, among the basalts and coal-measures of the south of Scotland; I had wrought for three more in the primary districts of the remote Highlands; I had been an explorer of caves and ravines, a wanderer along sea-coasts, a climber among rocks, a labourer in quarries. What I now chiefly wanted was such a knowledge of system as might enable me to employ my facts, and such an acquaintance with the vocabulary of the science as would qualify me to record them.

I had at fist some difficulty in conceiving how mere depositions of clay or sand should have hardened into vast beds of solid strata, but an early recollection served to lessen the wonder. Among the many springs that come gushing to the light along the sides of the hill of Cromarty, there is hardly one that is not of a petrifying quality. Grass and moss and nettle stalks of stone may be found beside a full score of them, and almost all the caves that open among the precipices are coated with stalactites. This I had discovered years before, and the object of more than one of my schoolboy excursions had been to procure some of the 'pretty white icicles of marble that the water had made.' Now, it did strike me as a great deal more wonderful that the solid strata among which I wrought should have existed at one time as mud or sand, than that grass and moss and nettle stalks should have been converted into stone.

I remarked further, that, in cutting most kinds of sandstone, there are what seem to be two different degrees of hardness in the same block; that it cuts with most ease in lines parallel to its bed in the quarry, and with most difficulty in lines rectangular to it. I found, too, that this arose from the peculiar structure of the stone, which is composed in most instances of minute particles of great hardness, bound together by a softer cement, and resting on their flatter sides in lines parallel to the line of the strata. Now, when hewing in the rectangular line, I had to cut through these harder particles, and when in the parallel one, merely to strike them apart by cutting through the cement; and thus quite in the way, that in making a horizontal fissure in a brick wall I had only to break through the lime, and raise a layer of brick from off their beds; while, in making a vertical one, I had to hew downwards through alternate layers of brick and lime. How was this peculiarity of texture to be accounted for? Only on the supposition that the strata had been formed on horizontal planes, where every harder particle settled on its side rather than on its edge, in the manner that slate or coin, or any other flat substances, rest on a floor when carelessly thrown upon it. When I therefore saw strata lying parallel to the horizon, I inferred that they still retained the position in which they had been formed; and concluded, when I found them raised on end, that their natural position had been altered. And the principle was the same, which, when in passing over a moor I saw a columnar mass of undressed stone laid at length on the surface, led me to think it unnecessary to account for its being there by any human agency; and to class it, when on the contrary I found it fixed upright, with the rude monuments of a former age.

All this, however, was but sailing along the shore. I met with a curious old book, a translation from the French, and bore out under its guidance into the open sea. But never before did poor voyager trust himself to so insane a pilot. The work was entitled *Telliamed*, or discourses between an Indian philosopher and a French missionary on the diminution of the sea, the formation of the earth, and the origin of men and animals; and it contained just enough of truth, in at least the earlier chapters, to give currency to its fictions.[2] Despite of the author's absurdities, however, he had awakened in me a strong love of theory, which continued to influence me years after I had ceased to believe in this book, and it was not long ere I found ample occasion to exercise it.

There was among my acquaintance of this period an old school-fellow, who was attending the classes at college, and who used occasionally to whet my curiosity with odds and ends of science borrowed from the lectures of his professors.[3] I showed him the shells and lignites I had brought from Eathie; he had seen such in the College Museum, and had learned regarding them that they constituted the strange records of a bygone creation, of which not so much as a single plant or animal continued to exist. How strange the conception! It filled my imagination with visions of the remote past, that teemed with wild poetry, and invested the subject of my studies with an obscure and terrible sublimity that filled the whole mind.

I was in the middle of the dreams it occasioned, when I stumbled by some rare chance on a number of the Edinburgh Review; I say rare chance, for seldom at this period did I meet with a book that had not been at least fifty years in print.[4] It was the number for October 1813, and contained, in a critique on Van Buch's Travels in Norway, a concise abstract of the geological system of Werner.[5] Nothing could be more wildly hypothetical, not even the strange fancies of *Telliamed* himself. Wild as it was, however, it presented me with such a nucleus, as, according to its own showing, the inner mass of the earth must have formed, when the materials of the external crust were suspended in the ocean over it – a nucleus on which all my previously acquired facts might precipitate and crystallise. It taught me, too, how to classify the various rocks under their two grand divisions of primary and secondary, and set me a-thinking in a new track. The belief that the motions of the heavenly bodies are regulated by other laws than those which obtain on earth, served as a sort of license to the old astronomers to speculate amid their cycles and epicycles as wildly as they chose. The very first assumption in the system of Werner rendered me nearly as independent of the fixed principles which I saw operating around me, as any old astronomer of them all. It led me to conceive the primary ocean as a mass of fluid stone – and yet as a mass rather watery than molten, seeing that, according to the theory, it owed none of its fluidity to heat. But what sort of an ocean could it have been? I had watched when a boy the herring-curers of Cromarty preparing brine for their fish. I had marked the fluid increasing in density as the salt dissolved, until the egg employed in testing the preparation, and which had at first lain heavily at the bottom, came floating to the top. It had not escaped me, however, that there is a certain point beyond which the gravity of the mixture cannot be increased, and that after the testing body has risen to the surface, whatever additional salt may be added, becomes indissoluble, and sinks to the bottom. But how could I conceive any such *last* degree of saturation in the primary ocean, seeing that its main characteristic, as introduced to me by the system, was an enormous and preternatural density. I could set no bounds to the gravity of an element which had contained, in a state of chemical solution, the whole materials of the earth's crust, from where the diluvium overlies the newer formations, to where the granite rests on the unknown nucleus beneath. True it was that it could not have been more ponderous than the stony matter which it precipitated; but, then, on the other hand, it might have been very little less so.

This inference, whether correctly deduced from the system, or otherwise, led me into a rather curious speculation. I had been employed ere now in well nigh half the quarries of the district, and had ascertained that each had its own variety of sandstone, which I could at once distinguish from all the sandstones of the others. Nay, in some instances I have found beds of very opposite qualities only a few yards apart – beds dissimilar in colour, in their degree of hardness, in the dip and direction of their strata, and withal so completely disjoined, that I could compare them to only the pieces of a dissected map. I had repeatedly attempted, though in vain, to account for this phenomenon, but the stony ocean of Werner furnished me with a solution at once. After the breaking up of a severe frost, I have seen floats of ice which had been formed perhaps miles apart, lying stranded together on the same narrow tract of beach. I had seen in the previous winter the porous snowy-looking masses which had formed over the brackish waters of the estuary, the browner covering of a massy pool, and the hard glassy sheets which had bound up the surface of a lake, all grounded side by side on the shore of one little bay. And might it not have been thus, I asked, with the sandstone beds whose striking dissimilarities of colour and texture had puzzled me so much? Might not they also have been formed far apart, and after some signal convulsion had first broken them up, might they not have been carried away by the waters of the primary ocean, to be stranded where we now find them? True, ere their first formation, even these waters must have lost much of their earlier weight; but if powerful currents in our own times can transport vast masses of rock to great distances, how much more might we not expect from the ocean of Werner though deprived of even half its original density!

A theory of a man's own forming is always much a favourite with him, and if unsuited to live abroad, he takes all the more care of it at home. It was the fate of this theory, however, though it amused me at the time, to die almost in the forming. I had barely completed it, when a brief paragraph in the Scotsman newspaper showed me that there is a school of geology opposed to that of Werner – a school in which the agency of fire is made to occupy at least as prominent a place as that of water; and though the paper contained little more than a hint on the subject, it had the effect of destroying my short-lived faith in the ocean of fluid stone. It is wonderful how whole hoards of observation, if they lie outside a favourite system, may be suffered to accumulate unnoticed in the bye corners of the mind, as little better than rubbish. It is scarcely less wonderful how suddenly the introduction of a single new principle can raise them into importance and value. My imperfect acquaintance with the system of Werner had left me an immense heap of residual facts, which I could make no use of whatever; my still more imperfect acquaintance with the system of Hutton furnished me with employment for them all. The hill of Cromarty is composed of an immense mass of gneiss, traversed by veins of quartz and granite, and lined by huge blocks of hornblende. The strata in some places assume a nearly vertical position. They are bent and twisted in others in almost every complexity of form, and yet retain their average thickness, even where their bends and curves are most abrupt – a proof surely that they could not have been so bent when forming on their beds. The hornblende, too, assumes in some places an appearance not very unlike that of the scoria of a glass-house; and how account for the fact, that the more modern gneiss – more modern, if, according to Werner, every successive layer of rock is a deposition from above – should be traversed by veins of the more ancient granite? I had thought nothing of all this before; I could now think of little else. I saw indeed that the several quarries in which I had wrought might be assigned to Werner, but the rocks of the hill were decidedly the property of Hutton.

The first fruit of this chance acquisition was a new theory. Cromarty is situated in nearly the middle of a vast tract of secondary rock, through the center of which there runs for more than twenty miles a rectilinear chain of primary hills. The hill of Cromarty is one of these. On the eastern side they are bounded by the depths of the Moray Firth, on the western the sandstones of the district lean against them in very high angles, or lie trampled and broken at their bases in every complexity of derangement. What more evident than that these primary masses had been forced wedge-like from below, through the secondary crust? And what other agency than that of fire and the expansive energy of steam could have produced this wonderful result?

A trader who had risen by his own exertions from comparative poverty to great wealth, used to remark that he had found more trouble in making his first thousand pounds, than in making all the rest. It is always thus with the student who has to force a way for himself from the lower levels of intelligence. He finds more of a difficulty in the first few stages than in all the other stages that come after. I read the little all on geology that came in my way; I examined every rock and stone and quarry; and the mingled mass of fact and opinion which I had thus gradually acquired, and which had been at first, like the chaos of Ovid, in a state of perpetual change, began at length to settle and consolidate, and to increase in amount, far beyond the earlier ratio, with every new acquisition. A chance paragraph served at times to give importance to whole hoards of fact and observation that had lain in the memory for years, without producing any thing. I have found shells and coralines in the mountain limestone of Linlithgowshire, and *equisetaceae* and *calamites* in a quarry amid the coal-measures of Mid-Lothian; but though they engaged me at the time, it was not until I had ascertained the group to which they belong, and learned some of its wonderful history, that they interested me most. The shells and lignites, too, which I had found in the white soft sandstones of Sutherlandshire, and the bituminous shales of Eathie, grew strangely into importance when I became aware that the strikingly marked fossils of the sandstone belong to the *oolite*, and those of the shale to the *lias*. I still remember the pleasure I felt on being first brought acquainted with the geological scale, as laid down by the best authorities, and on becoming skilful enough to ascertain that there occur vast gaps in the geology of my native district – the lias resting on the old red sandstone, and that on the granite gneiss. But still greater was my pleasure, when, after discovering in one of my rock excursions, that some of the upper beds of the old red sandstone abound in fossil remains – mostly fish – I found that the discovery was as new to some of the most respectable geologists in the kingdom as it had been to myself. Geology is still in that early stage, and it derives some of its interest from the fact, that the humblest observer may repay the pleasure he owes to it, by adding to the data from which it reasons and infers.

I may state briefly, ere I conclude, a few of the results of so long a course of inquiry; they are mostly of that obvious class, which, to be understood, require only to be enumerated. I may mention the pleasure to be derived from the continual exercise of the mental faculties; the exciting influence of a curiosity, which, the more it is gratified, still strengthens the more; and the ability of investing the commonest objects around us with all that interest of novelty which the traveller attaches to the productions of foreign climates. It is something, too, to have learned from experience that truth is more wonderful than even the wildest dreams of fiction. My course of geological reading, if course it may be termed, began with an ingenious though somewhat absurd romance, filled with the most improbable stories of sea men and women, and of men furnished, like those of Monboddo, with tails. It terminates for the time with the admirable treatise of Dr. Buckland – a work written with the strictest regard to fact, and in a calm and philosophical spirit, and yet filled with narratives, not merely more striking than those of the romance, but more marvellous even than the wildest fairy tales.[6] It is surely by steps like these that the humble and toil-worn labourer is enabled to elevate himself in the scale of rational beings, and to derive positive mental enjoyment of an enduring kind from pursuits which in ordinary circumstances are only productive of pain, or viewed with apathetic indifference.

NOTES

1. The first article ends here.
2. Benoît de Maillet, *Telliamed ou entretiens d'un philosophe indien* (1735). Miller used the 1750 English translation.

3. John Swanson.
4. 'We have here, unconsciously on the part of the writer, a most expressive proof of the rarity of copyright books among the common people. They can only afford the reprinyts of old books, and are thus apt to be at all times a half century behind the rest of the community in intelligence.' [note in original text]. Miller himself refers to the absence of geological books available to him in *Schools*, p. 311; see also p. 267.
5. [John Leslie], 'Von Buch's Travels in Norway and Lapland', *Edinburgh Review*, 22, 1813, pp. 145–78.
6. William Buckland, *Geology and Mineralogy Considered with Reference to Natural Theology*, 2 vols, London, 1836.

APPENDIX V

Works by Hugh Miller

Poems, Written in the Leisure Hours of a Journeyman Mason, Inverness: R. Carruthers, 1829, 268 pages.

Letters on the Herring Fishing in the Moray Frith, Inverness: R. Curruthers, 1829, 50 pages.

Letter from One of the People to the Author of 'Remarks on the Cromarty Chapel Case', Inverness: R. Carruthers, 1831, 36 pages.

The Traditional History of Cromarty, Inverness: R. Carruthers, 1834, 12 pages.

Scenes and Legends of the North of Scotland; or, the Traditional History of Cromarty, Edinburgh: A. & C. Black, 1835, 429 pages.

Letter from One of the Scotch People to the Right Hon. Lord Brougham & Vaux, on the Opinions Expressed by his Lordship in the Auchterarder Case, Edinburgh: John Johnstone, 1839, 15 pages.

The Whiggism of the Old School, as Exemplified by the Past History and Present Position of the Church of Scotland, Edinburgh: John Johnstone, 1839, 32 pages.

Picture of a Parish under Forced Settlement, Edinburgh: John Johnstone, 1839. 4 pages.

Memoir of William Forsyth, Esq. A Scotch Merchant of the Eighteenth Century, London: Stewart and Murray, 1839, 133 pages.

The Two Parties in the Church of Scotland, Exhibited as Missionary and Anti-Missionary; their Contendings in these Opposite Characters in the Past, and their Statistics Now, Edinburgh: John Johnstone, 1841, 47 pages.

The Old Red Sandstone; or, New Walks in an Old Field, Edinburgh: John Johnstone, 1841, 275 pages.

The Two Mr Clarks, Edinburgh: John Johnstone, 1843, 18 pages.

'Lochiel's Warning', Edinburgh: John Johnstone, 1843, 11 pages.

Sutherland as it Was and Is; or, How a Country May be Ruined, Edinburgh: John Johnstone, 1843, 39 pages.

The Riots in Ross, Edinburgh: John Johnstone, 1843, 11 pages.

Words of Warning to the People of Scotland, on Sir R. Peel's Scotch Currency Scheme, Edinburgh: John Johnstone, 1844, 80 pages.

A Word of Warning on Sir Robert Peel's Scotch Currency Scheme, Edinburgh: J. Johnstone, [1844], 12 pages.

A Voice from the Greyfriars, Edinburgh: John Johnstone, 1845, 12 pages.

The Tenant's True Quarrel, Edinburgh: John Johnstone, 1846, 16 pages.

Letter from Hugh Miller, Edinburgh: n.p., 14 January 1847. 30 pages.

First Impressions of England and its People, London: John Johnstone, 1847, 407 pages.

The Sites Bill and the Toleration Laws; being an Examination of the Resolutions of the Rev. Dr Alexander, of Argyle Square Congregational Chapel, Edinburgh, Edinburgh: John Johnstone, 1848, 16 pages.

Footprints of the Creator; or, the Asterolepis of Stromness, London: Johnstone and Hunter, 1849, 313 pages.

An Unspoken Speech, Edinburgh: John Johnstone and Hunter, 1850, 24 pages.

'Leading Articles on Various Subjects' by Hugh Miller, Edinburgh: W. P. Nimmo, 1850, 91 pages.

The Two Records: Mosaic and Geological. A Lecture . . . delivered before the Young Men's Christian Association in Exeter Hall, February 7, 1854, London: James Nisbet and Co., 1854, 33 pages.

My Schools and Schoolmasters; or, the Story of my Education, Edinburgh: Johnstone and Hunter, 1854, 537 pages.

The Fossiliferous Deposits of Scotland: being an Address to the Royal Physical Society, delivered on 22d November 1854, Edinburgh: John Shepherd, 1854, 32 pages.

Geology versus Astronomy: or, the Conditions and the Periods; being a View of the Modifying Effects of Geological Discovery on the Old Astronomic Inferences respecting the Plurality of Inhabited Worlds, Glasgow: James R. Macnair, [1855], 35 pages.

What is Criticism? And Whose Property are Letters written for the Press after they have reached their Destination? Being Report of Jury Trial, Rev. Nathan Davis v. the Proprietors of 'The Witness'. With Introductory Remarks by Hugh Miller, Edinburgh: Shepherd & Elliot, 1855, 75 pages.

Trinity College Church versus the Burns Monument, Edinburgh: Shepherd & Elliot, 1856, 14 pages.

Strange but True: Incidents in the Life of Dr John Kitto, Edinburgh: Shepherd and Elliot, [1856], 18 pages.

The Testimony of the Rocks; or, Geology in its Bearings on the two Theologies, Natural and Revealed, Edinburgh: Thomas Constable & Co., 1857, 500 pages.

Macaulay on Scotland: a Critique, Edinburgh: Miller & Fairly, [1856], 40 pages.

The Cruise of the Betsey; or, A Summer Ramble among the Fossiliferous Deposits of the Hebrides. With Rambles of a Geologist; or, Ten Thousand Miles over the Fossiliferous Deposits of Scotland, Edinburgh: Thomas Constable & Co., 1858, 486 pages.

Sketch-book of Popular Geology; being a Series of Lectures Delivered before the Philosophical Institution of Edinburgh, Edinburgh: Thomas Constable & Co., 1859, 358 pages.

The Headship of Christ, and the Rights of the Christian People, Edinburgh: Adam and Charles Black, 1861, 517 pages.

Essays, Historical and Biographical, Political and Social, Literary and Scientific, Edinburgh: Adam and Charles Black, 1862, 495 pages.

Tales and Sketches, Edinburgh: W. P. Nimmo, 1863, 389 pages.

Edinburgh and its Neighbourhood, Geological and Historical; With the Geology of the Bass Rock, Edinburgh: A. & C. Black, 1864, 313 pages.

Leading Articles on Various Subjects, Edinburgh: W. P. Nimmo, 1870, 453 pages.

Recollections of Burns, Glasgow: Wm. Mollison and Co., 1886, 97 pages.

INDEX

Note: 'n.' after a page reference indicates the number of a note on that page.